Scottish SECONDARY MATHEMATICS

R3

Tom Sanaghan

Jim Pennel

Carol Munro

Carole Ford

John Dalton

Elaine Walker

heinemann.co.uk

✓ Free online support
✓ Useful weblinks
✓ 24 hour online ordering

01865 888058

Heinemann

Contents

Introduction

Books R3 and R4 of the Scottish Secondary Mathematics series are designed to deliver a secure foundation for the study of Higher Mathematics in the senior school.

'Essential skills' chapters provide practice in the basic skills necessary for progression in mathematics at this level.

Every chapter is divided into sections. Each section begins with the learning intentions and continues with a graded exercise of examples.

At the end of each chapter there is a review exercise and a summary of the content.

At intervals throughout the book there is a cumulative review of the immediately preceding sections and of the work to date.

The use of calculators is at the teacher's discretion.

Curriculum for Excellence

The content is designed to deliver the four capacities of Curriculum for Excellence. *Successful learning* is intrinsic to the structure and content of the book. Particular content areas which contribute significantly to each of the other three capacities are indicated with icons:

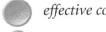 *effective contributor*

 confident individual

 responsible citizen

1 Essential skills: percentages

1.1 Finding percentages without a calculator

Learning intentions

For some commonly used percentages, equivalent fractions may be used to make the calculation easier.

Remember $10\% = \frac{10}{100} = \frac{1}{10}$

Percentage	Fraction
10%	$\frac{1}{10}$
50%	$\frac{1}{2}$
25%	$\frac{1}{4}$
75%	$\frac{3}{4}$

Percentage	Fraction
$33\frac{1}{3}\%$	$\frac{1}{3}$
$66\frac{2}{3}\%$	$\frac{2}{3}$

Percentage	Fraction
$12\frac{1}{2}\%$	$\frac{1}{8}$
1%	$\frac{1}{100}$
20%	$\frac{1}{5}$
5%	$\frac{1}{20}$

Example 1

Calculate:
(a) $12\frac{1}{2}\%$ of 296   (b) 30% of £57   (c) 7% of 40 litres

(a) $12\frac{1}{2}\%$ of 296
$= \frac{1}{8}$ of 296
$= 37$

(b) 10% of £57 = £5·70
30% of £57 = 3 × £5·70
$= £17·10$

(c) 1% of 40 litres = 0·4 litres
7% of 40 litres = 7 × 0·4 litres
$= 2·8$ litres

Example 2

Find the VAT at $17\frac{1}{2}\%$ payable on a freezer costing £350.

10% of £350 = £35
5%   = £17·50
$2\frac{1}{2}\%$ = £ 8·75
$17\frac{1}{2}\%$ of £350 = £61·25
The VAT payable is **£61·25**

Exercise 1.1

1 Calculate:
(a) $12\frac{1}{2}\%$ of 384 kg   (b) 20% of £52·80   (c) $33\frac{1}{3}\%$ of £105   (d) 75% of 6·8 m
(e) $66\frac{2}{3}\%$ of 25·5 km   (f) 10% of £34   (g) 60% of 510   (h) 30% of 97 mm
(i) 80% of 770 kg   (j) 40% of 5   (k) 70% of £125   (l) 3% of 80
(m) 9% of £4000   (n) 6% of 230 m   (o) 7% of £60   (p) 8% of 20 ml

2 Calculate:
(a) $17\frac{1}{2}\%$ of £180   (b) $17\frac{1}{2}\%$ of £57·60   (c) $17\frac{1}{2}\%$ of £392

3 In a year group of 270 pupils, $33\frac{1}{3}\%$ chose biology, 60% were female and 20% belonged to Allan House.
(a) How many pupils were in Allan House?
(b) How many pupils were male?
(c) If 40% of the pupils who chose biology were in Allan House, how many pupils in Allan House did not choose biology?

4 The prices for these items are given before VAT is added.

(**a**) car £6900   (**b**) laptop £260   (**c**) motorbike £3450

Find   (**i**) the VAT at 17·5 %

          (**ii**) the price including VAT.

5 Robert was preparing a plumbing bill for a customer.
Find the VAT at 17·5% and the total cost.

Labour: 2 hours at £45 per hour	£90
Parts:	£84
Subtotal:	___
VAT:	___
Total:	___

6 Jessica's annual council tax bill is £2560. If she is given a 25% single occupier discount, calculate:

(**a**) the discount

(**b**) her new council tax bill

(**c**) her monthly instalments if she pays in 10 equal monthly instalments.

7 The Trustee Bank saver account gives 3% interest per annum.
How much interest will Alex have after 1 year if he invests £4500?

8 Robertson's advertise that their crisps contain less than 6% fat. When a 25 gramme bag is tested it is found to contain 1·67 grammes of fat. Does this bag meet the manufacturer's claims? Give a reason for your answer.

9 The budget for the finance department of Ross & Baker in 2006 was £36 500. In 2007 it was increased by 15%.
What was the 2007 budget?

10 Find: (**a**) 10% of 50% of 80   (**b**) $33\frac{1}{3}$% of 1% of 6 000 000   (**c**) 35% of 40% of 60

1.2 Percentages with a calculator

Learning intentions

Example 1

Find 47% of £650

   47% of £650

= 0·47 × £650

= **£305·50**

$$\boxed{0.47 \times 650}$$

Example 2

Find the following percentages giving your answer to 2 decimal places.

(**a**) $17\frac{1}{2}$% of £80   (**b**) 8·3% of 44 m   (**c**) $2\frac{1}{4}$% of 18 kg

   $17\frac{1}{2}$% of £80

= 0·175 × £80

= **£14**

   8·3% of 44 m

= 0·083 × 44 m

= 3·652 m

= **3·65 m** to 2 d.p.

   $2\frac{1}{4}$% of 18 kg

= 0·0225 × 18 kg

= **0·405 kg**

= **0·41 kg** to 2 d.p.

Exercise 1.2

1 Calculate the following, giving your answers correct to 1 decimal place.

(**a**) 36% of 86 m   (**b**) 80% of 34 km   (**c**) 7% of 57 g   (**d**) 24% of 135 kg

(**e**) 98% of 270 kg   (**f**) 11·8% of 60 cm   (**g**) 8% of 240 ml   (**h**) 2·5% of 540 cm

(**i**) $8\frac{1}{4}$% of 225 kg   (**j**) $58\frac{1}{2}$% of 770 g   (**k**) 106% of 32 ml   (**l**) 117% of 920 km

2 Rayton's Bank gives an interest rate of 3·7% per annum.
How much interest will Bill earn if he invests £2500 for 1 year?

3 Clydewest Bank gives an interest rate of 4·2% per annum.
How much interest will Osian earn if he invests £3400 for:

(**a**) 1 year   (**b**) 6 months   (**c**) 1 month   (**d**) 10 months?

4 It is recommended that 6% of salary should be saved in a pension scheme. Anne earns £22 680 per annum.

(**a**) How much of this will go towards her pension?

(**b**) What is her monthly pension payment?

(**c**) If 13% of her salary is taken for national insurance, how much is this per month?

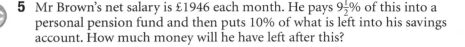

Discussion points

Find out about national insurance.

What are the benefits of joining a pension scheme as soon as you start working?

EC CI

5 Mr Brown's net salary is £1946 each month. He pays $9\frac{1}{2}$% of this into a personal pension fund and then puts 10% of what is left into his savings account. How much money will he have left after this?

6 Find the VAT charged at 17·5% for each item.

(**a**)
£119.00

(**b**)
£67.00

(**c**)
£8.50

7 A credit card company charges $2\frac{1}{4}$% interest per month. Pam spent £600 on her credit card in March. The next month she did not pay the bill. Calculate:

(**a**) the interest charged

(**b**) how much she now owes.

8 Calculate the annual interest for each of the following investments.

(**a**) Rachel – £650

(**b**) Robert – £1280

(**c**) Sarah – £10 700

R_B *Rayton's BANK*	
Interest rates per annum on savings	
£0–£499	3·25%
£500–£999	3·75%
£1000–£5000	4·05%
Over £5000	4·22%

9 There are 326 million cubic miles of water on Earth. Of this, 97% is in the oceans and 0·02% is in the lakes and rivers. The Amazon river contains 20% of this water. How much water is in:

(**a**) the oceans

(**b**) the Amazon?

10 Sofia can buy the washing machine she wants for £375 cash. She can also choose to pay for it using hire purchase.

How much more expensive is it to buy using hire purchase?

> **Hire Purchase agreement**
> 15% of the cash price
> +
> 12 instalments of £35

 11 Alex is buying a new car. He has two hire purchase options. Which one is cheaper?

Mega Motors cash price **£15 299**

> **Hire Purchase agreement**
> 18% of the cash price
> +
> 24 instalments of £510

Celebrity Cars cash price **£15 049**

> **Hire Purchase agreement**
> 15% of the cash price
> +
> 24 instalments of £505

12 *Economic Electrics* add 20% to the cash price when goods are bought using a credit agreement. Mr Wright bought a television with a cash price of £460 and decided to buy it on credit. He paid a deposit of 15% of the cash price followed by 12 equal instalments. Calculate:

(**a**) the total credit price   (**b**) each monthly instalment.

13 In a local election 72% of those eligible to vote turned out. Of those people 38% voted Labour. There were 82 300 people on the electoral roll. How many voted Labour?

1.3 Percentage increase and decrease

Learning intentions

Example 1

Joe earns £25 460 per annum. His salary is increased by 4%. Calculate his new salary.

The original amount is 100%.
Increase by 4%.
Original + 4% of original
100% + 4% = **104%**
  104% of £25 460
= 1·04 × £25 460
= **£26 478·40**

Example 2

A fridge costing £360 is reduced by 15% in a sale. Calculate the sale price.

The original amount is 100%
Decrease by 15%.
Original − 15% of original
100% − 15% = **85%**
  85% of £360
= 0·85 × £360
= **£306**

Exercise 1.3

1 Increase:

(**a**) £67 by 24%   (**b**) £130 by 82%   (**c**) £30·50 by 12%

2 Decrease:

(**a**) 38 litres by 18%   (**b**) 45 kilometres by 76%   (**c**) 20·7 tonnes by 55%

3 Mr Davis bought a painting for £8995 in 2005. In 2007, he sold it making a 37% loss. How much did he sell it for?

4 The Bank of Bradley made £25 500 000 profit in 2006.
In 2007 profits rose by 13%.

(**a**) What was the 2007 profit?   (**b**)   Calculate their profit per hour.

5 Vane's Furniture make a standard sized table that is 1·3 metres long and 80 centimetres wide. A customer asked for a table with an area that was 40% larger. What would be the area of the customer's table?

6 Calculate the price including VAT for each of these items:

(**a**)   £350 + VAT   (**b**)   £145 + VAT   (**c**)   £52 + VAT

7 Mrs Dover bought books for her school. She was given the following discounts.

> 5% off for books under £5
> 10% off for books £5 to £30
> 12% off for books over £30

Calculate her total bill if she bought 12 books at £4·99, 6 books at £8·50 and 2 books at £34.

8 Mr and Mrs Crawford bought their house in 1998 for £72 000. They sold it to Mr Alexander in 2006 making a profit of 38%.
How much did Mr Alexander pay?

9 The Wine Store is offering a 12% discount for every four bottles of wine purchased. Jay buys bottles costing £5·99, £7·50, £2·99 and £6·99.
How much will he pay for these in total?

10 *Movie Monthly* magazine costs £3·95 per issue.
Finlay subscribes to the magazine and saves 46%.
Find the subscriber cost per issue.

11 Joanna bought a pair of trousers originally costing £45, but reduced by 25% in the sale. When she returned to the shop 3 days later it was *Orange cross day* where all sale prices are reduced by a further 10%.
How much could she have saved by waiting for the *Orange cross day*?

12 A 750 gramme box of bran flakes has $12\frac{1}{2}$% extra free. If the box costs £1·27 find the cost per 100 grammes.

1.4 Appreciation and depreciation

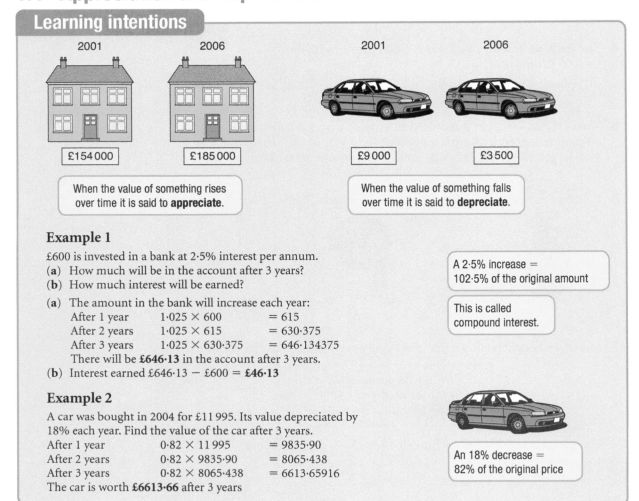

Learning intentions

2001   2006   2001   2006

£154 000   £185 000   £9 000   £3 500

When the value of something rises over time it is said to **appreciate**.

When the value of something falls over time it is said to **depreciate**.

Example 1

£600 is invested in a bank at 2·5% interest per annum.
(a) How much will be in the account after 3 years?
(b) How much interest will be earned?

(a) The amount in the bank will increase each year:
After 1 year	1·025 × 600	= 615
After 2 years	1·025 × 615	= 630·375
After 3 years	1·025 × 630·375	= 646·134375

There will be **£646·13** in the account after 3 years.
(b) Interest earned £646·13 − £600 = **£46·13**

> A 2·5% increase = 102·5% of the original amount

> This is called compound interest.

Example 2

A car was bought in 2004 for £11 995. Its value depreciated by 18% each year. Find the value of the car after 3 years.

After 1 year	0·82 × 11 995	= 9835·90
After 2 years	0·82 × 9835·90	= 8065·438
After 3 years	0·82 × 8065·438	= 6613·65916

The car is worth **£6613·66** after 3 years

> An 18% decrease = 82% of the original price

Exercise 1.4

1 Calculate the compound interest for the following investments.

(a) £6000	(b) £2500	(c) £12 400	(d) £9 000
3% p.a.	2% p.a.	4% p.a.	6% p.a.
2 years	3 years	4 years	3 years

2 It was predicted that house prices would rise by 12% each year in Gilmerton. How much would a house valued at £152 000 be worth 3 years later?

3 Lucas bought a new car for £8995. The value of the car depreciated by 11% each year. What was the value of the car after 3 years?

4 It is estimated that the number of cells in a biology experiment will grow by 6% every hour. If there were originally 40 cells, how many would there be after 4 hours?

5 After a chemical spill in the River Bowent it is estimated that each annual clean up operation reduces the amount of chemical by 40%. A safe level of the chemical is 2 milligrams per litre. If the amount of pollutant is originally 30 milligrams per litre, will the river be safe after 5 years?

6 Ronnie bought a car for £6545. In the first year the value depreciated by 22%, in the second year by 18% and in the third year by 15%. How much was the car worth after 3 years?

7 Frieda works for Boxy office supplies and earns £1658 each month. The staff at Boxy were given a pay increase of 0·8% in April 2006 and a further increase of 2·3% in September 2006. How much would Frieda earn after each pay rise?

8 A house valued at £245 000 in 2004 appreciated by 19% each year. How many years would it take for the value to double?

9 The mass of an iceberg is reducing by 2·24% each year due to climate change. After how many years will the iceberg have lost 10% of its mass?

1.5   Longer calculations

Learning intentions

Example

The value of a house in Abbeywood appreciates by 6% every year. How much will a house costing £82 000 be worth after 10 years? Give your answer to the nearest pound.

After 1 year	$1{\cdot}06 \times 82\,000$	$= (1{\cdot}06)^1 \times 82\,000 = 86\,920$
After 2 years	$1{\cdot}06 \times (1{\cdot}06) \times 82\,000$	$= (1{\cdot}06)^2 \times 82\,000 = 92\,135{\cdot}20$
After 3 years	$1{\cdot}06 \times (1{\cdot}06)^2 \times 82\,000$	$= (1{\cdot}06)^3 \times 82\,000 = 97\,663{\cdot}312$
After 4 years	$1{\cdot}06 \times (1{\cdot}06)^3 \times 82\,000$	$= (1{\cdot}06)^4 \times 82\,000 = 103\,523{\cdot}1107$
After n years	$1{\cdot}06^n \times 82\,000$	

So after 10 years the value is $(1{\cdot}06)^{10} \times 82\,000 = £146\,849{\cdot}5111$

The house will be worth **£146 850** to the nearest pound.

Exercise 1.5

1 Samantha saves £3000 in an account giving 4·5% interest per annum. How much money will there be in the account after 15 years?

2 Elliot puts £3000 into a savings account with an interest rate of 3·7% per annum. Euan puts £2900 into a savings account with an interest rate of 4% per annum. Who will have the most money after

(**a**) 10 years   (**b**) 20 years?

3 Marie has £500 in a bank account paying interest of 2·25% per annum. How long will it take for her money to double?

4 It is estimated that the rainforest in a certain country reduces at a rate of 0·8% per year. If the area in 1990 was 50 000 square kilometres, find the area remaining after:

(**a**) 1 year   (**b**) 10 years   (**c**) 25 years.

1.6 Annual percentage rate

Learning intentions

The annual percentage rate (APR) is often used for comparison.
Interest on a store card is charged at 2% per month.
To find the APR
$(1·02)^{12} = 1·26824 = 126·824\%$
The annual percentage rate is 26·8% to 1 d.p.
Over 1 year the amount on the card would increase by 26·8%

$1·26824 = 126·824\%$
$= (100 + 26·824)\%$

Exercise 1.6

1 Calculate the APR for a monthly interest rate of:

(**a**) 3%   (**b**) 1%   (**c**) 4%   (**d**) 6%

2 Calculate the APR for a monthly interest rate of:

(**a**) 2·9%   (**b**) 1·839%   (**c**) 2·225%   (**d**) 0·915%

3 A credit card has a monthly interest rate of 1·232% for purchases.

(**a**) What is the annual percentage rate?

(**b**) If £700 was spent on the credit card how much would be owed after one year?

Discussion point

By looking at the APR offered on several credit or store cards, decide which one would offer best value. An internet search might be useful.

EC **CI**

1.7 Percentage of a total

Learning intentions

Example 1

A painting was bought for £1200 and resold for £1650. Calculate the percentage profit.

Profit = £1650 − £1200 = £450   Profit as a fraction of original cost $= \dfrac{450}{1200} = \dfrac{3}{8}$

Percentage profit $= 37\frac{1}{2}\%$

Example 2

A car bought for £6500 depreciated to £2800. Calculate the percentage depreciation of the car.

Depreciation = £6500 − £2800 = £3700
Depreciation as a fraction of original value $= \dfrac{3700}{6500} = 0.56923 = 56·9\%$

Percentage depreciation = 56·9% to 1 decimal place

Exercise 1.7

1 Find:

(**a**) 36 as a percentage of 120   (**b**) 18 as a percentage of 40   (**c**) 68 as a percentage of 170

(**d**) 15 as a percentage of 62   (**e**) 206 as a percentage of 15 000   (**f**) 0·7 as a percentage of 23

2 Peter has received his marks for five third year exams. Find each of these marks as a percentage, giving your answer to the nearest percent.

Maths	English	French	History	Physics
$\frac{37}{45}$	$\frac{48}{62}$	$\frac{27}{64}$	$\frac{56}{75}$	$\frac{38}{40}$

3 After a stocktake in a DVD rental shop the numbers were:

Certificate	U	PG	12/12A	15	18
Number of titles	47	143	190	145	112

What percentage of the titles are:

(**a**) a 15 rating?　　　　　　　　　(**b**) suitable for 10 year old children?

4 The value of a house in 2005 was £50 000. By 2007 the value had risen to £87 000. What was the percentage appreciation?

5 In 2006, the population of Rainey was 17 406. By 2007, it had dropped to 16 637. Find the percentage decrease in the population.

6 Arthur earns £26 420 per annum. If he saves £300 each month what percentage of his salary does he save?

7 Bill paid £1420 council tax in 2006. In 2007 council tax increased by 7%. In 2008 it increased again by 15%. A local newspaper reported that since 2006 council tax had increased by 23%. Is this correct? Give a reason for your answer.

8 Richard saves £350 per month. He decides to reduce his savings by 15%.

(**a**) How much does he save now?

(**b**) When he is given a pay increase a year later he decides to increase the amount he saves by 15%. How much does he save now?

(**c**) Find the percentage reduction in his savings.

9 When Roisin moved to a new job she took a 10% pay cut. After 6 months she was given a 10% pay increase. Show that she now earns less than her original salary.

10 The table shows the number of pupils at Braid High School in 2006.

(**a**) What percentage of the total school roll is male?

(**b**) What percentage of the total school roll is in S3?

(**c**) What percentage of S5 is female?

(**d**) What percentage of the school roll is in S4 or above?

(**e**) What percentage of the pupils in S1 is male?

(**f**) Which is greater, the percentage of males in S1 or the percentage of males in S5?

Year	Male	Female
S1	200	220
S2	196	180
S3	180	170
S4	190	192
S5	98	114
S6	60	57

(**g**) In 2007 the school roll increased by 17% then in 2008 it decreased by 4%. What was the overall percentage change from 2007 to 2008?

1.8 Calculating the original amount

Learning intentions

Example 1

A DVD player, which has been reduced by 15%, has a sale price of £52·70.
Calculate its original cost.

Adding on 15% will not work!
Use a table.

%	£
85	52.70
1	52.70 ÷ 85 = 0·62
100	0.62 × 100 = 62

The sale price is 85% of the original price.

The original cost was **£62**.

Example 2

The price of a set of car tyres including VAT is £411·25.
Calculate the price excluding VAT.

%	£
117·5	411.25
1	411·25 ÷ 117·5 = 3·50
100	3·50 × 100 = 350

VAT is 17·5%

The price excluding VAT is **£350**.

Exercise 1.8

1 Calculate the original costs of the following items.

(a)

| 20% off |
| now only |
| £468 |

(b)

| 15% off |
| now only |
| £108·12 |

(c)

| 60% off |
| now only |
| £45 |

2 The owner of a shop decides that on a certain day in February he will give 15% of all sales to charity. He would like to give at least £600. How much would the sales have to be if this is to be achieved?

3 Niall earns a basic wage of £300 per week plus 12% commission on all sales made.
What were the value of his sales in a week where his wage was £570?

4 Calculate the price excluding VAT for the following items:

(a)
Price including VAT
£423

(b)
Price including VAT
£279·65

5 Calculate the VAT paid on each of the following items:

(a)

£141 inc VAT

(b)

£764 inc VAT

6 The Megabucks coffee company increased the number of outlets each year by 25%. If the company had 125 outlets in 2007, how many did they start with in 2005?

Review exercise 1: Am I a successful learner?

1 Find:
(a) 10% of 48   (b) 25% of 62   (c) $33\frac{1}{3}$% of 324   (d) 12·5% of 424
(e) 7% of 38   (f) 70% of £435   (g) 45% of £340   (h) 32% of 520 m

2 Calculate the VAT at 17·5% on the following:

(a)

£12 800

(b)

£950

(c)

£2 630

3 Calculate:
(a) 12·4% of £67   (b) $53\frac{1}{2}$% of £82   (c) $2\frac{3}{4}$% of 324   (d) 9·6% of 424

4 Increase:
(a) £420 by 12%   (b) 132 metres by 48%   (c) 308 kg by 6·5%

5 Decrease:
(a) 350 m by 18%   (b) £426 by 87%   (c) £87 by $4\frac{1}{2}$%

6 *Aitkens* have a table for the cash price of £326. The hire purchase price is 15% more than this.
(a) Calculate the hire purchase price.
(b) Maia buys the table on hire purchase. She pays a 10% deposit and the rest in 12 equal monthly payments. How much is each payment?

7 The table below shows pollution levels at 4 areas in a city.

Wardour Street	175 units
Haymarket	164 units
Heathcote Road	173 units
Bridge Street	150 units

Health regulations state that pollution levels should be less than 135 units. The council plans to introduce measures to reduce the level of pollution by 8% each year for the next three years. Which places will meet the regulations after 3 years?

8

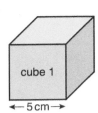
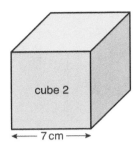

cube 1

←5 cm→

cube 2

←— 7 cm —→

Calculate the surface area of cube 1 as a percentage of the surface area of cube 2.

9 In 2006, a house was valued at £150 000 and the contents at £70 000. The value of the house appreciates by 6% each year. The value of the contents depreciates by 7% each year. What will be the total value of the house and contents in 2008?

10 A new cinema with 370 seats has opened. During the first week, the cinema was open 7 days and ran 3 shows per day. A total of 6200 tickets were sold.

The manager has a target of selling at least 80% of the available seats for the first week. Did the manager meet the target? Explain your answer.

11 In a survey, 60% of houses contained two or more people. Of those homes containing only one person, 35% contained a male. What percentage of all houses contain exactly one female and no males?

12 In a recent election Labour won 26 451 votes, Conservative won 22 675 votes and Liberal Democrats won 18 290 votes. If 75% of those eligible to vote did so, what was the total number of eligible voters?

13 Richard pays the bill for a meal at a restaurant. 12% service charge has been included. The bill total was £62·72.
What was the bill before the service charge was added?

14 Blueberry jam is on special offer. The special offer jar contains 12·5% more than a standard jar.

A jar on special offer contains 450 grammes of jam. How much does a standard jar contain?

BLUEBERRY JAM

12·5% extra FREE
450g for the price
of ⬤

15 The value of a car depreciates by 12% each year.
How many years will it take for the car to reach half of its original value?

16 The half life of a drug is the period of time required for the concentration or amount of drug in the body to be reduced by one-half. At 11 am a patient is given a 200 milligram dose of a drug. The amount of the drug in the bloodstream decreases by 15% every hour.

(**a**) What amount of drug is present in the patient at midday?

(**b**) What is the half life of the drug?

Summary 1: What I learned in this chapter.

Finding a percentage

Percentage	Fraction
10%	$\frac{1}{10}$
50%	$\frac{1}{2}$
25%	$\frac{1}{4}$
75%	$\frac{3}{4}$
$33\frac{1}{3}$%	$\frac{1}{3}$
$66\frac{2}{3}$%	$\frac{2}{3}$

Percentage	Fraction
$12\frac{1}{2}$%	$\frac{1}{8}$
1%	$\frac{1}{100}$
20%	$\frac{1}{5}$
5%	$\frac{1}{20}$

Non calculator

VAT at $17\frac{1}{2}$% payable on a freezer costing £350.

10% of £350	= £35
5%	= £17·50
$2\frac{1}{2}$%	= £ 8·75

$17\frac{1}{2}$% of £350 = £61·25

The VAT payable is **£61·25**

Calculator

47% of £650
= 0·47 × £650
= **£305·50**

$2\frac{3}{4}$% of £86
= 0·0275 × £86
= £2·365
= **£2·37**

Percentage increase and decrease

To increase by 4% :
Original + 4% of original
100% + 4% = **104%**
To find 104% multiply by 1·04

To decrease by 15% :
Original − 15% of original
100% − 15% = **85%**
To find 85% multiply by 0·85

Appreciation and depreciation

A car was bought in 2004 for £11 995. Its value depreciates by 18% each year.

After 1 year	0·82 × 11 995	= 9835·90
After 2 years	0·82 × 9835·90	= 8065·438
After 3 years	0·82 × 8065·438	= 6613·65916

The car is worth **£6613·66** after 3 years

> When the value of something rises over time it is said to appreciate.

> When the value of something falls over time it is said to depreciate.

Finding a percentage of a total

A painting was bought for £1200 and resold for £1650. Calculate the percentage profit.

Profit = £1650 − £1200 = £450

Profit as a fraction of original cost $= \frac{450}{1200} = \frac{3}{8}$

Percentage profit = **$37\frac{1}{2}$%**

Finding the original amount

The price of a set of car tyres including VAT is £411.25.

The price excluding VAT:

%	£
117·5	411·25
1	411·25 ÷ 117·5 = 3·5
100	3·5 × 100 = 350

The price excluding VAT is **£350**.

2 Essential skills: algebra

2.1 Evaluating expressions

Learning intentions

Expressions may be evaluated by replacing variables with numbers.

Example

If $p = -3$, $q = 5$, $r = -4$ and $s = 10$ evaluate:

(a) $s + pr$

(b) $\dfrac{pqr}{s}$

(c) $\dfrac{2q^2 - s}{p - q}$

(a) $s + pr$
$= 10 + (-3) \times (-4)$
$= 10 + 12$
$= \mathbf{22}$

(b) $\dfrac{pqr}{s}$
$= \dfrac{(-3) \times 5 \times (-4)}{10}$
$= \dfrac{60}{10}$
$= \mathbf{6}$

(c) $\dfrac{2q^2 - s}{p - q}$
$= \dfrac{2 \times (5)^2 - 10}{(-3) - 5}$
$= \dfrac{2 \times 25 - 10}{-8}$
$= \dfrac{40}{-8}$
$= \mathbf{-5}$

Exercise 2.1

1 Given $w = -2$, $x = 5$, $y = -3$ and $z = 1$, calculate the value of:

(a) $wx + z$
(b) $wy + 4z$
(c) $xy - x$
(d) $wx - 2y$

(e) $wz + xz$
(f) $wx + yz$
(g) $wy - xy$
(h) $(2w)^2 + 2y$

(i) $x^2 + yz$
(j) $4z^2 - 3x$
(k) $5y^2 - 3wz$
(l) $4x^2 + yz^2$

2 Given that $k = -10$, $m = -6$, $n = -4$, $x = 0$ and $p = 5$, evaluate:

(a) mnp
(b) $\dfrac{kmn}{12}$
(c) $\dfrac{kn}{2p}$
(d) kmx

(e) $\dfrac{4mp}{n^2}$
(f) $\dfrac{k^2 + m^2}{n}$
(g) $\dfrac{4p^2 + 5n^2}{2k}$
(h) $\dfrac{3k^3}{5np}$

(i) $\dfrac{px}{mk}$
(j) $\dfrac{mp}{k^2}$
(k) $\dfrac{p^2 x}{m}$
(l) $\dfrac{kx - k}{p}$

2.2 Simplifying expressions

Learning intentions

It may be possible to simplify algebraic expressions.

Example

Simplify:
(a) $6a + 2y - 4a - 8y$

(b) $3x + 8y - 5x + 3z - y$

(c) $4x^2 + 8 - 6x^2 + x - 14$

(a) $6a + 2y - 4a - 8y$
$= 6a - 4a + 2y - 8y$
$= \mathbf{2a - 6y}$

(b) $3x + 8y - 5x + 3z - y$
$= 3x - 5x + 8y - y + 3z$
$= \mathbf{-2x + 7y + 3z}$

(c) $4x^2 + 8 - 6x^2 + x - 14$
$= 4x^2 - 6x^2 + x + 8 - 14$
$= \mathbf{-2x^2 + x - 6}$

Exercise 2.2

1 Simplify each expression:

(a) $5b + 8c - 3b + 6c$

(b) $12x - 3y + 7x + 5y$

(c) $7p + 2q - 3p + 5q - 4p$

(d) $6a + 9y - 4 - 6a - 3y$

(e) $12w + 30z - 15w - 17z$

(f) $5y + 4x - 8y - 6x + 3y + 2x$

(g) $4t - 9s - 8t + 12s$

(h) $5v + 4w - 2v + 2w - 15v$

(i) $3 - t + 10 + 5t - 6$

(j) $6d - 3e - 9d + 2 - 4e$

(k) $7 - 6x - 3y - 9 + 4x - 2y$

(l) $8 - 9t + 8r + 2 + 10t - 8r$

2 Simplify:

(a) $4t - 9s - 8t - s$

(b) $-3x + 4y - 8x - 7y$

(c) $6x + 7y - 20z + 2z + y$

(d) $5a - 6b + c + 2a - 3b - 5c$

(e) $-3f + 4g + 16 - 4f + 5g + 1$

(f) $15d + 6e + 6 - 10d + 3e - 5d$

(g) $4z - 9t + 2r - 5t - 7r - 15z$

(h) $6y - 12 - 9y + 15 - 3y - 3$

(i) $7f + 8g + 5h - 4g - 6f - 4g$

(j) $-13 + 8v - 4 - 9v + 16w + 8$

3 Simplify:

(a) $16x^2 - 5 - 9x^2 - 7$

(b) $4y^2 + 3x + 7y^2 - 2x + y^2$

(c) $9 - c^2 + 5c^2 - 7 + 3c^2 - 3$

(d) $20x^2 + 3y - 2x^2 + 4y$

(e) $14w^2 + 3w - 9w^2 + 5w$

(f) $3b^2 + 4b - 2b^2 - 6b + 4b^2 + 7$

(g) $5k + 3k^2 - 8k - 6k^2 + k^2 + 12k$

(h) $ab + 2xy + 4ab - 5xy$

(i) $3xy - 7y + 4xy + 11y - 8xy$

(j) $6st - 8at + 3st + 9at - at + 2st$

(k) $14x^2y - 9x^2y + 5x^2y$

(l) $6ab^2 - 3a^2b + 9ab^2 + 8a^2b$

(m) $4yz + 6y^2z + 2yz^2 + 4yz + 2yz^2$

(n) $7m^2n - 9mn^2 - 6m + mn^2$

(o) $-gh + gh^2 - g^2h - 3gh + 3gh^2$

(p) $x^3 + 3x^2 - 4x - 3x - 8 + 6x^2 + 5x - 2$

2.3 Simplifying using the distributive law

Learning intentions

Example

Expand and simplify:

(a) $-9(3p - 2)$

(b) $5(3x + 6) - 7x$

(c) $-5(10m + 1) - (m - 5)$

(a) $-9(3p - 2)$
$= -27p + 18$

(b) $5(3x + 6) - 7x$
$= 15x + 30 - 7x$
$= 8x + 30$

(c) $-5(10m + 1) - (m - 5)$
$= -50m - 5 - m + 5$
$= -51m$

Exercise 2.3

Multiply out the brackets:

1 (a) $5(2y - 7)$

(b) $6(2 + 3x)$

(c) $4(5z + 2w)$

(d) $7(2a - 5b)$

(e) $-3(4b + 3)$

(f) $-5(q - 3)$

(g) $-7(6 - 2t)$

(h) $2(6x - 5)$

(i) $10(5 - 2a + 4b)$

(j) $-4(3c - 6d - 7)$

(k) $-8(4e + 2f - 6)$

(l) $-3(-x + 2y - 5z)$

2 Multiply out the brackets and simplify:

(a) $4(2x + 4) - 3x$

(b) $3(5y - 9) + 5y$

(c) $5(3c + 4d - e) + 2c$

(d) $6(3x + 6 - y) - 20$

(e) $-3(4y + 7) + 3y$

(f) $-4(3w - 2v) + 5v$

(g) $8(a - 2b - c) - 4a$

(h) $-3(2d - 4e + f) + 10d$

(i) $16 + 5(3g - h - 2)$

(j) $9 - 2(3j + 1) - j$

(k) $11k - 3(2k - 1) + 6$

(l) $m - 2n - 3(n - m)$

3 Multiply out the brackets and simplify:

(a) $4(2a + b) + 3(a + 2b)$

(b) $4(3e + 1) - 5(2e + 1)$

(c) $5(f + 6) - 3f(6 - f)$

(d) $5(g + 2h) - (g - 3h)$

(e) $2(x + y + 2z) + 3(x + 2y + z)$

(f) $4(a + 3b - c) - 2(a - 3b + c)$

(g) $-9(2 + 3y) + 3(3 + y)$

(h) $-5(3 - 2m) + 8 - m$

(i) $-3(10d + 1) - (d - 4)$

(j) $-20(3x - y) - (2x - 2y)$

(k) $3(4a + 5) + 5(3a - 2b - 3) + 6b$

(l) $5(y - 7) + 8y - 3(2x - y - 6)$

(m) $16x - (x + 2y + 8) + 3(x + y)$

(n) $-6(3a + b - 1) - 4b - 2b(a - b + 7)$

2.4 Common factors

Learning intentions

5 is a **common factor** of $15x + 45$ since 5 is a factor of both $15x$ and 45.

$$15x + 45$$
$$= 5(3x + 9)$$

Check this mentally by expanding the bracket.

This is called **factorising** or **factorisation**.
When factorising, the convention is to use the largest common factor.

Example

Factorise each expression using a common factor:

(a) $32y - 40$

(b) $7m + 14n - 28$

(c) $ax + bx$

(a) $32y - 40$
$= 8(4y - 5)$

(b) $7m + 14n - 28$
$= 7(m + 2n - 4)$

(c) $ax + bx$
$= x(a + b)$

Exercise 2.4

1 Factorise each expression:

(a) $2x + 6$

(b) $3y + 24$

(c) $4y + 36$

(d) $15m - 35$

(e) $18t + 36$

(f) $20t - 35$

(g) $30f + 50$

(h) $32s + 16t - 20$

(i) $35a - 77b + 49$

2 Factorise where possible:

(a) $6r + 2s - 8$

(b) $16x + 4$

(c) $20x + 15y - 25$

(d) $18t + 9s$

(e) $20t + 36u - 28$

(f) $33 - 21g$

(g) $20f - 10g$

(h) $8r + 49s - 14$

(i) $16f - 8g$

(j) $30r + 25s - 15$

(k) $18m + 36n - 24$

(l) $5f - 20g$

3 Factorise where possible:

(a) $40m - 25n - 55$

(b) $10d + 28e - 12$

(c) $11r - 33s + 99$

(d) $40x - 80y$

(e) $500f + 700g - 600$

(f) $52x - 26y + 39$

(g) $42m - 63n + 77p$

(h) $7x + 21y$

(i) $4g + 6h - 14$

(j) $16f - 14g$

(k) $20x + 80y$

(l) $30s + 35t$

(m) $30x + 45y - 75$

(n) $21r + 40s$

(o) $22x - 55y + 88z$

4 Factorise where possible:

(**a**) $cx + dx$ (**b**) $fx + gx$ (**c**) $ay + by$

(**d**) $ax - bx$ (**e**) $xy - zy$ (**f**) $ab + ac$

(**g**) $hm - hf$ (**h**) $ax + x$ (**i**) $by - y$

(**j**) $x^2 - ax$ (**k**) $by - y^2$ (**l**) $2x + ax$

2.5 Solving equations

Learning intentions

Equations may be solved by keeping each side of the equation balanced.

Example

Solve:

(**a**) $3p + 7 = 16$

(**b**) $5y + 3 = 3y - 13$

(**c**) $5 - 4p = 6 - 2p$

(**a**) $3p + 7 = 16$
$-7 \quad -7$
$3p = 9$
$\div 3 \quad \div 3$
$p = 3$

(**b**) $5y + 3 = 3y - 13$
$-3y \quad -3y$
$2y + 3 = -13$
$-3 \quad -3$
$2y = -16$
$\div 2$
$y = -8$

(**c**) $5 - 4p = 6 - 2p$
$+4p \quad +4p$
$5 = 6 + 2p$
$-6 \quad -6$
$-1 = 2p$
$\div 2 \quad \div 2$
$-\frac{1}{2} = p$
$p = -\frac{1}{2}$

Exercise 2.5

1 Solve each equation:

(**a**) $2p + 5 = 13$ (**b**) $6x + 2 = 32$ (**c**) $4y - 2 = 22$

(**d**) $5 + 3p = -1$ (**e**) $2 + 8g = -22$ (**f**) $-7 + 6b = 5$

(**g**) $28 = 5c + 18$ (**h**) $7 = 4y + 5$ (**i**) $9x - 4 = -7$

2 Solve:

(**a**) $3 = 6 - 3x$ (**b**) $12 = 20 - 2y$ (**c**) $24 = 60 - 6f$

(**d**) $28 - 5y = 26$ (**e**) $16 = 8 - 2z$ (**f**) $35 = 17 - 6b$

(**g**) $130 = -40m + 30$ (**h**) $17 = -9x + 23$ (**i**) $95 - 20y = 110$

3 Solve:

(**a**) $7y + 3 = 3y + 11$ (**b**) $9b - 5 = 3b + 1$ (**c**) $10z - 8 = 5z + 42$

(**d**) $8y + 8 = 5y - 1$ (**e**) $6y + 10 = y$ (**f**) $b = 9b + 40$

(**g**) $2g = 3 - 4g$ (**h**) $5y - 6 = 10y - 8$ (**i**) $16z - 10 = 4z - 19$

4 Solve:

(**a**) $5 - 3p = 4 - 2p$ (**b**) $10 - 4y = 6 - 3y$ (**c**) $7 - 12x = 15 - 8x$

(**d**) $9 - 6z = 29 - 2z$ (**e**) $6t + 8 = 26 - 3t$ (**f**) $14 - 5b = 7b + 26$

(**g**) $7 + 6x = 5 + 3x$ (**h**) $5 - 4y = 6 - 2y$ (**i**) $29 - 8z = 2 + 10z$

2.6 Solving equations using the distributive law

Learning intentions

Example

Solve the equations:

(a) $2(y + 1) = -4$ 　　　(b) $10 + 2(3w - 1) = 23$ 　　　(c) $15 - 2(2x - 3) = 3(9 - x)$

(a) $2(y + 1) = -4$
$$2y + 2 = -4$$
$$2y = -6$$
$$y = -3$$

(b) $10 + 2(3w - 1) = 23$
$$10 + 6w - 2 = 23$$
$$8 + 6w = 23$$
$$6w = 15$$
$$w = 2\tfrac{1}{2}$$

(c) $15 - 2(2x - 3) = 3(9 - x)$
$$15 - 4x + 6 = 27 - 3x$$
$$21 - 4x = 27 - 3x$$
$$21 = 27 + x$$
$$-6 = x$$
$$x = -6$$

Exercise 2.6

1 Solve the equations:

(a) $3(x + 2) = 12$ 　　　(b) $5(z - 4) = 20$ 　　　(c) $6(2b + 1) = -30$
(d) $4(3y - 7) = -16$ 　　(e) $7(1 + 2x) = 0$ 　　(f) $4(2 - w) = 26$
(g) $2(9 - 3t) = 33$ 　　(h) $15 = 3(4b + 3)$ 　　(i) $-20 = 5(2 + 7x)$
(j) $-18 = 9(3 - 2x)$ 　　(k) $7(1 + 5b) = -14$ 　　(l) $120 = 12(3 - 2z)$

2 Solve:

(a) $3(y + 8) + 5 = 35$ 　　　　　(b) $2(b - 6) + 7 = 17$
(c) $4 + 5(2x - 1) = -41$ 　　　　(d) $16 + 3(4t - 5) = 7$
(e) $-9 + 5(2w - 3) = -64$ 　　　(f) $10 - 2(z + 3) = 1$
(g) $-5 - (3x + 6) = -12$ 　　　　(h) $8 - 3(5z - 2) = 34$
(i) $-4(3g - 11) + 20 = 52$ 　　　(j) $-3(4b + 5) - 16 = -11$

3 Solve:

(a) $2(3y + 5) = 5(y + 1)$ 　　　　(b) $3(x - 4) = 2(x - 7)$
(c) $6(z - 3) = 3(z + 1) + 3$ 　　　(d) $4(y - 4) = 2(y + 25) - 4$
(e) $5(x - 3) + 6 = 10(x - 6) + 9$ 　(f) $8(x + 3) + 7 = 4(x + 5) + 15$
(g) $3(3z - 9) = -4 - (5 - 2z)$ 　　(h) $6 - 7(b - 3) = 3(2b + 1)$
(i) $3(2w - 2) + 5 = 9 - 2(3w + 1)$ 　(j) $7 - 3(b - 1) = 8 + 3(b - 4)$

2.7 Solving more complex equations

Learning intentions

Example

Solve:

(a) $2x + 11 = \dfrac{x}{6}$ 　　Multiply both sides by 6

(b) $\dfrac{y}{3} = \dfrac{y + 2}{5}$ 　　15 is the lowest common multiple of 3 and 5 Multiply both sides by 15

(c) $\dfrac{x}{2} + \dfrac{3x}{4} = \dfrac{x + 2}{3}$ 　　12 is the lowest common multiple of 2, 3 and 4 Multiply both sides by 12

(a) $2x + 11 = \dfrac{x}{6}$

$$6(2x + 11) = \tfrac{x}{6} \times 6$$
$$12x + 66 = x$$
$$11x + 66 = 0$$
$$11x = -66$$
$$x = -6$$

(b) $\dfrac{y}{3} = \dfrac{y + 2}{5}$

$$15 \times \tfrac{y}{3} = 15 \times \tfrac{(y + 2)}{5}$$
$$5y = 3(y + 2)$$
$$5y = 3y + 6$$
$$5y - 3y = 6$$
$$2y = 6$$
$$y = 3$$

(c) $\dfrac{x}{2} + \dfrac{3x}{4} = \dfrac{x + 2}{3}$

$$12 \times \tfrac{x}{2} + 12 \times \tfrac{3x}{4} = 12 \times \tfrac{x + 2}{3}$$
$$6x + 9x = 4(x + 2)$$
$$15x = 4x + 8$$
$$11x = 8$$
$$x = \tfrac{8}{11}$$

Exercise 2.7

1 Solve each equation:

(a) $\dfrac{y}{2} = 2y - 18$

(b) $4b + 22 = \dfrac{b}{3}$

(c) $\dfrac{x}{2} = x + 5$

(d) $3z + 85 = \dfrac{x}{6}$

(e) $2x - 9 = \dfrac{x}{4}$

(f) $\dfrac{x}{4} = 5x - 19$

(g) $\dfrac{3y}{4} = 6y - 7$

(h) $\dfrac{x}{5} = 2(x + 9)$

(i) $\dfrac{6x}{3} = 4(x - 9)$

2 Solve:

(a) $\dfrac{y}{3} = \dfrac{y + 2}{4}$

(b) $\dfrac{z}{3} = \dfrac{z - 6}{5}$

(c) $\dfrac{y + 2}{3} = \dfrac{y - 6}{5}$

(d) $\dfrac{w - 2}{3} = \dfrac{w - 5}{4}$

(e) $\dfrac{y + 9}{7} = \dfrac{y - 3}{5}$

(f) $\dfrac{a + 1}{2} = \dfrac{a - 8}{5}$

3 Solve:

(a) $\dfrac{x}{3} + \dfrac{x}{6} = \dfrac{x + 3}{5}$

(b) $\dfrac{z + 2}{3} + \dfrac{z}{2} = \dfrac{z - 9}{4}$

(c) $\dfrac{3m - 1}{15} + \dfrac{m - 1}{3} = \dfrac{m + 8}{5}$

(d) $\dfrac{4x}{3} + \dfrac{2x - 2}{6} = \dfrac{x - 3}{2}$

(e) $\dfrac{2y - 1}{4} + \dfrac{y + 2}{3} = \dfrac{y - 6}{6}$

(f) $\dfrac{8b + 2}{8} = \dfrac{b - 1}{4} + \dfrac{4b}{2}$

2.8 Forming equations

Learning intentions

Remember   An equation may be used to model a situation.

Example 1

Adnan thinks of a number.
He subtracts 5 then triples his answer.
His final answer is −27.
With what number did he start?

Call his number n.

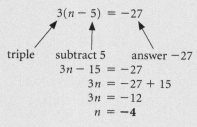

$3(n - 5) = -27$

triple   subtract 5   answer −27

$3n - 15 = -27$

$3n = -27 + 15$

$3n = -12$

$n = -4$

Example 2

Find the length and breadth of the rectangle, if its perimeter is 54 centimetres and the length is 3 less than 4 times the breadth.
Call the breadth x.

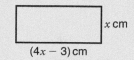

x cm

$(4x - 3)$ cm

$2 \times \text{length} + 2 \times \text{breadth} = \text{perimeter}$

$2(4x - 3) + 2x = 54$

$8x - 6 + 2x = 54$

$10x - 6 = 54$

$10x = 54 + 6$

$10x = 60$

$x = 6$

length $= (4x - 3)$ breadth $= x$

$ = (4 \times 6 - 3)$ $ = 6\,\text{cm}$

$ = 24 - 3$

$ = 21\,\text{cm}$

Exercise 2.8

1 Zara thinks of a number. She adds 6 then doubles her answer.
   Her total is 34. What number did she start with?

2 Thomas adds 9 to 3 times a number, then multiplies the total by 3. His answer is 18. What is the number?

3 Fifteen is added to 4 times a number. The answer is 33. What is the value of the number?

4 Form an equation for each diagram and find the value of x.

(a)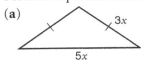

5x

Perimeter = 88 mm

(b)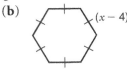

$(x - 4)$

Perimeter = 48 cm

(c)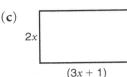

2x

$(3x + 1)$

Perimeter = 42 m

5 Two children, Zein and Mandy, have the same number of sweets.
Zein has 8 packets of sweets and 3 extra sweets.
Mandy has 4 packets and 43 extra.
Make an equation and solve it to find the number of sweets in each packet.

6 The owner of a cafe buys 15 full crates and 4 loose cans of cola.
He puts 124 cans on the shelf and has 9 full crates left.
Make an equation and solve it to find the number of cans in each crate.

7 Carol is a joiner. At the start of a job she has 5 bags of nails and 2 loose nails. She uses 102 nails and has 3 bags left.
Make an equation and solve it to find the number of nails in each bag.

2.9   Solving inequations

Learning intentions

Example 1

Solve:

(a) $4x - 4 \leqslant 2x - 10$ (b) $-2(3y - 1) - 3y \geqslant 56$

(a) $4x - 4 \leqslant 2x - 10$
$\ 2x - 4 \leqslant -10$
$\ \ 2x \leqslant -6$
$\ \ \ \ x \leqslant -3$

(b) $-2(3y - 1) - 3y \geqslant 56$
$\ -6y + 2 - 3y \geqslant 56$
$\ \ \ \ -9y + 2 \geqslant 56$
$\ \ \ \ 2 - 56 \geqslant 9y$
$\ \ \ \ \ \ \ -54 \geqslant 9y$
$\ \ \ \ \ \ \ \ -6 \geqslant y$
$\ \ \ \ \ \ \ \ \ \ y \leqslant -6$

Example 2

Solve on the set of numbers {0, 1, 2 … … … … 10}

$3(2p - 5) > 24$

$3(2p - 5) > 24$
$\ 6p - 15 > 24$
$\ \ \ \ 6p > 39$
$\ \ \ \ \ \ p > \frac{39}{6}$
$\ \ \ \ \ \ p > 6\frac{1}{2}$
$\ \ \ \ \ \ p = 7, 8, 9, 10$

Exercise 2.9

1 Solve the inequations:

(a) $7y + 11 < 2y - 24$ (b) $13x - 23 > 6x + 19$ (c) $15z + 57 \leqslant 5z - 43$

(d) $-5b + 3 \geqslant -2b + 15$ (e) $5w + 2 > 3w - 10$ (f) $-6x + 3 \geqslant -2x - 9$

(g) $-p - 7 < 3p + 1$ (h) $4y + 3 \leqslant 8y + 1$ (i) $15w - 9 < -5w - 13$

(j) $6z + 11 \leqslant 10z - 4$ (k) $-9p + 3 < 3p + 9$ (l) $7y + 2 \leqslant 3y - 8$

2 Solve the inequations on the set of numbers
$\{-6, -5, -4, -3, -2, -1, 0, 1, 2, 3, 4, 5, 6\}$

(a) $3(x - 4) \geqslant 6$

(b) $5(2w + 3) \leqslant 25$

(c) $-2(7p - 4) \leqslant -20$

(d) $-(3x + 1) > 8$

(e) $5(4 - 2z) \leqslant 30$

(f) $-3(5 + 3w) > 30$

(g) $8(3x - 2) - 3 < 5$

(h) $10 + 2(3y - 8) \leqslant 6$

(i) $3 - 5(3y - 2) \geqslant 28$

3 Solve:

(a) $4(y + 7) > 6(y + 2)$

(b) $5(2x + 1) \geqslant 7(x + 2)$

(c) $2(w - 3) < 3(8 - w)$

(d) $3(2z + 4) \geqslant 4(8 - z)$

(e) $6(m + 2) < 3(m - 4)$

(f) $7(2p + 6) \leqslant 4(3p + 12)$

(g) $3(2y + 10) < 2(5 - 2y)$

(h) $4(x - 3) \leqslant -5(x + 1)$

(i) $3(2x + 7) \geqslant 2(5x - 3)$

(j) $3(2p - 1) \geqslant 2(2p + 3)$

(k) $2(4 - 3w) < 4(w - 5)$

(l) $\frac{1}{3}(6y - 9) > \frac{1}{2}(10y + 8)$

4 Solve:

(a) $5(y + 2) - 2y > 13$

(b) $4(z + 1) - 3z \geqslant 6$

(c) $5(w - 1) + 3w < 3$

(d) $6(2x - 3) + 4x \geqslant -26$

(e) $3(2 + 4y) - 6y < 15$

(f) $15x - 3(4 + 6x) \leqslant 3$

(g) $-2(3 - 8z) + 16z \leqslant 66$

(h) $7(x + 1) + 3(x + 2) > 23$

(i) $3(6 - z) + 4(2z + 3) > 50$

(j) $3(y + 2) < 8 - 2(y - 1)$

(k) $3(7 - 2w) \geqslant 3(w + 5) - 84$

(l) $-9(y - 1) - (4y + 5) \geqslant -5y$

2.10 Forming inequations

Learning intentions

Remember   An inequation may be used to model a situation.

Example 1

If the area of the rectangle is greater than the area of the square, find the possible values of x.

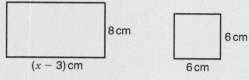

Area $\boxed{}$ > Area $\square$

$8(x - 3) > 6 \times 6$

$8x - 24 > 36$

$\quad 8x > 36 + 24$

$\quad 8x > 60$

$\quad x > 7\frac{1}{2}$

Example 2

The safety regulations for a lift state that the maximum weight that can be carried is 510 kilograms.
Najma, who weighs 65 kilograms, enters a lift with 5 people already in it.
What is the restriction on the average weight of the 5 people for the safety regulations not to be broken?

Let x be the average weight

$5x + 65 \leqslant 510$

$\quad 5x \leqslant 510 - 65$

$\quad 5x \leqslant 445$

$\quad x \leqslant \mathbf{89}$

The average weight must **not be over 89 kg**.

Exercise 2.10

1 Form an inequation for each diagram and find the possible values of x.

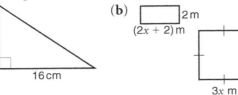

(a)

$x$cm

16 cm

(b)

2 m

$(2x + 2)$ m

3x m

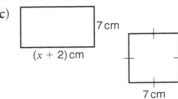

(c)

7 cm

$(x + 2)$ cm

7 cm

7 cm

The area of the triangle is less than 40 cm².

The perimeter of the square is greater than the perimeter of the rectangle.

The area of the rectangle is less than or equal to the area of the square.

2 David and Uzma are organising a cake and candy stall to raise money for charity.
They want to raise at least £140.
David bakes 200 muffins and Uzma makes 300 cookies.
They decide to charge twice as much for a muffin as a cookie.
What is the minimum cost of each if they are to make their target?

3 For safety reasons, the maximum weight a van can transport is 960 kilograms.
The van is being used to transport boxes, each weighing 12 kilograms.
The driver has already loaded some boxes and puts in another 20.
What is the maximum number of boxes already in the van if the safety regulations are not broken?

Review exercise 2: Am I a successful learner?

1 Calculate the value of each expression if $e = 6$, $w = -4$, $x = -5$ and $y = -6$:

(a) $2w + xy$　　　　(b) $3x^2 - 2ew$　　　　(c) $\frac{8e}{w}$

(d) $\frac{2y^2}{e}$　　　　(e) $\frac{2x^2 + 5y}{w + e}$　　　　(f) $\frac{xw^2 + (y - x)}{w + x}$

2 Simplify each expression:

(a) $-8x - 2y + 3x + 4y$　　　　　　(b) $-7r - 3r - 4v - 6v$

(c) $14st + 3xy - 5st - 11xy$　　　　(d) $3c^2 - 4ab - c^2 + 6ab + 2c^2 + ab$

(e) $11gh^2 - 5gh - 5gh^2 + gh$　　　(f) $2x^2 + 4x - x^2 - 9x + x^3 - 3$

3 Multiply out the brackets and simplify:

(a) $6(3d - 2)$　　　　(b) $4(5x - 5y)$　　　　(c) $3(2x^2 - 9) + 5x^2$

(d) $9 - 3(4f - 3)$　　(e) $5(6z - 3) + 3(4 + 2z)$　(f) $12b - 3(4b - 8) + 8(3b + 1)$

4 Factorise each expression

(a) $15x - 35y$　　　(b) $28p + 21$　　　(c) $6a - 12b + 42$

5 Solve each equation:

(a) $4y - 9 = 31$　　　(b) $3x + 11 = 13$　　　(c) $120 = -6z + 78$

(d) $16b - 10 = 4b - 19$　(e) $12w + 6 = 54 - 4w$　(f) $8 - 3y = 6y + 4$

6 Solve:

    (a) $3(x + 3) = -27$ **(b)** $-18 = 6(5y - 4)$ **(c)** $4(3z - 1) + 16 = 48$

    (d) $15 - 2(w - 9) = 35$ **(e)** $5(2b + 3) = 4(3 + 4b)$ **(f)** $3(4x - 8) - 3 = 5(2x - 9) + 10$

7 Solve:

    (a) $\dfrac{y}{3} = 4y + 22$ **(b)** $\dfrac{3x}{2} = 3(x - 5)$ **(c)** $\dfrac{x}{2} = \dfrac{x - 2}{3}$

    (d) $\dfrac{2w}{3} = \dfrac{w - 5}{4}$ **(e)** $\dfrac{x}{6} + \dfrac{2x + 1}{3} = \dfrac{x - 3}{2}$ **(f)** $\dfrac{z - 2}{3} + \dfrac{z}{2} = \dfrac{z + 9}{4}$

8 Solve each inequation:

    (a) $5y - 11 \leqslant 10y + 4$ **(b)** $7z - 2 \leqslant 3z + 8$ **(c)** $8 + 2(3x + 8) \leqslant -6$

    (d) $4(w - 7) > 6(w - 2)$ **(e)** $5(y - 2) + 2y > -13$ **(f)** $3(1 + 2z) \geqslant 3(z - 5) + 8$

9 Form an equation for each diagram and find the value of x.

    (a) 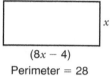   **(b)** 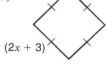   **(c)**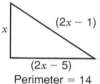

10 James adds 11 to $2y$ then multiplies the total by 3. His answer is 45.
    What number is y?

11 Katie thinks of a number. She subtracts 5 and then multiplies the answer
    by 4. The result is -28.
    What number did Katie first think of?

12 Form an inequation for each diagram and find the value of x.

    (a) 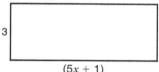   **(b)**

      The area of the rectangle is less   The perimeter of the
      than 33 m².   pentagon is greater than
                                             or equal to 50 cm.

13 Carole and John are selling juice and crisps in a tuck shop to raise funds
    for their school.
    Their target is to raise at least £30.
    Carole sells 50 cartons of juice and John sells 100 packets of crisps.
    They decide to charge twice as much for a carton of juice as a packet of
    crisps.
    What is the minimum cost of each if they are to make their target?

Summary 2: What I learned in this chapter.

Evaluating expressions

Evaluate $\dfrac{2q^2 - s}{p + q}$ if $p = -1$, $q = 5$ and $s = -4$

$$= \frac{2 \times (5)^2 - (-4)}{-1 + (-5)} = \frac{2 \times 25 + 4}{-6}$$

$$= \frac{54}{-6}$$

$$= -9$$

Simplifying using the distributive law

Simplify: $5(4x + 5) + 5(3x - 2y - 3) - 8y$

$5(4x + 5) + 5(3x - 2y - 3) - 8y$

$= 20x + 25 + 15x - 10y - 15 - 8y$

$= 20x + 15x - 10y - 8y + 25 - 15$

$= \mathbf{35x - 18y + 10}$

> Expand the brackets

> Simplify by collecting like terms

Solving equations and inequations

Solve:

(a) $3(3x + 9) = 4 - (5 - 2x)$

$9x + 27 = 4 - 5 + 2x$

$9x + 27 = -1 + 2x$

$9x - 2x = -1 - 27$

$7x = -28$

$x = -\dfrac{28}{7}$

$x = \mathbf{-4}$

(b)

$$\frac{2y - 1}{5} + \frac{y + 2}{2} = \frac{y - 8}{10}$$

$$10 \times \frac{2y - 1}{5} + 10 \times \frac{y + 2}{2} = 10 \times \frac{y - 8}{10}$$

$$2(2y - 1) + 5(y + 2) = y - 8$$

$$4y - 2 + 5y + 10 = y - 8$$

$$9y + 8 = y - 8$$

$$9y - y = -8 - 8$$

$$8y = -16$$

$$y = -\frac{16}{8}$$

$$y = \mathbf{-2}$$

(c) $16 - 2(x - 1) \leqslant 3(x + 2)$

$16 - 2x + 2 \leqslant 3x + 6$

$16 + 2 - 6 \leqslant 3x + 2x$

$12 \leqslant 5x$

$\dfrac{12}{5} \leqslant x$

$x \geqslant 2\dfrac{2}{5}$

Forming equations and inequations

An equation or inequation may be used to model a situation.

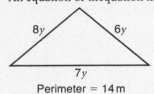

8y   6y

7y

Perimeter = 14 m

$8y + 7y + 6y = 14$

$21y = 14$

$y = \dfrac{14}{21}$

$y = \dfrac{2}{3}$ **metres**

3 Essential skills: proportion

3.1 Direct proportion

Learning intentions

Two quantities are in **direct proportion** if they increase or decrease in the same ratio.

Number of books
Cost of books

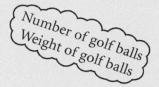
Number of golf balls
Weight of golf balls

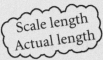
Scale length
Actual length

Example

8 balls of wool cost £52.
    (a) Calculate the cost of 11 balls.

                      (b) How many balls can be bought for £32·50?

(a)

Balls of wool	Cost (£)
$\div 8$ ⟨ 8	52
1	$52 \div 8 = 6{\cdot}50$
$\times 11$ ⟨ 11	$6{\cdot}50 \times 11 = 71{\cdot}50$

11 balls cost **£71.50**

(b)

Cost (£)	Balls
52	8
1	$8 \div 52$
32·50	$\frac{8}{52} \times 32{\cdot}5 = 5$

£32.50 would buy **5** balls

Exercise 3.1

1 Six balls of wool cost £19·80.
Calculate the cost of   (a) 10 balls   (b) 4 balls

2 Three weeks' rent for an apartment is £810.
Calculate the rent for 8 weeks.

3 A car travels 352 kilometres on 32 litres of petrol.
How far should it travel on 50 litres?

4 A breadmaker produces 260 loaves in 4 hours. If the machine is in use
from 5am until 2pm, how many loaves should it produce?

5 A garden centre sold 70 flower bulbs for £8·40.
How much should 120 bulbs cost?

6 A bundle of 25 catalogues weighs 10 kilogrammes.
How much would 48 catalogues weigh?

7 A case of wine holds 12 bottles.
Jim bought 4 cases of wine which cost him £254·40.
What is the cost of $7\frac{1}{2}$ cases of wine?

8 In a 5 month period John pays £615 in pension contributions.
How much would he pay for a full year?

9 A building 24 metres high casts a shadow 16·4 metres long.
At the same time of day, what height is a tower which has a shadow 28·2
metres long?

10 A tool rental company charges £56·50 for 4 days' hire of a floor sander.
What would the charge be for
(**a**) 7 days   (**b**) 13 days?

11 Fiona owns 950 shares in a chemical company. In one year she earned a
£76 dividend. How much would the dividend have been on 1250 shares?

12 Chloe earned £33·20 commission on sales of £830. How much would she
earn on sales of
(**a**) £652   (**b**) £1004?

13 A map has a scale of 1:1000. What distance on the ground, in kilometres,
is represented by
(**a**) 17 cm   (**b**) 8·2 cm?

14 On a map with scale 1 : 20 000, what distance on the map, in centimetres,
represents
(**a**) 8 km   (**b**) 24·6 km?

15 A distance of 12 centimetres on a map represents 1·8 kilometres.
Calculate
(**a**) the real distance for a map distance of 8·2 centimetres
(**b**) the distance on the map for a real distance of 4·4 kilometres.

16 A scale model of a yacht is 48 centimetres long. The actual length of the
yacht is 38 metres. The mast on the model is 54 centimetres high.
How high is the real mast?

17 In the Home Economics class Mrs Macfarlane has a recipe for
6 scones.
Calculate how much of each ingredient is needed for a batch of
45 scones.

Scones recipe	
Flour	100g
Butter	30g
Sugar	25g

18 An electric fire uses 4·8 units of electricity in a 3 hour period.
If 32 units are used, for how long has the fire been switched on?

19 A car travels 23 metres in one second. What is this speed in
(**a**) metres per hour   (**b**) kilometres per hour?

3.2 Direct proportion with rounding

Learning intentions

Example

At Kirkdale School 853 pupils used 175 432 pages of photocopying paper.
If the roll drops to 785, calculate the number of pages required, to 3 significant figures.

Pupils	Pages
853	175 432
1	$\dfrac{175\,432}{853}$
785	$\dfrac{175\,432 \times 785}{853} = 161\,446{\cdot}79$

The number of pages is **161 000**, to 3 significant figures.

Exercise 3.2

1 On a shelf, 64 copies of a physics book use up 396 centimetres of space.
Calculate to 1 decimal place how much shelf space is required for

(**a**) 83 books   (**b**) 132 books.

2 Morag uses 10·85 metres of ribbon to trim 12 baby dresses.
How much ribbon, to 2 decimal places, will she need for 30 dresses?

3 The weight of 35 bags of bulbs is 27 kilogrammes.
To 1 decimal place, how much will 64 bags weigh?

4 At a football match 1353 fans generate a profit of £620 for the club.
Calculate, to 2 significant figures, the expected profit from 1750 fans.

5 At a disco the school made £456 when 385 pupils attended.
If the school wishes to raise at least £550, how many pupils need to
attend? Give your answer correct to 2 significant figures.

6 A factory produced 1760 chairs during a 5 day period. Calculate how many
chairs should be produced in 28 days, to 2 significant figures.

7 A restaurant uses 2·6 kilogrammes of pasta for 8 portions.
How much pasta is required for 35 portions, to 1 decimal place?

8 A transport company spends £1456 on fuel in a week when the
trucks travel a total of 125 400 kilometres. If the trucks travel 223 544
kilometres, how much will this cost, to 3 significant figures?

9 The council raises £456 890 of tax on property valued at £43 600 000.
If property values rise to £58 750 000, how much tax will be raised, to 1
significant figure?

10 Copy and complete the table, correct to 2 decimal places.

Distance on map (cm)	5·30	8·95	14·65	
Distance on ground (km)		4·40		34·8

3.3 Inverse proportion

Learning intentions

Two quantities are in **inverse proportion** if, as one increases, the other decreases in the same ratio.

Example 1

A builder estimates that a team of 4 men will complete a project in 6 days.
If he employs only 3 men, how long should the project take?

Men	Days
4	6
1	$6 \times 4 = 24$
3	$\frac{24}{3} = 8$

One person will take 4 times as long.

$\frac{24}{3} = 8$ The project will take **8** days.

Example 2

Deirdre has just enough money to buy 9 boxes of chocolates at £6.50 each.
If she decides to buy boxes which cost £9.75, how many can she afford?

Cost per box (£)	Boxes she can afford
6·50	9
1	$9 \times 6{\cdot}50$
9·75	$\frac{9 \times 6{\cdot}50}{9{\cdot}75} = 6$

She can afford **6** boxes.

Exercise 3.3

1 A building project will take 16 days to complete with 3 men working.
How long should it take if there are 8 men available to work?

2 A maths department has a fixed sum for jotters. Last session they bought
2400 at 58p each. If the price rises to 60p each, how many can they
afford?

3 A cyclist takes 40 minutes at a speed of 28 kilometres/hour to complete
a journey. If he travels at 32 kilometres/hour how long will the journey
take?

4 Ian is using 1·5 metre edging slabs around the perimeter of a flower bed.
He needs exactly 36 slabs. If he buys 1·8 metre slabs instead, how many
will he need?

5 A caterer estimates she has enough paper napkins to set places at
3 meal times for 120 people. If she only has to cater for 24 people at how
many meal times could she set places?

6 A bookshelf will hold 24 books each 4 centimetres wide.
How many books 6 centimetres wide will fit on the shelf?

7 Pete is draining a small pond and estimates it will take 6 days if he uses
4 pumps. If he can only hire 3 pumps how long should it take to drain
the pond?

8 New drainage pipes are being laid in a sports field. The contractor estimates he will need 240 pipes each 3·2 metres long. If he switches to 2·8 metre pipes, how many should he need?

9 Ian has chosen to buy 12 fruit trees at £25 each. If he selects a different type of tree which costs £17·50, how many more trees could he buy for the same cost?

10 A vet has sufficient supplies to inoculate 4800 hens with 2·5 milligrams of vaccine each. Instead she is asked to inoculate turkeys with 3·6 milligrams. How many turkeys can she treat?

11 The grass on Jane's pasture land will support a herd of 42 cattle for 8 days. If she buys 14 more cows, for how long will the grass support the herd?

12 A new school building is to be completed in 360 working days with 44 workers on site. The finish date is brought forward by 30 days. How many more workers will be required to meet the new deadline?

13 Donald has a contract to deliver 3400 pairs of jeans. He estimates he will need 8 employees to complete the order in 9 days. If he is asked to deliver in 6 days, how many more workers will he need?

3.4 Foreign exchange

Learning intentions

Foreign currencies are in direct proportion to each other.

Discussion points

Example

$£1 = 1.40$ euros

(a) Change £35 into euros   **(b)** Change 236 euros into pounds

(a)

£	euros
1	1·40
35	$1·40 \times 35 = 49$

£35 is worth **49 Euros**

(b)

euros	£
1·40	1
1	$\dfrac{1}{1·40}$
236	$\dfrac{1 \times 236}{1·40} = 168·5714$

236 euros is worth **£168.57**

How many different currencies have the class used and in which countries?

Where can foreign currency be bought?

How do you find out about exchange rates?

Investigate different exchange rates and where to find the best value for euros.

EC CI

Exercise 3.4

1 Change into euros

$£1 = 1.40$ euros

    (a) £46   **(b)** £256   **(c)** £356.50   **(d)** £478.80

2 Change into pounds

    (a) 36 €   **(b)** 89 €   **(c)** 346 €   **(d)** 785.5 €

3 Michael changed £350 into euros and was given 475 €. What rate of exchange is this?

4 At the Europe Express travel agency the rates of exchange are shown on a table.

   (**a**) Change £176 into
      (**i**) euros   (**ii**) dollars   (**iii**) krone

   (**b**) Use the rates to change into pounds
      (**i**) 455 €   (**ii**) $385   (**iii**) 624 krone

Europe Express

£1 buys
1.50 euros
1.72 dollars
14 krone

5 Sally changed £75 at the bank and received $127·50.
How much would George expect to receive for £126?

6 Which company gives the best rate of exchange?
Explain your answer.
Bank of Caledonia exchanged £250 for 360 euros.
Euro Express exchanged £175 for 262.50 euros.
Burnfoot Travel exchanged £320 for 424 euros.

7 Ian changed £240 into dollars at the rate of $1·72 to the pound.
He did not spend any money and later changed his money back into pounds at the rate of $1·81 to the pound.
How much money did he lose by doing this?

8 In May Sam was paid $4500 when the rate was $1·64 to the pound.
In December he earned $4800 when the rate was $1·82 to the pound.
In which month did he earn the most, in sterling, and by how much?

Review exercise 3: Am I a successful learner?

1 Eight rose plants cost £42·40.
   (**a**) Calculate the cost of 5 plants.
   (**b**) How many plants can be bought for £37·10?

2 A bus travels 840 kilometres on 80 litres of diesel.
How much fuel should it require for a journey of 1260 kilometres?

3 A box of soaps contains 6 bars. Sheila bought 7 boxes which cost her £37·45.
How much should she pay for 11 boxes?

4 Greta's 835 shares in a hotel business earned her a £751·50 dividend.
Tom earned a dividend of £832·50. How many shares does he have?

5 A car is travelling at 85 kilometres per hour.
What is this speed in metres per second?

6 Ian used 33·68 metres of trim to edge 8 small tables.
How much trim does he need for 15 tables?
Give your answer correct to 1 decimal place.

7 At a nightclub an attendance of 525 people brings in a profit of £2780.
To make a profit of £3580, how many people need to attend, to 2 significant figures?

8 For a meal for 35 people, a caterer makes 6·5 kilograms of coleslaw.
How much should he make for 78 people, correct to 2 decimal places?

9 A landscaper needs 5 men to complete a project in 12 days.
If he uses 6 men for the task, how long should it take?

10 £1 is worth $1·72. Change into dollars:
  (**a**) £73   (**b**) £136

11 £1 is worth 2.65 Australian dollars. Change into pounds:
  (**a**) $356   (**b**) $16·50

 12 Who got the best rate of exchange?

> Mike changed £135 into $189   Stan changed £126 into $168·84

Summary 3: What I learned in this chapter.

Direct proportion

42 bags of seed potatoes weigh 142·8 kilograms.
What would 317 bags weigh, correct to 3 significant figures?

Bags	Weight (kg)
42	142·8
1	$\frac{142·8}{42}$
317	$\frac{142·8}{42} \times 317 = 1077·8$

÷42, ×317

317 bags weigh **1080** kg to 3 sig. figs.

Inverse proportion

5 men will take 12 days to build a swimming pool.
How long should 6 men take?

Men	Days
5	12
1	12×5
6	$\frac{12 \times 5}{6} = 10$

It should take **10** days.

Foreign exchange

£1 is worth $1·72

(**a**) Change £235 into dollars

(**b**) Change $396 into pounds

(**a**)

£	$
1	1·72
235	$1·72 \times 235 = 404·2$

£235 is **$404·20**

(**b**)

$	£
1·72	1
1	$\frac{1}{1·72}$
396	$\frac{1 \times 396}{1·72} = 230·2325$

$396 is **£230·23**

4 Area

4.1 Area of square, rectangle and triangle

Remember

Area of a triangle
$A = \frac{1}{2} \times$ base $\times$ height
$A = \frac{1}{2}bh$

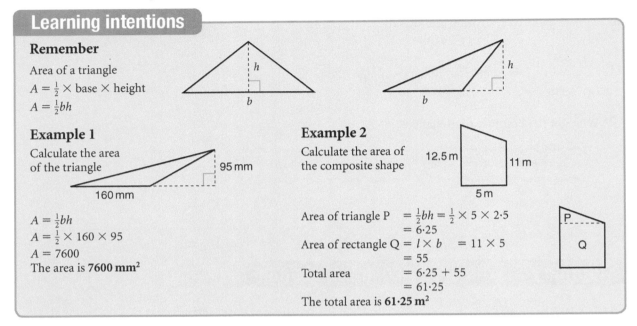

Example 1

Calculate the area
of the triangle

95 mm

160 mm

$A = \frac{1}{2}bh$
$A = \frac{1}{2} \times 160 \times 95$
$A = 7600$
The area is **7600 mm²**

Example 2

Calculate the area of
the composite shape

12.5 m   11 m

5 m

Area of triangle P $= \frac{1}{2}bh = \frac{1}{2} \times 5 \times 2.5$
$= 6.25$
Area of rectangle Q $= l \times b$ $= 11 \times 5$
$= 55$
Total area $= 6.25 + 55$
$= 61.25$
The total area is **61.25 m²**

P

Q

Exercise 4.1

1 Calculate the area of each shape.

(a) 30 cm
1.5 m

(b) 3.5 mm

(c) 24 cm
68 cm

(d)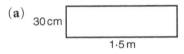
3.5 cm
20 mm

(e)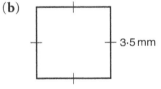
65 cm
1.35 m

(f)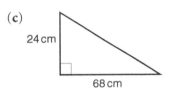
3.4 m
230 cm

2 Find the area of each shape.

(a)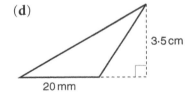
30 m
10 m
50 m
20 m

(b)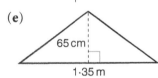
17.5 cm
9.5 cm
15 cm

(c)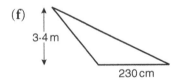
7.2 cm
1.2 cm
6.6 cm
2.8 cm
1.2 cm
7.2 cm

(d)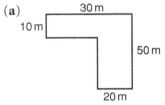
2.2 m
0.6 m
4.6 m

(e)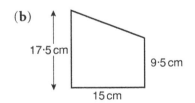
64 mm
26 mm
38 mm

(f)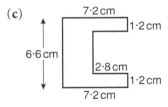
11.3 cm
8.9 cm
6.5 cm

3 Calculate the cost of resurfacing this childrens' play park if the special surface costs £44.99 per square metre.

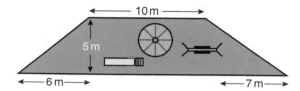

4 David uses pieces of glass to make stained glass windows. The area of each piece of glass is shown.

(**a**) Find the length of the base.   (**b**) Find the height.

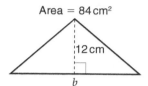

Area = 84 cm²

12 cm

b

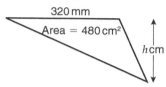

320 mm

Area = 480 cm²

h cm

4.2 Area of rhombus and kite

Learning intentions

Remember

The area of a rhombus or kite is half the area of the surrounding rectangle.

Area of a rhombus or kite,

$A = \frac{1}{2} \times$ breadth $\times$ length

$A = \frac{1}{2} \times diagonal_1 \times diagonal_2$

$A = \frac{1}{2} d_1 d_2$

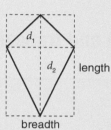

length

breadth

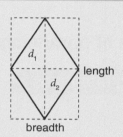

length

breadth

Example 1 Calculate the area of the kite

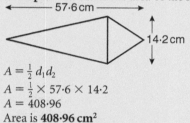

57·6 cm

14·2 cm

$A = \frac{1}{2} d_1 d_2$

$A = \frac{1}{2} \times 57{\cdot}6 \times 14{\cdot}2$

$A = 408{\cdot}96$

Area is **408·96 cm²**

Example 2 Find the missing dimension

$A = \frac{1}{2} d_1 d_2$

$250 = \frac{1}{2} \times x \times 25$

$250 = 12{\cdot}5x$

$x = \frac{250}{12{\cdot}5}$

$x = 20$ cm

x is **20 cm**

x cm

25 cm

Area 250 cm²

Exercise 4.2

1 Calculate the area of each kite.

(**a**)

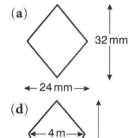

32 mm

24 mm

(**b**)

2·7 m

3·5 m

(**c**)

9·5 cm

14·2 cm

(**d**)

4 m

12·8 m

(**e**)

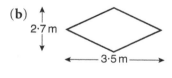

3·1 mm

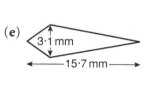

15·7 mm

(**f**)

35 cm

22 cm

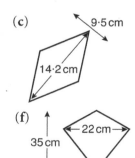

2 Find the missing dimension for each kite.

(a)

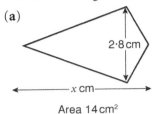

2·8 cm

x cm

Area 14 cm²

(b)

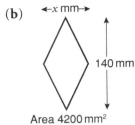

←x mm→

140 mm

Area 4200 mm²

(c)

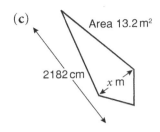

Area 13.2 m²

2182 cm

x m

3 Sophia uses congruent rhombus patches to create patterns on a patchwork quilt.
Calculate the area of the patch and each pattern.

(a)

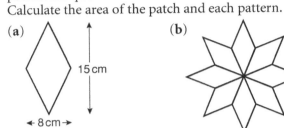

15 cm

← 8 cm →

(b)

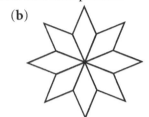

(c)

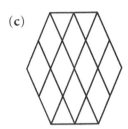

4.3 Area of parallelogram and trapezium

Learning intentions

Remember

Area of a parallelogram = base × height
$$A = bh$$

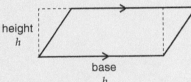

height
h

base
b

The area of a trapezium is the average of the outer rectangle and the inner rectangle. This is equivalent to calculating breadth times average length.

Outer rectangle $A = bL$ Inner rectangle $A = bl$

Area of a trapezium $A = \dfrac{(bL + bl)}{2}$ or $A = \dfrac{b(L + l)}{2}$

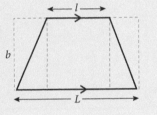

A trapezium has one pair of parallel lines.

Example

Find the area of each shape. **(a)**

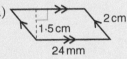

2 cm

1·5 cm

24 mm

(b)

24 cm

8 cm

36 cm

$A = bh$

$A = 2·4 \times 1·5$

$A = 3·6$

Area is **3·6 cm²**

$A = \dfrac{b(L + l)}{2}$

$A = \dfrac{8(36 + 24)}{2}$

$A = \dfrac{480}{2}$

$A = 240$

Area is **240 cm²**

Discussion point

How could you find the area of a trapezium without using the formula $A = \dfrac{b(L + l)}{2}$?

Exercise 4.3

1 Calculate the area of each parallelogram or trapezium.

(a)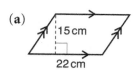

(b)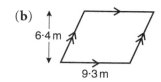

(c)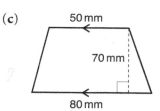

(d)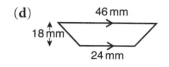

(e)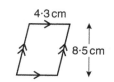

(f)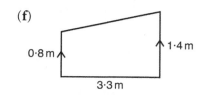

2 Fahim uses small trapezium shaped pieces of tile to make designs.
(a) Calculate the area of this tile.

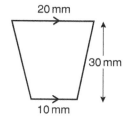

(b) Calculate the area of this design, made with congruent tiles.

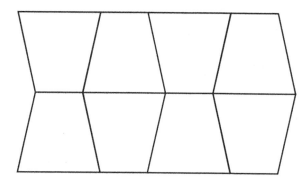

3 Find the missing dimension for each shape..

(a)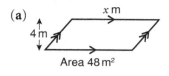

(b)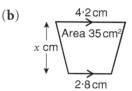

(c)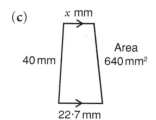

4.4 Circles

Learning intentions

Remember

Circumference of a circle $= \pi d = 2\pi r$
Area of a circle $= \pi r^2$

$\pi = 3 \cdot 14$ to 2 decimal places

Example 1

Calculate the circumference and area of this circle.

13 cm

$C = \pi d$
$C = \pi \times 26$
$C = 81 \cdot 68$
Circumference is **81·7 cm** to 3 sig. figs.

$A = \pi r^2$
$A = \pi \times 13^2$
$A = 530 \cdot 929$
Area is **531 cm²** to 3 sig. figs.

Example 2

Find the diameter of a circle with area 628 cm²

$A = \pi r^2$
$628 = \pi \times r^2$
$\dfrac{628}{\pi} = r^2$
$199 \cdot 89 = r^2$
$\sqrt{199 \cdot 89} = r$
$r = 14 \cdot 134$

Diameter $= 2 \times 14 \cdot 134$
$= 28 \cdot 277$
Diameter is **28·3 cm** to 1 dec. place.

Exercise 4.4

1 Find the circumference and area of each circle. Round answers to 3 significant figures.

(a)

22 cm

(b)

6·2 mm

(c)
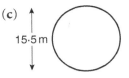
15·5 m

2 Bushra is trimming the bottom edge of a lampshade.
She uses lace ribbon which costs £4.95 per metre.
The bottom of the lampshade has a radius of 21 centimetres.
How much does it cost to trim the lampshade?

3 An indoor cycle track is 200 metres long.
The front wheel on a racing bicycle has diameter 63 centimetres.
How many revolutions does the front wheel make to complete one lap of the track?

4 Find the area of each shape.

(a)
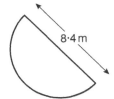
8·4 m

(b)
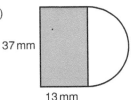
37 mm
13 mm

(c)
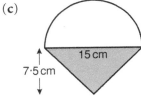
15 cm
7·5 cm

5 A circular table with diameter 1.4 metres is covered with a circular table cloth. The table cloth has diameter 175 centimetres.
What is the area of cloth which overhangs?

6 Find the area of each circle, leaving the answer as a multiple of π.

(a) 2 cm

(b)  10 mm

(c) 10 m

7 Calculate the radius of each circle.

(a) 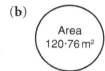 Area 28·3 cm²

(b) 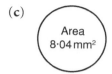 Area 120·76 m²

(c) Area 8·04 mm²

8 A square jigsaw puzzle fits exactly on to a circular table as shown. The area of the table top is 191·13 square centimetres. What is the length of the jigsaw's diagonal?

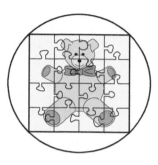

4.5 Arc length

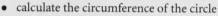

Learning intentions

Remember

An arc is a section of the circumference of a circle.
The length of an arc is proportional to the angle at the centre.

To find the length of an arc:
- calculate the circumference of the circle
- find the fraction $\frac{x}{360}$
- find the length of an arc by multiplying $\frac{x}{360} \times$ circumference $= \frac{x}{360} \times \pi d$

Example

For this circle find the length of the minor arc.

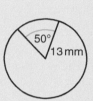

$C = \pi d$
$C = \pi \times 26$
$C = 81 \cdot 68$

Length of arc $= \frac{50}{360} \times 81 \cdot 68$

Length of arc $= 11 \cdot 344$

Length of arc is **11·3 mm** to 3 sig. figs.

Exercise 4.5

1 Calculate the length of each arc.

(a) 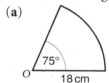 75° 18 cm

(b) 23 cm O

(c)  O 145° 17·2 mm

(d)  25° 4·4 m O

(e) 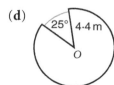 16·2 cm 230° O

(f) 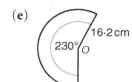 125° 36 mm O

2 Calculate the perimeter of each shape.

(a)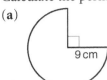
9 cm

(b)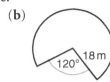
120° 18 m

3 A sector of a circle is created on the floor as a door swings open.
Calculate the length of the arc created when a door, 70 centimetres
wide, swings through 100°.

4 The throwing area for the hammer event at an athletics ground is part of
the sector of a circle with angle at the centre 75°.
The groundsman has to mark off arcs within the sector at 10 metre
increments. Calculate the length of each of the arcs for radii of 40, 60
and 80 metres.

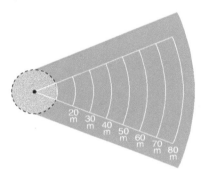

5 The windscreen wipers on a car clear an area on the window
like the one shown in the diagram below. The windscreen
wiper measures 58 centimetres and the blade is 42 centimetres.
The wiper sweeps through an angle of 165°.
What is the difference between the length of the arcs created
by the top and bottom of the blade?

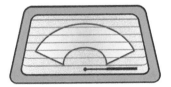

6 Show that the arc length can be written as $\frac{5\pi}{3}$ centimetres.

O 60°
5 cm

7 Write each arc length in terms of π.

(a)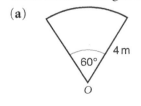
4 m
60°
O

(b)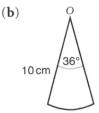
O
36°
10 cm

(c)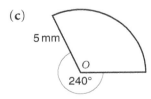
5 mm
O
240°

4.6 Area of a sector

Learning intentions

Remember

A sector is a section of a circle enclosed by two radii and an arc.
The area of a sector is proportional to the angle at the centre.

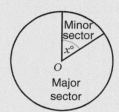

To find the area of a sector
- calculate the area of the circle
- find the fraction $\frac{x}{360}$
- find the area of the sector by multiplying $\frac{x}{360} \times$ area $= \frac{x}{360} \times \pi r^2$

Example

Find the area of the major sector.

$$A = \pi r^2$$
$$= \pi \times 12^2$$
$$= 452 \cdot 389$$

$x = 360 - 120 = 240°$

$$A = \frac{240}{360} \times 452 \cdot 389$$

$$A = 301 \cdot 592$$

Area is **302 m²** to 3 sig. figs.

Exercise 4.6

1 Calculate the area of each sector.

(a)

(b)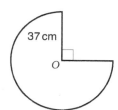

(c)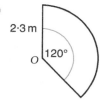

(d)

(e)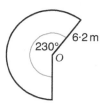

(f)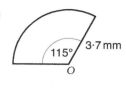

2 A magician's hat is made from the piece of card shown.
What area of card is used?

3 Popcorn is sold in conical containers. The cones are made from cardboard
sectors with radius 80 millimetres and angle at the centre 235°.
Find the area of card needed for each container.

4 A goat is tethered by a length of rope to the corner of a shed in the middle of a field. The area of grass the goat can eat is 9·42 square metres. Assuming the length and breadth of the shed are greater than the radius, find the length of rope that has been used to tether the goat.

5 Show that the area of the sector can be written as $\frac{49\pi}{3}$ square metres.

6 Write the area of each sector in terms of π.

(a)

(b)

(c)

7 Calculate the area of each minor sector. Answers should be given as a multiple of π.

(a)

(b)

(c)

4.7 Working backwards

Learning intentions

The radius, diameter or angle at the centre of a circle may be found from the arc length or area of a sector.

Example 1

Find the radius of a circle with length of arc 12·5 centimetres and angle at the centre 45°.

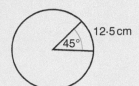

$$\text{arc length} = \frac{x}{360}\pi d$$

$$12\cdot5 = \frac{45}{360} \times \pi \times d$$

$$12\cdot5 = 0.393 \times d$$

$$\frac{12\cdot5}{0\cdot393} = d$$

$$31\cdot81 = d$$

$$r = 31\cdot81 \div 2 = 15\cdot905$$

Radius is **15·9 cm** to 1 dec. place.

Example 2

Calculate the angle at the centre of a circle for a sector with radius 7·5 centimetres and area 14·73 square centimetres.

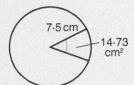

$$A = \frac{x}{360}\pi r^2$$

$$14\cdot73 = \frac{x}{360} \times \pi \times 7\cdot5^2$$

$$14\cdot73 = \frac{x}{360} \times 176\cdot715$$

$$\frac{14\cdot73}{176\cdot715} \times 360 = x$$

$$30\cdot006 = x$$

Angle at the centre is **30°** to nearest degree.

Exercise 4.7

1 Find the radius of a circle with length of arc 6·28 centimetres and angle at the centre 72°.

2 Calculate the diameter of a circle for a sector with angle at the centre 150° and arc length 16·49 metres.

3 Calculate the angle at the centre of a circle for a sector with radius 30 millimetres and area 471·24 millimetres squared.

4 Calculate the diameter of a circle for a sector with angle at the centre 75° and area 23·56 centimetres squared.

5 Find the radius of a sector of a circle with angle at the centre 220° and area 191·99 metres squared.

6 For a sector with radius 6 centimetres and area 14·14 centimetres squared·
   (**a**) calculate the angle at the centre
   (**b**) calculate the length of the minor arc.

7 For a sector with radius 2.4 metres and arc length 6·07 metres
   (**a**) calculate the angle at the centre of the circle
   (**b**) calculate the area of the sector.

8 If an arc length of 15 centimetres subtends an angle of 40° at the centre
   (**a**) calculate the arc length for an angle of 60°
   (**b**) find the angle subtended by an arc of 67·5 centimetres.

9 If the area of a sector is 30 centimetres square with an angle of 25° at the centre
   (**a**) calculate the area of a sector subtended by an angle of 40°
   (**b**) find the angle subtended by a sector area of 45 centimetres squared.

Review exercise 4: Am I a successful learner?

1 Calculate the area of each shape.

(**a**)
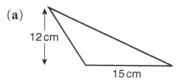
12 cm
15 cm

(**b**)
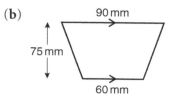
90 mm
75 mm
60 mm

(**c**)
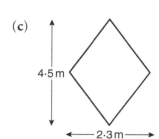
4·5 m
2·3 m

2 How much paint does John require to cover the wall, if one litre of paint covers 2·25 square metres?

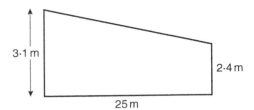

3·1 m

2·4 m

25 m

3 Find the circumference and area of each circle.

(a) 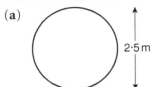 2·5 m

(b) 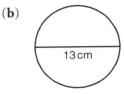 13 cm

(c) 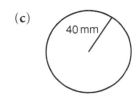 40 mm

4 The edging on a stained glass window needs to be replaced. What length of edging is required?

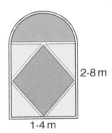

2·8 m

1·4 m

5 For each shape find the length of the arc and the area of the sector.

(a)  275° 8 cm

(b) 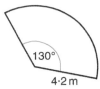 130° 4·2 m

(c) 35° 17 mm

6 (a) Show that the length of the arc can be written as 7π metres.
   (b) Express the area of the sector in terms of π.

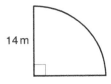

14 m

7 Calculate the angle at the centre of a circle for a sector with radius 2·4 metres and area 1·51 metres squared.

8 If an arc length of 24 centimetres subtends an angle of 136°
   (a) calculate the arc length for an angle of 48°.
   (b) find the angle subtended by an arc of 30 centimetres.

Summary 4: What I learned in this chapter.

Area of rectilinear shapes

Triangle

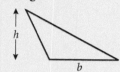

$A = \frac{1}{2} \times$ base $\times$ height

$A = \frac{1}{2}bh$

Rhombus and kite

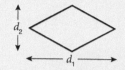

$A = \frac{1}{2} \times$ breadth $\times$ length

$A = \frac{1}{2} \times diagonal_1 \times diagonal_2$

$A = \frac{1}{2}d_1d_2$

Parallelogram

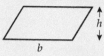

$A =$ base $\times$ height

$A = bh$

Trapezium

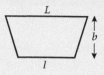

$A = \dfrac{b(L + l)}{2}$

Circles

Circumference of a circle

$C = \pi d$ or $C = 2\pi r$

Area of a circle

$A = \pi r^2$

Arcs and sectors

Length of an arc

To find the length of an arc:

- calculate the circumference of the circle
- find the fraction $\dfrac{x}{360}$
- find the length of an arc by multiplying

$\dfrac{x}{360} \times$ circumference $= \dfrac{x}{360} \times \pi d$

Area of a sector

To find the area of a sector:

- calculate the area of the circle
- find the fraction $\dfrac{x}{360}$
- find the area of the sector by multiplying

$\dfrac{x}{360} \times$ area $= \dfrac{x}{360} \times \pi r^2$

Example

Calculate the angle at the centre of a circle for a sector with radius 7.5 centimetres and area 14.73 square centimetres.

$$A = \frac{x}{360}\pi r^2$$

$$14{\cdot}73 = \frac{x}{360} \times \pi \times 7{\cdot}5^2$$

$$14{\cdot}73 = \frac{x}{360} \times 176{\cdot}715$$

$$\frac{14{\cdot}73}{176{\cdot}715} \times 360 = x$$

$$30{\cdot}006 = x$$

x is **30°** to nearest degree.

5 Similarity

5.1 Enlarging and reducing

When photographs are enlarged, all lengths in the original are increased by the same **scale factor**.

- All dimensions are increased by same scale factor.
- Photograph is an enlargement

- Not all dimensions are enlarged by same scale factor.
- Photograph is **not** an enlargement.

A shape may be enlarged or reduced using a scale factor.
A scale factor multiplies the length of every side of a shape.

An enlargement using a scale factor of 3

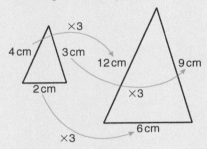

A reduction using a scale factor of $\frac{1}{2}$

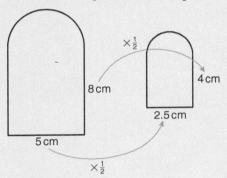

A scale factor **greater than 1 enlarges** a shapes.
A scale factor **less than 1 reduces** a shape.

Example

Find the scale factor to make this enlargement.

6 cm

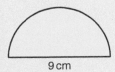
9 cm

Compare dimensions.   Scale factor $= \frac{9}{6} = \frac{3}{2}$

Exercise 5.1

1 Copy each shape and draw an enlargement or reduction using the scale factor given.

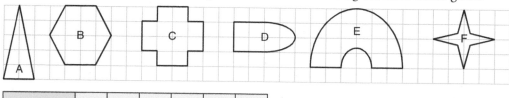

Shape	A	B	C	D	E	F
Scale factor	2	3	$\frac{1}{2}$	1.5	$\frac{1}{2}$	2.5

2 Draw an enlargement or reduction of each letter using the scale factor given.

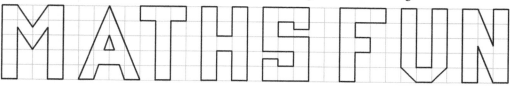

Letter	M	A	T	H	S	F	U	N
Scale factor	$\frac{1}{2}$	2	3	1.5	2	2.5	2	1

3 Find the scale factor used to make each enlargement.

(a)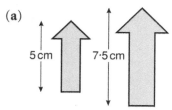

(b)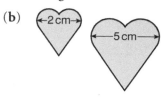

(c)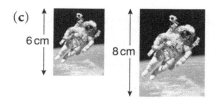

4 Find the scale factor used to make each reduction.

(a)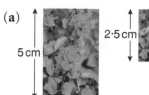

(b)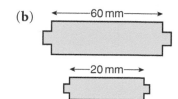

(c)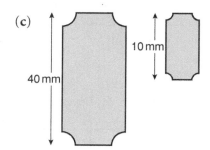

5 Find the value of x in each enlargement or reduction.

(a)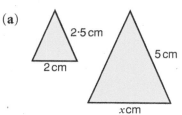

(b)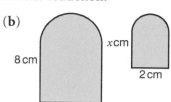

(c)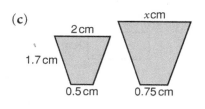

5.2 Similar shapes

Learning intentions

For enlargements or reductions, corresponding angles are equal **and** corresponding sides are in equal ratio. Shapes are **similar** if one is an enlargement or reduction of the other.

Example

Which pairs of shapes are similar?

(a)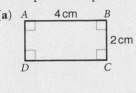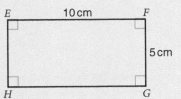

Shapes are equiangular.

$\dfrac{EF}{AB} = \dfrac{10}{4} = 2{\cdot}5$

$\dfrac{FG}{BC} = \dfrac{5}{2} = 2{\cdot}5$ Ratios are equal.

Since *ABCD* and *EFGH* are equiangular, and the ratios of corresponding sides are equal, the shapes are **similar**.

(b)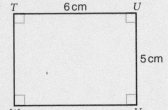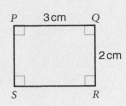

Shapes are equiangular.

$\dfrac{PQ}{TU} = \dfrac{3}{6} = 0{\cdot}5$

$\dfrac{QR}{UV} = \dfrac{2}{5} = 0{\cdot}4$ Ratios are not equal.

Despite being equiangular, since the ratios of corresponding sides are not equal, the rectangles are **not similar**.

(c)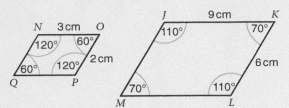

$\dfrac{JK}{NO} = \dfrac{9}{3} = 3$

$\dfrac{KL}{OP} = \dfrac{6}{2} = 3$ Ratios are equal.

Shapes are not equiangular.

Despite equal ratios, since *NOPQ* and *JKLM* are not equiangular, the shapes are **not similar**.

Exercise 5.2

1 Which pairs of shapes are similar? In each case explain your answer fully.

(a) 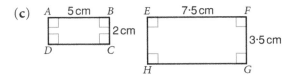   (b)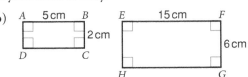

(c)   (d)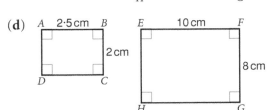

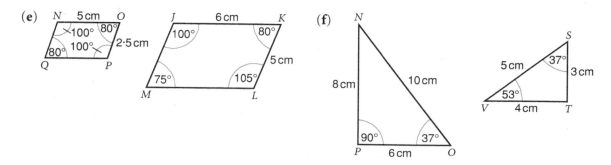

(e) N 5 cm O — 100° 80° — 80° 100° 2·5 cm — 80° 100° — Q P

J 6 cm K — 100° 80° — 5 cm — 75° 105° — M L

(f) N — 8 cm — 10 cm — 90° 37° — P 6 cm O

S — 5 cm 37° 3 cm — 53° — V 4 cm T

2 Which of the triangles are similar to triangle A? In each case explain your answer fully.

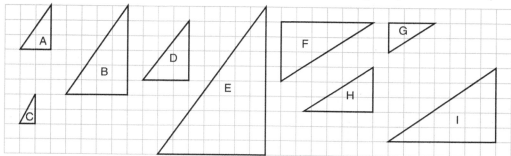

3 The diagram shows Saltires of different sizes. Which flags are similar? Explain fully.

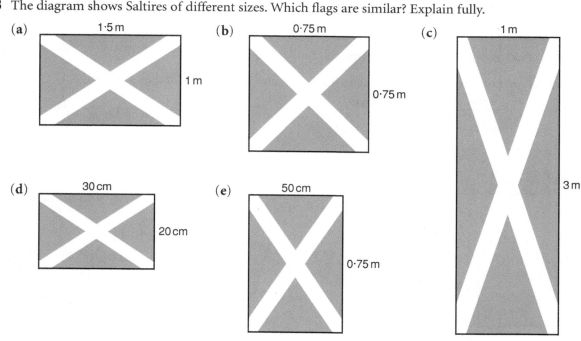

(a) 1·5 m — 1 m

(b) 0·75 m — 0·75 m

(c) 1 m — 3 m

(d) 30 cm — 20 cm

(e) 50 cm — 0·75 m

4 Are all rectangles similar? Explain your answer fully.

5 Are all squares similar? Explain fully.

6 Are all circles similar? Explain fully.

5.3 Calculations in similar shapes

Learning intentions

Scale factors may be used to calculate unknown lengths.

Example 1

These photographs are similar. Find the scale factor and hence find the value of x.

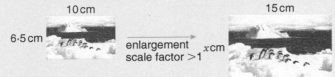

Scale factor $= \frac{15}{10} = 1\frac{1}{2}$

$x = 1 \cdot 5 \times 6 \cdot 5$

$= 9 \cdot 75$

x is **9·75 cm**.

Example 2

The shapes are similar. Find the value of x.

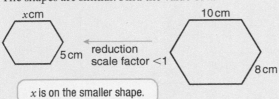

x is on the smaller shape.

Scale factor $= \frac{5}{8}$

$x = \frac{5}{8} \times 10$

$= \frac{50}{8}$

$= 6\frac{1}{4}$

x is **$6\frac{1}{4}$ cm**.

Exercise 5.3

For questions 5 and 6 you require a protractor, ruler and pair of compasses.

1 For each pair of similar shapes, calculate the scale factor and hence find the value of x.

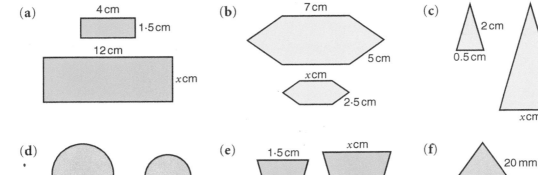

2 Each pair of photographs is similar. Find the scale factor and hence calculate the value of x.

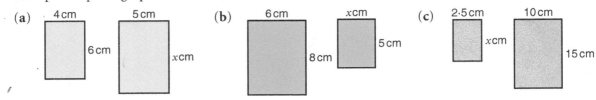

3 A model car is similar to the real car. If the height of the real car is 1·8 metres, find the scale factor and hence find the length of its wheel base.

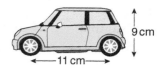

4 International paper sizes are given as A0, A1 … A9, A10.
A4 is a common size of paper.
It measures 297 millimetres by 210 millimetres.
A5 is half of A4, A6 is half of A5 and so on, as shown in the diagram.

(**a**) Find the length and breadth of a piece of A6 paper.
(**b**) Show that A4 and A6 paper are similar and calculate the scale factor.
(**c**) Find the length and breadth of a piece of A8 paper.
(**d**) Are A6 and A8 papers similar? Explain your answer.
(**e**) What do you notice about the scale factors in each case?
(**f**) Without measuring, calculate the dimensions of an A10 piece of paper.
(**g**) Calculate the dimensions of an A0 piece of paper.

5 You need a protractor and ruler.
(**a**) Accurately construct two different sized triangles which have the angles shown.
(**b**) Measure the length of the sides of each triangle.
(**c**) Are the triangles similar? Explain fully.
(**d**) Construct a third triangle with the same angles. Explain why this triangle is similar to the other two?

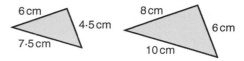

6 You need a pair of compasses, ruler and protractor.
(**a**) Accurately construct the triangles with the sides given.
(**b**) Are the triangles similar? Explain fully.
(**c**) Construct a third triangle with sides 3 centimetres, 4 centimetres and 5 centimetres.

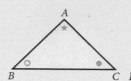
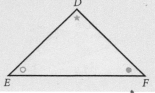

7 (**a**) Examine your results for question 5 and 6. Make a conjecture about triangles and similarity.
(**b**) Check your conjecture by repeating these questions for different sets of triangles.

5.4 Similar triangles

Learning intentions

For all triangles, *if* corresponding angles are equal *then* the ratios of corresponding sides are equal. Conversely, *if* the ratios of corresponding sides are equal *then* corresponding angles are equal. Hence, to prove similarity in triangles, either property is sufficient.

If $\begin{cases} \angle A = \angle D, \\ \angle B = \angle E \\ \angle C = \angle F \end{cases}$ then $\dfrac{AB}{DE} = \dfrac{AC}{DF} = \dfrac{BC}{EF}$

and triangles ABC and DEF are similar.

Example

Prove that each pair of triangles is similar and hence calculate the value of x.

(a)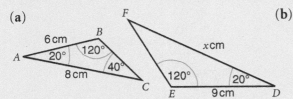

(b)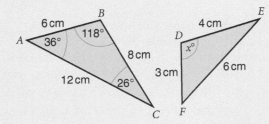

(a) Sketch the triangles in the same orientation.

Since $\angle A = 20° = \angle D$,

$\angle B = 120° = \angle E$

$\angle C = 40° = \angle F$

triangles ABC and DEF are similar.

Scale factor $= \frac{9}{6} = \frac{3}{2}$

$x = \frac{3}{2} \times 8$

$= 12$

The length of side DF is **12 cm**

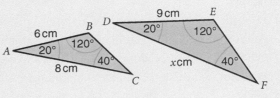

(b) Sketch the triangles in the same orientation.

$\frac{AB}{FD} = \frac{6}{3} = 2$

$\frac{BC}{DE} = \frac{8}{4} = 2$

$\frac{AC}{FE} = \frac{12}{6} = 2$

Since ratios are equal, the triangles are similar.

$\angle B = 118°$ $(180° - 36° - 26°)$

Hence, $x = \mathbf{118°}$

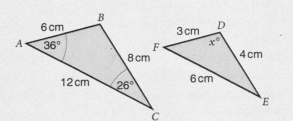

Exercise 5.4

1 For each pair of triangles, either prove or disprove that they are similar.

(a)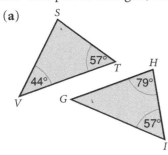

(b)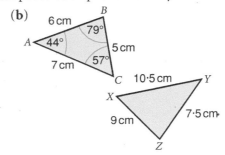

(c)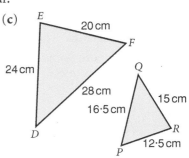

2 Prove that each pair of triangles is similar and hence find the values of x and y.

(a)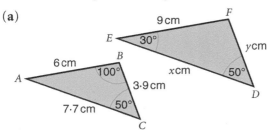

(b)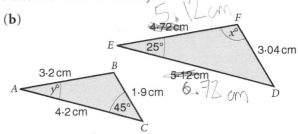

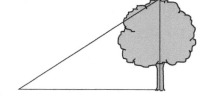

3 At 3 pm the length of the shadow of a vertical
3 metre pole is 4 metres.
Find the height of a tree which casts a shadow
of 25 metres at the same time.

4 The three sails shown are similar. Find the value of x, y and z.

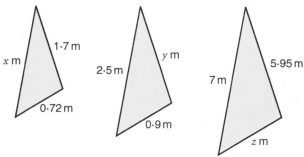

5.5 More complex similar triangles

Example 1

Prove that the triangles are similar and hence calculate the value of x.

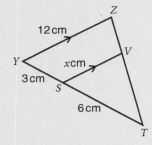

Since $\angle T \quad = \angle T$,
$\angle TYZ = \angle TSV$ (corresponding angles)
$\angle TZY = \angle TVS$ (corresponding angles)
triangles TYZ and TSV are similar.

Sketch triangles separately
Scale factor $= \frac{6}{9} = \frac{2}{3}$

$$x = \frac{2}{3} \times 12$$
$$= 8$$

The value of x is **8 cm**

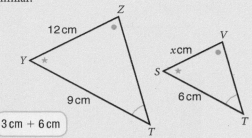

3 cm + 6 cm

Example 2

Prove that the triangles are similar and hence calculate the value of x.

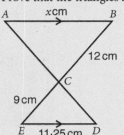

Since $\angle A \quad = \angle D$ (alternate angles)
$\angle B \quad = \angle E$ (alternate angles)
$\angle BCA = \angle DCE$ (vertically opposite angles)
triangles ABC and DEC are similar.

Sketch triangles separately.
Scale factor $= \frac{12}{9} = \frac{4}{3}$

$$x = \frac{4}{3} \times 11 \cdot 25$$
$$= 15$$

x is **15 cm**

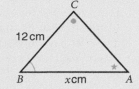

Exercise 5.5

1 Calculate the value of *x* in the following diagrams.

(**a**)

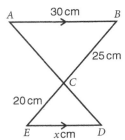

(**b**)

(**c**)

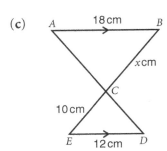

2 For each diagram find the lengths listed.

(**a**) *AC* and *ED*

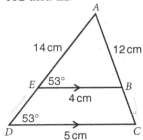

(**b**) *AE* and *AB*

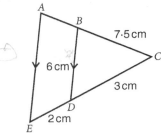

(**c**) *BE*

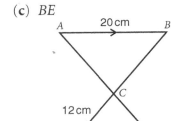

3 Find the length marked *x* in each of these diagrams.

(**a**)

(**b**)

(**c**)

(**d**)

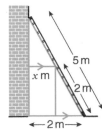

(**e**)

(**f**)

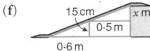

4 Chiara measures 20 metres from the foot of a house wall.
From here the top of a tree, 5 metres from the foot of the wall,
is in line with the top of the house, as shown in the diagram.
The house is 7 metres high.
Chiara's eyelevel is 1·5 metres from the ground.

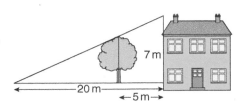

(**a**) Calculate the height of the tree above eye level.

(**b**) If the tree falls down, could it hit the house?

5 Calum wants to know the width of the canal. He places a stick at B on the opposite bank of the canal from a tree marked A. Starting directly opposite the tree, he walks along the bank to C and then walks at right angles to the bank to D. From D the stick B and the tree are seen in line. Calculate the width of the canal.

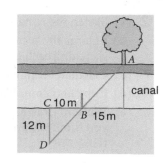

6 Mairi stood 122 metres from the Scott Monument in Edinburgh. She held a ruler 30 centimetres long 60 centimetres from her eye. The ruler, held vertically, just blocked the monument from her view. Calculate the height of the monument.

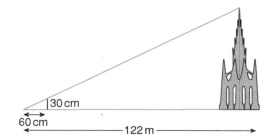

7 Rod makes different designs for roof trusses as shown in the diagrams. By identifying similar triangles, calculate the length of the truss marked x in each diagram.

(**a**) This design is symmetrical.

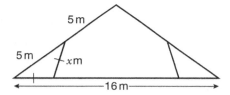

(**b**) $\angle$SRV = $\angle$SUT

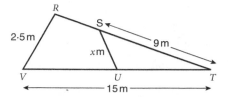

8 The two right angled triangles are similar. If the area of triangle ABC is 24 square centimetres, find the length of x and y.

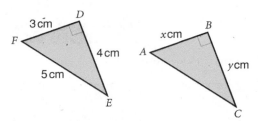

5.6 Investigating areas of similar shapes

Exercise 5.6

1 (**a**) Sketch the square shown on squared paper.

(**b**) Enlarge the square by scale factors, 2, 3 and 4, sketching each enlargement.

(**c**) Calculate the area for each enlargement.

(**d**) Copy and complete the table.

(**e**) Without drawing further squares, what do you think the area will be of a square enlarged by scale factor
(**i**) 5   (**ii**) n?

Scale factor	Area (cm²)
1	1
2	
3	
4	

2 (a) Sketch the rectangle shown on squared paper.
 (b) Enlarge the rectangle by scale factors 2, 3 and 4, sketching each enlargement.
 (c) Calculate the area for each enlargement.
 (d) Copy and complete the table.
 (e) Without drawing further rectangles, what do you think the area will be of a rectangle enlarged by scale factor
  (i) 5   (ii) n?

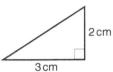

2 cm
1 cm

Scale factor	Area (cm²)
1	2
2	
3	
4	

3 (a) Sketch the triangle angle shown on squared paper.
 (b) Enlarge the triangle by scale factors 2, 3 and 4, sketching each enlargement.
 (c) Calculate the area for each enlargement.
 (d) Copy and complete the table.
 (e) Without drawing further triangles, what do you think the area will be of a triangle enlarged by scale factor
  (i) 5   (ii) n?

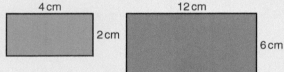

2 cm
3 cm

Scale factor	Area (cm²)
1	3
2	
3	
4	

4 Make a conjecture about the connection between the area and the scale factor.

5.7 Similar areas

Learning intentions

The diagram shows two similar rectangles. The scale factor is 3.

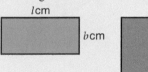

4 cm
2 cm
12 cm
6 cm

Area of blue rectangle = 9 × Area of red rectangle

The diagram shows two similar rectangles. The scale factor is s.

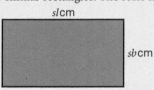

l cm
b cm
sl cm
sb cm

Area of blue rectangle = s^2 × Area of red rectangle

If the linear scale factor is **s**, then the area scale factor is s^2.

Example

The diagram shows a photograph and an enlargement. The scale factor is 1·5. The area of the original photograph is 24 square centimetres. Find the area of the enlargement.

Linear scale factor = s = 1·5
Area scale factor = s^2 = 1·5² = 2·25
Area of enlargement = 2·25 × 24
          = 54

The area of the enlargement is **54 cm²**

Exercise 5.7

1 Find the area of each enlargement.

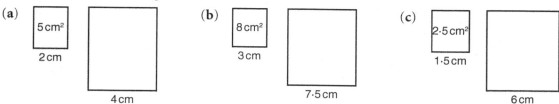

(a) 5 cm² · 2 cm · 4 cm

(b) 8 cm² · 3 cm · 7·5 cm

(c) 2·5 cm² · 1·5 cm · 6 cm

2 In three different models of car, the windscreen wiper sweeps through the same angle.
If the area cleaned by the wiper on model A is 900 cm², calculate the area cleaned on model B and model C.

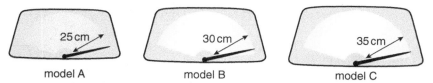

25 cm — model A   30 cm — model B   35 cm — model C

3 These rugs, similar in shape, are priced in proportion to their area.
If the smaller rug costs £450, find the cost of the larger rug.

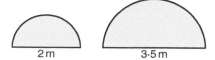

2 m   3·5 m

4 Raymond makes sails of similar shapes for dinghies and yachts.
  (a) Calculate the areas of the two smaller sails.
  (b) Size 2 has a length half of size 5. Find its area.

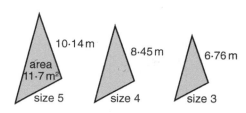

10·14 m — area 11·7 m² — size 5   8·45 m — size 4   6·76 m — size 3

5 The scale of an OS map is 1 : 50 000. Maggie is surveying an area of wetland for birds. If the marsh on the map is 1·5 centimetres long and covers an area of 0·75 square centimetres, what is the true area of land in square kilometres?

6 On this map of Scotland the scale is 1 : 7 500 000.
The area of land mass on the map is 14 square centimetres.
What is the true land area of Scotland in square kilometres?

7 For these two similar shapes find:
  (a) the area scale factor
  (b) the linear scale factor
  (c) the length of the larger hexagon.

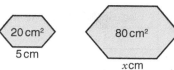

20 cm² · 5 cm   80 cm² · x cm

8 For this photograph and enlargement find:
  (a) the area scale factor
  (b) the linear scale factor
  (c) the length of the enlargement.

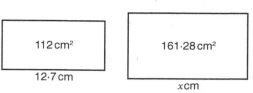

112 cm² · 12·7 cm   161·28 cm² · x cm

5.8 Investigating volumes of similar solids

Exercise 5.8

1 (a) Calculate the volume of the yellow cube.

(b) The yellow cube has been enlarged by scale factor 2. Calculate the volume of the enlargement.

(c) Enlarge the dimensions of the yellow cube by scale factor 3 and 4. Calculate the volume of each enlargement.

(d) Copy and complete the table.

(e) What do you think the volume will be of a cuboid enlarged by scale factor
(i) 5 (ii) n?

Scale factor	Volume (cm³)
1	1
2	
3	
4	

2 (a) Calculate the volume of the yellow cuboid.

(b) The yellow cuboid has been enlarged by scale factor 2. Calculate the volume of the enlargement.

(c) Enlarge the dimensions of the yellow cuboid by scale factor 3 and 4. Calculate the volume of each enlargement.

(d) Copy and complete the table.

Scale factor	length	breadth	height	Volume (cm³)
1	2	1	3	6
2				
3				
4				

(e) What do you think the volume will be of a cuboid enlarged by scale factor (i) 5 (ii) n?

3 (a) Calculate the volume of the yellow cylinder.

(b) Each dimension of the yellow cylinder has been enlarged by scale factor 2. Calculate the volume of the enlargement.

(c) Enlarge the dimensions of the yellow cylinder by scale factor 3 and 4. Calculate the volume of enlargement.

(d) Copy and complete the table.

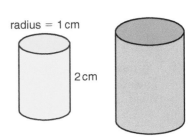

radius = 1 cm

2 cm

Volume of a cylinder = $\pi r^2 h$

Scale factor	radius	height	Volume (cm³)
1	1	2	6·28
2			
3			
4			

(e) What do you think the volume will be of a cylinder enlarged by scale factor (i) 5 (ii) n?

4 Make a conjecture about the connection between the volume and the scale factor.

5.9 Similar volumes

The diagram shows two cubes. The red cube has been enlarged by scale factor 2.

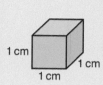

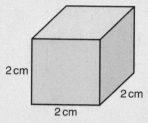

Volume = $1 \times 1 \times 1 = 1\ cm^3$.   Volume = $2 \times 2 \times 2 = 8\ cm^3$.

Volume of blue cube = $8 \times$ Volume of red cube

The diagram shows two cubes. The red cube has been enlarged by scale factor s.

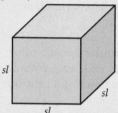

Volume = $l \times l \times l = l^3$ Volume = $sl \times sl \times sl = s^3 l^3$

Volume of blue cube = $s^3 \times$ Volume of red cube
                    = $s^3 l^3$

If the linear scale factor is **s**, then the volume scale factor is s^3.

Example 1

The diagram shows a miniature bottle and a similar larger bottle.
The scale factor is 2·5. Find the volume of the larger bottle if the
volume of the miniature is 50 millilitres.

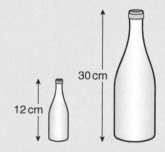

  Linear scale factor = 2·5
  Volume scale factor = $2\cdot5^3$
                      = 15·625
  Volume of enlargement = 15·625 × 50
                        = 781·25

The volume of the larger bottle is **781·25 ml**.

Example 2

The volumes of two similar milk cartons are shown
in the diagram. If the height of the smaller carton is
7 centimetres, find the height of the larger carton to
the nearest millimetre.

Volume scale factor = $\dfrac{1000}{330}$

Linear scale factor = $\sqrt[3]{\dfrac{1000}{330}}$

Height = $\sqrt[3]{\dfrac{1000}{330}} \times 7 = 10\cdot1296 = 10\cdot1\ cm$ (to nearest mm)

Height is **10·1 cm**

Exercise 5.9

1 For each pair of similar bottles, find the volume of the second bottle.

(a)

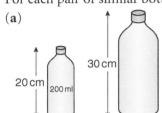

20 cm   30 cm   200 ml

(b)

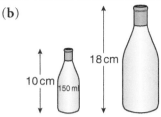

10 cm   18 cm   150 ml

(c)

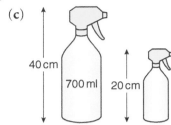

40 cm   700 ml   20 cm

2 A can has a height of 10 centimetres and has a volume of 200 cubic centimetres. A can with a similar shape has a height of 12 centimetres. Find the volume of the larger can.

3 A box has a volume of 50 cubic centimetres and a width of 8 centimetres. A similar box has a width of 12 centimetres. Find the volume of this box.

4 The two flasks shown are similar to each other. The diameter of the larger flask is 12 centimetres and has a volume of 500 millilitres. If the smaller flask has a diameter of 8 centimetres, calculate its volume.

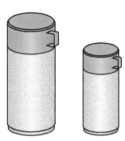

5 The normal size and selling prices of small and medium toothpaste tubes are shown. If the tubes are similar, is the medium tube value for money?

mint BRUSH-BRIGHT Toothpaste 25 ml £0.99

8 cm

mint BRUSH-BRIGHT Toothpaste £3.99

16 cm

6 The true volume of the boot of the car is 500 litres.
A model of the car is made to a scale of 1 : 8.
Find the volume of the boot in the model.

7 (a) A cereal packet has its dimensions increased by 20%.
   By what percentage is the volume of the packet increased?

(b) The manufacturer claims that a new packet contains 25% more.
   Find the percentage increase needed in the dimensions of the packet to make this claim true.

8 Whisky bottles are made in three different sizes, 50 millilitres, 200 millilitres and 700 millilitres. If the 200 millilitre bottle is 160 millimetres high, how tall are the other two to the nearest millimetre?

9 *Canit* designs cans to be similar. If two of the cans have capacities of 400 millilitres and 1350 millilitres, what will be the width of the larger can?

←9 cm→

10 *Boxclever* makes similar boxes. Find
(**a**) the height of size 2
(**b**) the volume of size 1.

Size 1

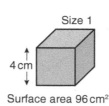

4 cm

Surface area 96 cm²

Size 2

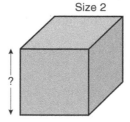

?

Surface area 864 cm²
Volume 1728 cm³

Review exercise 5: Am I a successful learner?

1 Photographic prints are made in the following standard sizes.

Which sizes are similar? Explain fully.

4 × 6

5 × 7·5

8 × 10

12 × 18

2 For each pair of similar shapes, calculate the scale factor and hence find *x*.

(**a**)

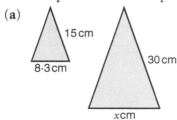

15 cm

8·3 cm

30 cm

x cm

(**b**) 5·3 cm

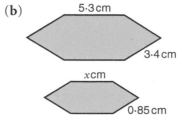

3·4 cm

x cm

0·85 cm

(**c**)

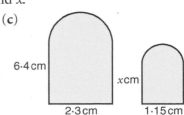

6·4 cm

2·3 cm

x cm

1·15 cm

3 This model car is similar to the real car. If the length of the real car is 3·2 metres, find the diameter of the wheel of the car.

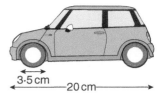

3·5 cm

20 cm

4 Prove that the following pairs of triangles are similar and hence find the values of *x* and *y*.

(**a**)

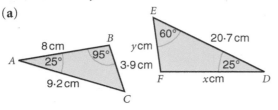

E

8 cm   B   *y* cm   60°   20·7 cm
A   25°   95°   3·9 cm   25°
    9·2 cm   F   *x* cm   D
         C

(**b**)

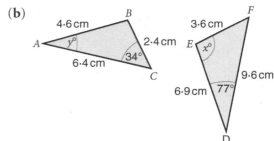

4·6 cm   B   3·6 cm   F
A   *y*°   2·4 cm   E   *x*°
    6·4 cm   34°   9·6 cm
         C   6·9 cm   77°
                         D

5 At 4 pm the length of the shadow cast by Appleton Tower is 100 metres. The length of shadow cast by a 1·15 metre stick is 2·5 metres at this time.
Calculate the height of Appleton tower.

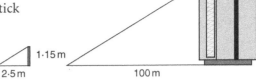

6 Calculate *x* and *y* in the following diagrams.

(**a**)

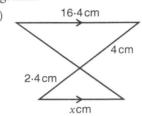

(**b**)

(**c**)

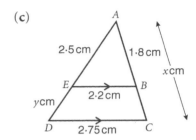

7 A camping table is stable when the top is parallel to the ground.
Calculate the distance between the feet if the table is stable.

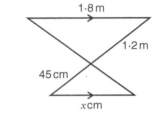
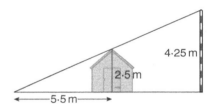

8 The shed in Colin's garden is near a transmitter. When he is 5·5 metres from the shed, the top of the transmitter cannot be seen. His shed is 2·5 metres high. If the transmitter is known to be 4·25 metres high, could it hit his shed if it is blown over in a gale?

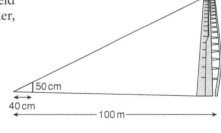

9 Nicola stood 100 metres from the Glasgow Science Tower. She held a ruler 50 centimetres long, 40 centimetres from her eye. The ruler, held vertically, just blocked the monument from her view.
Calculate the height of the tower.

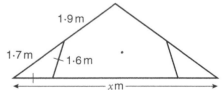

10 The diagram shows the side elevation of a design for a tent. The design is symmetrical to ensure stability.
Calculate *x*, the space needed to pitch the tent.

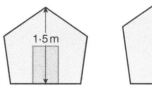

11 *Garden Designs* makes similar polytunnels in different sizes. The area of the end of a small tunnel is 3·5 square metres.
Calculate the area of the medium-sized tunnel.

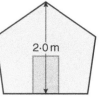

12 A spare piece of land is to be used for a car park. The land available is shown on the plan with scale 1 : 5000. The area required to make the car park economical must be no less than 1 250 square metres. Can the car park be economic?

0.6 cm²

13 For this photograph and its enlargement find
  (**a**) the area scale factor
  (**b**) the linear scale factor
  (**c**) the length of the enlargement.

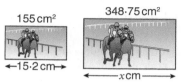

155 cm²

←15·2 cm→

348·75 cm²

←——x cm——→

14 Two wine bottles have similar shapes. The standard bottle has a height of 30 centimetres and the small bottle has a height of 24 centimetres. The volume in the small bottle is 350 millilitres. What is the volume of the large bottle?

RC **15** These cola tins are similar in shape. Which gives better value for money?

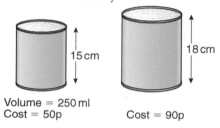

15 cm

18 cm

Volume = 250 ml
Cost = 50p

Cost = 90p

16 *Parfuma* make perfume in similar shaped bottles. The heights of the bottles are 4·5 centimetres and 6 centimetres. The larger bottle contains 60 millilitres. It is claimed that the smaller bottle contains 26 millilitres. Is this claim true?

17 These bottles of washing up liquid are similar to each other. If the height of the smaller bottle is 10 centimetres, calculate the height of the larger bottle.

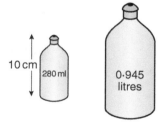

10 cm

280 ml

0·945 litres

18 *Bigger Biscuits* claim to have increased the size of their biscuits by 70%, while keeping the design similar. Is this claim correct?

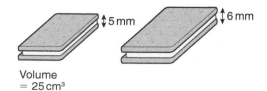

5 mm

6 mm

Volume = 25 cm³

Summary 5: What I learned in this chapter.

Similar shapes

Any shape may be enlarged or reduced using a scale factor.

A scale factor multiplies the length of every side of a shape.

A scale factor **greater than 1 enlarges** a shape.

A scale factor **less than 1 reduces** a shape.

Shapes are said to be **similar** if corresponding angles are equal and corresponding sides are in equal ratio. Scale factors may be used to calculate unknown lengths.

Example

These photographs are similar. Find the scale factor and hence find the size of the side marked x.

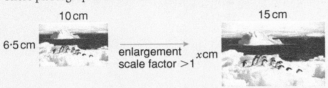

$$\text{Scale factor} = \frac{15}{10} = 1\frac{1}{2}$$
$$x = 1 \cdot 5 \times 6 \cdot 5$$
$$= 9 \cdot 75$$

The side is **9·75 cm.**

Similar triangles

For all triangles, *if* corresponding angles are equal *then* the ratios of corresponding sides are equal. Conversely, *if* the ratios of corresponding sides are equal *then* corresponding angles are equal. Hence, to prove similarity in triangles, either property is sufficient.

If $\left\{ \begin{array}{l} \angle A = \angle D, \\ \angle B = \angle E, \\ \angle C = \angle F, \end{array} \right.$ then $\dfrac{AB}{DE} = \dfrac{AC}{DF} = \dfrac{BC}{EF}$

and triangles ABC and DEF are similar.

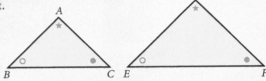

Similar areas

If the linear scale factor is s, then the area scale factor is s^2.

Example

The diagram shows a photograph and an enlargement.
The area of the original photograph is 24 square centimetres.
Find the area of the enlargement.

Linear scale factor $= \frac{6}{4} = 1 \cdot 5$
Area scale factor $= 1 \cdot 5^2 = 2 \cdot 25$
Area of enlargement $= 2 \cdot 25 \times 24$
$= 54$

The area of the enlargement is **54 cm²**

Similar volumes

If the linear scale factor is s, then the volume scale factor is s^3.

Example

The diagram shows a miniature bottle and a similar larger bottle.
Find the volume of the larger bottle if the volume of the miniature is 50 millilitres.

Linear scale factor $= \frac{30}{12} = 2 \cdot 5$
Volume scale factor $= 2 \cdot 5^3$
$= 15 \cdot 625$
Volume of enlargement $= 15 \cdot 625 \times 50$
$= 781 \cdot 25$
The volume of the larger bottle is **781·25 ml.**

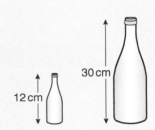

6 Pythagoras' theorem

6.1 Areas of squares

Exercise 6.1

1 Each diagram on the page shows a right angled triangle with a square drawn on each side.
The lengths of the sides are in centimetres.
Copy and complete the table.

Triangle	A	B	C	D
Area of smallest square in cm²	$3 \times 3 = 9$			
Area of middle-sized square in cm²	$4 \times 4 = 16$			
Area of largest square in cm²				

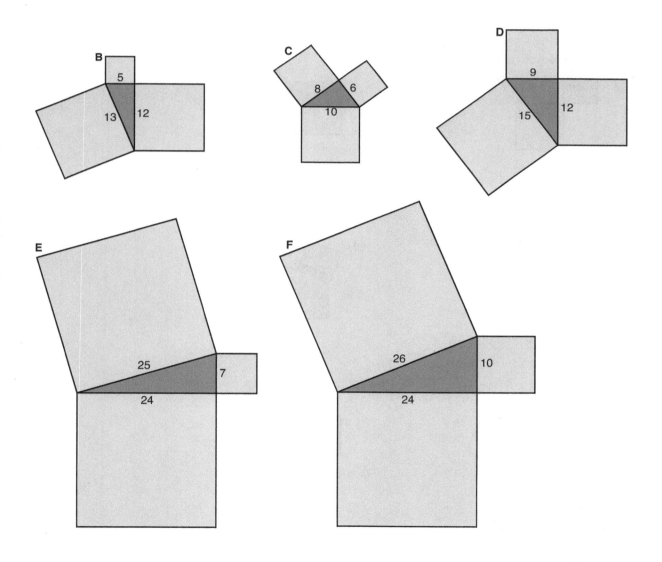

Learning intentions

Pythagoras' theorem

Your answers to question 1 should show that

Area of the square C = Area of the square A + Area of the square B

This result has been used by mathematicians for over 3000 years.

It was first known to the Babylonians and is referred to as **Pythagoras' theorem** after a Greek mathematician who first proved it around the sixth century BC.

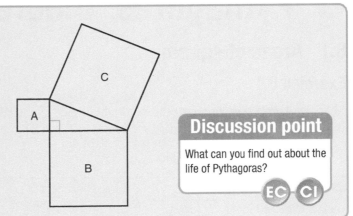

Discussion point

What can you find out about the life of Pythagoras?

EC **CI**

2 For each right angled triangle:
  (i) calculate the areas of the yellow and blue squares
  (ii) hence find the area of the green square.

(a)

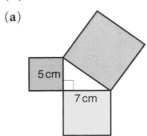

5 cm

7 cm

(b)

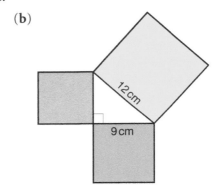

12 cm

9 cm

(c)

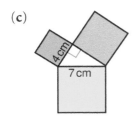

4 cm

7 cm

(d)

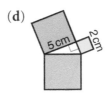

5 cm 2 cm

(e)

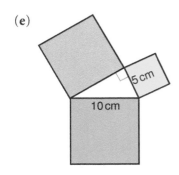

5 cm

10 cm

(f)

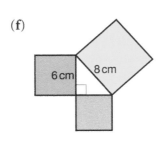

6 cm 8 cm

6.2 Lengths of sides

Learning intentions

Pythagoras' theorem

If a triangle is right angled the square on the hypotenuse is equal to the sum of the squares on the other two sides.

> The longest side in a right angled triangle is called the **hypotenuse**. It is the side opposite the right angle.

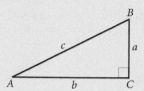

In triangle ABC, if angle C is a right angle then
$$c^2 = a^2 + b^2$$

Pythagoras' theorem is used to calculate the length of a side in a right angled triangle.

Example

(a) Calculate the hypotenuse

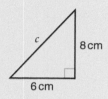

(b) Find a

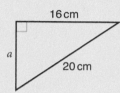

(c) Find the length of PQ

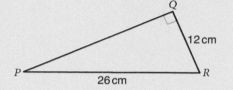

(a) $c^2 = a^2 + b^2$
$c^2 = 6^2 + 8^2$
$c^2 = 36 + 64$
$c^2 = 100$
$c = \sqrt{100}$
$c = \textbf{10 cm}$

(b)
$c^2 = a^2 + b^2$
$20^2 = a^2 + 16^2$
$400 = a^2 + 256$
$400 - 256 = a^2$
$144 = a^2$
$\sqrt{144} = a$
$12 = a$
$a = \textbf{12 cm}$

(c)
$PR^2 = PQ^2 + QR^2$
$26^2 = PQ^2 + 12^2$
$676 = PQ^2 + 144$
$676 - 144 = PQ^2$
$532 = PQ^2$
$\sqrt{532} = PQ$
$23.065125 = PQ$
$PQ = \textbf{23 cm}$

Exercise 6.2

1 Which side is the hypotenuse in each right angled triangle?

(a)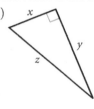
(b)
(c)
(d)
(e)

2 Calculate the length of the side marked x in each triangle.

(a)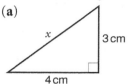
(b)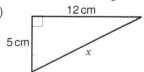
(c)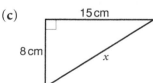

3 Calculate the value of *x* in each triangle.

(a)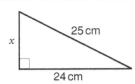
25 cm, x, 24 cm

(b)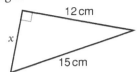
12 cm, x, 15 cm

(c)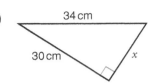
34 cm, 30 cm, x

4 Calculate the length of the unknown side in each triangle.
Give your answers correct to one decimal place.

(a)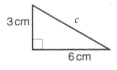
3 cm, c, 6 cm

(b)
7 cm, 8 cm, b

(c)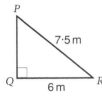
P, 7·5 m, Q, 6 m, R, b

(d)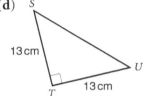
S, 13 cm, U, 13 cm, T

(e)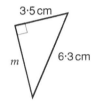
3·5 cm, m, 6·3 cm

(f)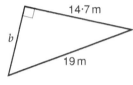
14·7 m, b, 19 m

6.3 Practical applications

Learning intentions

Example
The picture shows a lifeboat station with a slipway.
Calculate the length of the sloping edge of the slipway.

Draw a right angled triangle.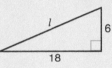

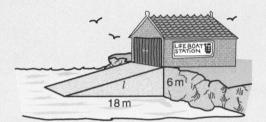

From Pythagoras' theorem
$l^2 = 18^2 + 6^2$
$l^2 = 324 + 36$
$l^2 = 360$
$l = \sqrt{360}$
$l = 18{\cdot}973\ldots$
The length of the sloping edge is **19·0 m** rounded to one decimal place.

Exercise 6.3

1 Calculate the marked lengths in each diagram.
Round your answers to one decimal place.

(a) A ladder against a wall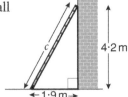
c, 4·2 m, 1·9 m

(b) A farm gate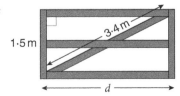
1·5 m, 3·4 m, d

(**c**) Buttress supporting an old building

(**d**) Support carrying a railway's overhead power line

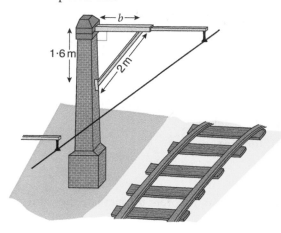

(**e**) Crane on a building site

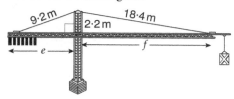

(**f**) Girders of a railway bridge

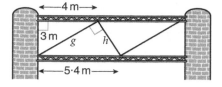

(**g**) Frame for a coal wagon

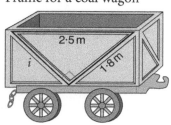

(**h**) Support beams for a barn roof

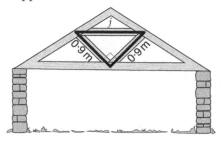

(**i**) Roof girders for a factory

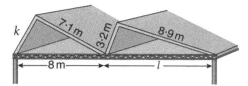

(**j**) Straps holding an attic floor

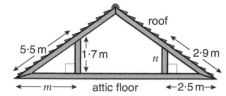

2 How much shorter is the path through the wood than the road around the two sides?

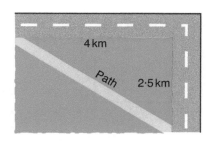

3 A ship leaves port and sails 10 kilometres due east. It then alters
course and sails 7 kilometres due north.
How far would it have to sail to return directly to port?

4 Jack and Jill had an argument. Jack walked off north at 4 kilometres per
hour and Jill walked off east at 5 kilometres per hour.
After two hours, how far apart were Jack and Jill?

5 For each isosceles triangle calculate:
  (**i**) the height
 (**ii**) the area.

(**a**)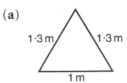

(**b**)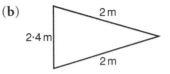

6 Use Pythagoras' theorem to calculate the value of x and y in each diagram below.

(**a**)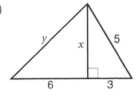

(**b**)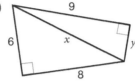

(**c**)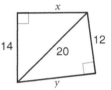

6.4 Further examples

Learning intentions

Example 1

The diagonal of the square is 8 centimetres long.
Find the length of each side.

$$8^2 = s^2 + s^2$$
$$64 = 2s^2$$
$$32 = s^2$$
$$\sqrt{32} = s$$
$$s = 5 \cdot 6568$$

s is 5·7 cm to 1 decimal place

Example 2

Find the length of space diagonal EC.

From the base, triangle EHG is right angled

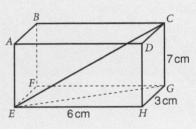

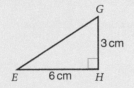

$$EG^2 = 6^2 + 3^2$$
$$= 36 + 9$$
$$= 45$$
$$EG = \sqrt{45}$$

Triangle EGC is right angled

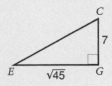

$$EC^2 = (\sqrt{45})^2 + 7^2$$
$$= 45 + 49$$
$$= 94$$
$$EC = \sqrt{94} = 9 \cdot 695$$

EC is 9·7 cm to 2 sig. figs.

Exercise 6.4

1 Find the value of *x* in each diagram.

(a)

(b)

(c)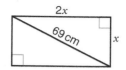

2 The distance across the diagonal of a square field is 130 metres.
Calculate the length of a side of the field.

3 The diagram shows a cube with each
edge 5 centimetres long.

(a) What is the shape of each face of the cube?

(b) Name the right angle in triangle *GBC* and
calculate the length of *BG*.

(c) If angle *BGH* is a right angle, calculate the
length of *BH*.

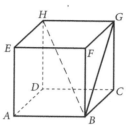

4 The diagram shows a cuboid with edges 8 centimetres,
6 centimetres and 4 centimetres long.

(a) Name the right angle in triangle RPQ and calculate the
length of PR.

(b) Angle PRV is a right angle. Calculate the length of PV.

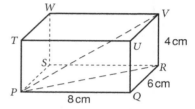

5 Find the height of each cone.

(a)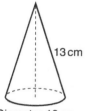

(b)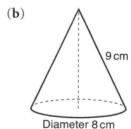

6 In square based pyramid *PQRST*, *PQ* is 10 centimetres and *TQ* is
13 centimetres

(a) If *M* is the midpoint of *QR*, find the length of *TM*.

(b) Calculate the length of *TO*.

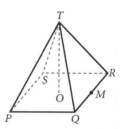

7 The dimensions of the PE department's storage container are
8 metres by 3 metres by 4 metres.
Is it possible to store an 11 metre mast in the container?

8 For this cuboid calculate the value of x given that the length of the space diagonal is 26 metres.

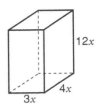

6.5 The distance between two points

Learning intentions

To find the distance between two points, A and B, on a coordinate diagram:
- join A to B
- draw a right angled triangle with AB as hypotenuse
- mark in the lengths of the two shorter sides
- use Pythagoras' theorem to calculate the length of AB

Example

Find the distance between $A(2, 3)$ and $B(6, 6)$.

$AB^2 = 3^2 + 4^2$
$AB^2 = 9 + 16$
$AB^2 = 25$
$AB = \sqrt{25}$
$AB = 5$

The distance between A and B is **5 units**.

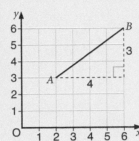

Exercise 6.5

1 In each diagram the coordinates of A and B are given.
Use Pythagoras' theorem to calculate the length of AB for each.

(a)

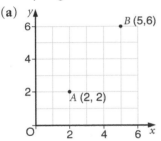

(b)

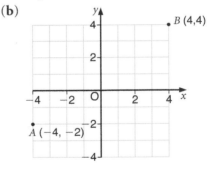

2 Plot each pair of points on a coordinate diagram.
Calculate the distance between each pair correct to one decimal place.

(a) $P(1, 2)$ and $Q(7, 10)$ **(b)** $S(1, 0)$ and $T(9, 5)$ **(c)** $V(3, 7)$ and $W(9, 2)$
(d) $C(0, 10)$ and $D(9, 2)$ **(e)** $E(9, 9)$ and $F(2, 3)$ **(f)** $K(8, 0)$ and $L(0, 8)$

3 Plot the points $P(1, 7)$, $Q(4, 7)$, $R(6, 2)$ and $S(1, 4)$ on a coordinate diagram and join them to form a quadrilateral.
(a) Calculate the length of diagonal SQ.
(b) Calculate the length of diagonal PR.

4 The vertices of a triangle are $A(0, 6)$, $B(6, 7)$ and $C(5, 1)$.
(a) Calculate the lengths of the three sides of the triangle.
(b) What type of triangle is ABC?

6.6 The distance formula

Learning intentions

In the diagram, A has coordinates (x_1, y_1) and B has coordinates (x_2, y_2).

Horizontal distance is $x_2 - x_1$.

Vertical distance is $y_2 - y_1$.

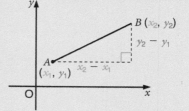

By Pythagoras' theorem
$$AB^2 = (x_2 - x_1)^2 + (y_2 - y_1)^2$$
$$AB = \sqrt{(x_2 - x_1)^2 + (y_2 - y_1)^2}$$

This is called the **distance formula** and is used to calculate the distance between two points on a coordinate diagram.

Example

Triangle ABC has vertices $A(-2, 1)$, $B(4, 4)$ and $C(1, -2)$.
Calculate the lengths of sides AB and BC to show
that triangle ABC is isosceles.

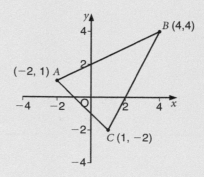

$$AB = \sqrt{(x_2 - x_1)^2 + (y_2 - y_1)^2}$$
$$AB = \sqrt{(4 - (-2))^2 + (4 - 1)^2}$$
$$= \sqrt{6^2 + 3^2}$$
$$= \sqrt{36 + 9}$$
$$= \sqrt{45}$$

$$BC = \sqrt{(x_2 - x_1)^2 + (y_2 - y_1)^2}$$
$$BC = \sqrt{(1 - 4)^2 + (-2 - 4)^2}$$
$$= \sqrt{(-3)^2 + (-6)^2}$$
$$= \sqrt{9 + 36}$$
$$= \sqrt{45}$$

Since **AB = BC** the triangle is **isosceles**.

Exercise 6.6

1 Calculate the distance between each pair of points.

   (a) the origin and $P(3, 4)$

   (b) the origin and $Q(8, -6)$

   (c) $O(0, 0)$ and $R(-5, -12)$

   (d) $S(-2, 5)$ and $T(3, -7)$

   (e) $U(4, -11)$ and $V(-5, 1)$

   (f) $W(-1, -1)$ and $Z(-4, -4)$

2 The vertices of a triangle are $A(4, 4)$, $B(-2, 3)$ and $C(3, -2)$.
Use the distance formula to show that ABC is an isosceles triangle.

3 Calculate the lengths of the four sides and both diagonals in the
quadrilateral whose vertices are $A(-1, 1)$, $B(3, 2)$, $C(5, 5)$ and $D(1, 4)$.

6.7 The converse of Pythagoras' theorem

Learning intentions

Theorem
If triangle ABC is right angled at C then $c^2 = a^2 + b^2$.

Converse
If $c^2 = a^2 + b^2$ then triangle ABC is right angled at C.

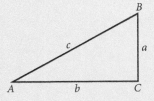

Example
(a) Is triangle PQR right angled?
(b) Name the right angle.

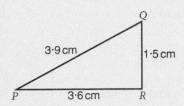

(a) Longest side
$$PQ^2 = 3 \cdot 9^2$$
$$= 15 \cdot 21$$

Shorter sides
$$QR^2 + PR^2 = 1 \cdot 5^2 + 3 \cdot 6^2$$
$$= 2 \cdot 25 + 12 \cdot 96$$
$$= 15 \cdot 21$$

Since $PQ^2 = QR^2 + PR^2$ **triangle PQR is right angled.**

(b) PQ is the longest side so **angle PRQ is a right angle.**

Exercise 6.7

1 Use the converse of Pythagoras' theorem to find which of these triangles is right angled.

(a)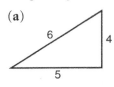
(b)
(c)
(d)
(e)

2 Jock is a joiner and has made this window frame.
The frame has to be a perfect rectangle.
Has Jock made it properly?

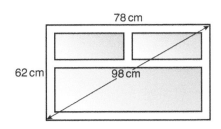

3 Kanwal is a bricklayer. In the wall she built, she had to leave a perfectly square hole for a window.
Did Kanwal do the job properly?

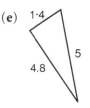

4 Billy claims this isosceles triangle is right angled. Is he correct?

5 If this quadrilateral is a rhombus, its diagonals must bisect each other at right angles.
Is the quadrilateral a rhombus?

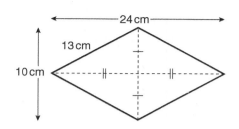

6 When joined, each set of three points forms a triangle.
Use the distance formula and the converse of Pythagoras' theorem to find if each triangle is right angled.

(**a**) $P(2, 6)$, $Q(7, 5)$ and $R(6, 0)$

(**b**) $S(6, 5)$, $T(8, 1)$ and $U(-4, 3)$

(**c**) $D(4, -4)$, $E(-4, -1)$ and $F(-1, 6)$

(**d**) $K(8, 4)$, $L(-4, 2)$ and $M(-3, -4)$

6.8 Pythagorean triples

Learning intentions

A Pythagorean triple is a set of three whole numbers a, b and c which satisfy the rule $c^2 = a^2 + b^2$.

The most common Pythagorean triples are

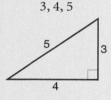

3, 4, 5

5, 12, 13

$5^2 = 25$

$3^2 + 4^2 = 9 + 16 = 25$

$13^2 = 169$

$12^2 + 5^2 = 144 + 25 = 169$

Exercise 6.8

1 Which of these sets of numbers is a Pythagorean triple?

(**a**) 8, 15, 17

(**b**) 6, 8, 10

(**c**) 12, 16, 20

(**d**) 4, 5, 6

(**e**) 20, 21, 29

(**f**) 6, 9, 12

(**g**) 10, 24, 26

(**h**) 24, 32, 40

(**i**) 7, 24, 25

(**j**) 30, 40, 50

(**k**) 9, 40, 41

(**l**) 20, 48, 52

2 3, 4, 5 and 6, 8, 10 are Pythagorean triples.

(**a**) Check that 9, 12, 15 is a Pythagorean triple.

(**b**) Do you notice anything about these sets of triples?

(**c**) Generate three similar sets of Pythagorean triples.

3 5, 12, 13 and 10, 24, 26 are Pythagorean triples.

(**a**) Check that 15, 36, 39 is a Pythagorean triple.

(**b**) What do you notice?

(**c**) Generate three similar sets of Pythagorean triples.

4 (a) Choose two natural numbers x and y, such that $x > y$.

(b) Use these numbers to calculate a, b and c where

$$a = 2xy$$
$$b = x^2 - y^2$$
$$c = x^2 + y^2$$

(c) Check that $c^2 = a^2 + b^2$

(d) Copy and complete the table for these values of x and y.

(e) Find another four sets of Pythagorean triples.

x, y	a	b	c
2, 1			
3, 1			
3, 2			
4, 1			
4, 2			
4, 3			

5 State the value of x in each triangle without using a calculator.

(a)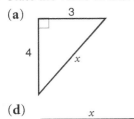

(b)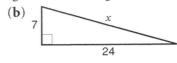

(c)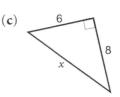

(d)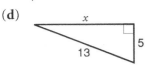

(e)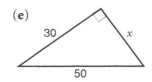

(f)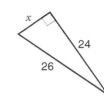

Review exercise 6: Am I a successful learner?

1 Calculate the length of the unknown side in each triangle.
Give your answer correct to one decimal place.

(a)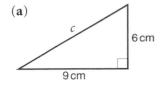

(b)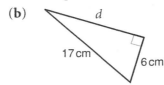

(c)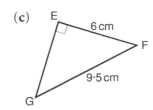

2 Calculate the marked lengths in each diagram.
Round your answers to one decimal place.

(a) Television transmitter with support cables at two heights

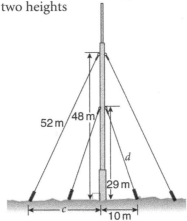

(b) Footbridge over a stream

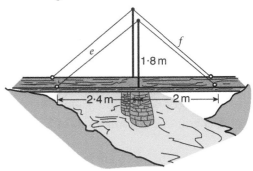

(c) Girders holding a semi-circular bridge under repair.

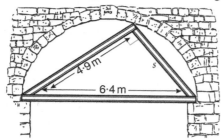

3 Jim and John are at an oasis in the desert.
Jim sets off walking north east at 6 kilometres per hour and John goes
south east at 4 kilometres per hour.
How far apart are they after 2 hours?

4 Calculate the length of the side of a square with diagonal 14 centimetres.

5 The diagram shows a cuboid with edges 9 cm, 7 cm and 5 cm.

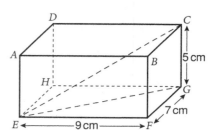

(a) Use triangle EFG to calculate the length of EG.
(b) Use triangle EGC to calculate the length of EC.

6 (a) Use the distance formula to calculate the lengths of the sides of a
triangle with vertices $P(5, 0)$, $Q(-3, -4)$ and $R(-7, 4)$.
(b) Is triangle PQR right angled?

7 Karim is a joiner and has made this door.
The door has to be a perfect rectangle.
Has Karim made the door properly?

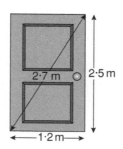

8 Prove that triangle ACD is right angled.

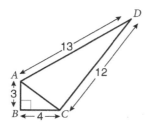

Summary 6: What I learned in this chapter.

Pythagoras' theorem

If a triangle is right angled then the square on the
hypotenuse is equal to the sum of the squares
on the other two sides.

$$c^2 = a^2 + b^2$$

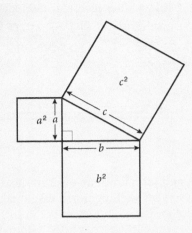

Calculating a side

Find the length of the hypotenuse.

Calculate the value of x in the triangle

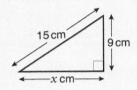

$c^2 = a^2 + b^2$
$c^2 = 6^2 + 8^2$
$c^2 = 36 + 64$
$c^2 = 100$
$c = \sqrt{100}$
$c = 10$

The hypotenuse is **10 m**

$c^2 = a^2 + b^2$
$15^2 = x^2 + 9^2$
$225 = x^2 + 81$
$225 - 81 = x^2$
$144 = x^2$
$x = \sqrt{144}$
$x = 12$

x is **12 cm**

The distance formula

$$AB = \sqrt{(x_2 - x_1)^2 + (y_2 - y_1)^2}$$

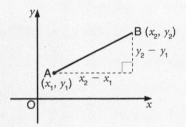

Converse of Pythagoras' theorem

If $c^2 = a^2 + b^2$ then the triangle is right angled at C

Longest side
$3 \cdot 9^2 = 15 \cdot 21$

Shorter sides
$3 \cdot 6^2 + 1 \cdot 5^2 \quad = 12 \cdot 96 + 2 \cdot 25$
$= 15 \cdot 21$

Since $3 \cdot 9^2 = 3 \cdot 6^2 + 1 \cdot 5^2$ the triangle is right angled.

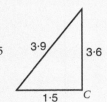

Review 1

Percentages

1 Find:

   (**a**) 1% of £345   (**b**) 10% of 450 kg   (**c**) 75% of £48   (**d**) $12\frac{1}{2}$% of 488ml

2 A washing machine costs £350 excluding VAT.
Calculate:

   (**a**) the VAT at $17\frac{1}{2}$%   (**b**) the total price of the washing machine.

3 Calculate:

   (**a**) 35% of £216   (**b**) 17·5% of 82 kg   (**c**) $33\frac{1}{3}$% of 339 ml   (**d**) 5·25% of £789

4 *Castle Furnishings* offer this chair on hire purchase but it costs $12\frac{1}{2}$%
more than the cash price.
Fahrida buys the chair on hire purchase. She has to pay a deposit of 10%
and the rest in 6 equal monthly instalments.
How much is each monthly payment?

£328

5 *Acme Electronics* agree to a wage deal with their workers that will mean a
3·5% wage increase each year for the next three years.
If Ben earns £33 250 per year at the moment, what will he be earning in
three years time?

6 Mr Singh buys bottles of lemonade for 96 pence and sells them for £1·28.
Calculate his profit as a percentage of the cost price.

7 *Hillhouse Fine Arts* bought two paintings last month, one for £3750 and
the other for £7895. The first painting has appreciated by 9% but the
second painting was stolen. If insurance refunded 85% of the value of
the second painting, calculate the total value of the paintings now.

8 Mrs. Beaton calculated that her family's weekly food bill increased by 4%
last year and is now £124. What was the weekly bill a year ago?

Algebra

9 Evaluate each expression if $p = 5$, $q = -3$, $r = -6$ and $s = 0$.

   (**a**) $\dfrac{2p^2 + 5q}{p}$ (**b**) $\dfrac{r^2 - 8s}{q + r}$ (**c**) $\dfrac{5p - qr}{(r - 7s)^2}$

10 Simplify each expression:

   (**a**) $2m^2 - 8kl + m^2 + 5kl - 3m^2 + 2kl$ (**b**) $x^2 - 3x^3 - x + 5x + 7x^3 - 2x^2$

11 Expand and simplify:

   (**a**) $9(3z - 5w) + 6(w + 3z)$ (**b**) $21s - 4(6s - 9) - (12 - 3s)$

12 Solve each equation:

   (**a**) $17x + 9 = 86 + 6x$ (**b**) $6 - 2p = 10p - 18$

   (**c**) $7n + 21 = 12n + 20$ (**d**) $3(5d - 3) = 8(d - 2)$

   (**e**) $4(3x - 9) - 21 = 7(5x - 9) + 29$

13 Solve each equation:

(a) $\dfrac{a}{4} + \dfrac{3a + 1}{2} = \dfrac{a - 9}{8}$

(b) $\dfrac{v - 8}{3} + \dfrac{5v}{6} = \dfrac{3v + 8}{2}$

14 Solve each inequation:

(a) $3x + 4 < x - 9$

(b) $4(y - 8) - (3y - 9) \geqslant 0$

(c) $6 + 5(2x + 3) \leqslant -9$

(d) $2(7 + 3z) - 8 > 4(2z + 1)$

15 Bill thought of a number. He added 5 and then multiplied the total by 6. The result was -12. What was Bill's number?

16 The area of the triangle is less than 22 square centimetres. Form an inequation and solve it to find possible values for x.

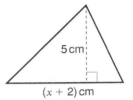
5 cm
$(x + 2)$ cm

Proportion

17 Paul uses 2500 grammes of lawn feed for an area of 55 square metres. What weight of lawn feed does he need for 75 square metres? Give your answer in kilogrammes and round to 2 significant figures.

18 An engineer calculated that a flooded mine shaft could be cleared in 24 hours by 5 identical pumps. However, only 4 pumps were available. How long did it take to clear the water?

19 John hired a car to drive from Brisbane to Sydney. The hire charge was $156. The hotel and return flight cost $638. The exchange rate was £1 = 1.45 Australian dollars. What was the total cost in pounds?

Area

20 Calculate the area of each shape.

(a)
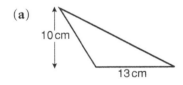
10 cm
13 cm

(b)
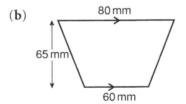
80 mm
65 mm
60 mm

(c)
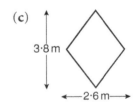
3·8 m
2·6 m

21 Find the circumference and area of each circle.

(a)
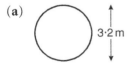
3·2 m

(b)

11 cm

(c)

30 mm

22 A stained glass window is made from a rectangle and a semicircle. The edging needs to be replaced. What length of edging is required?

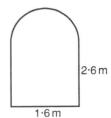
2·6 m
1·6 m

23 For each shape, find the length of the arc and the area of the sector.

(a)

270°

8 cm

(b)

140°

4·2 m

(c)

40° 17 mm

24 (a) Show that the length of the arc may be written as 6π metres.
   (b) Express arc length in terms of π and calculate the length of the arc.

12 m

O

25 Work out the angle at the centre of a circle for a sector with radius 2·8 m and area 2·05 m².

Similarity

26 For each pair of similar shapes, calculate the scale factor and hence find x.

(a)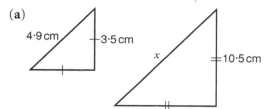

4·9 cm   3·5 cm

x =10·5 cm

(b)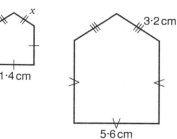

x 3·2 cm

1·4 cm

5·6 cm

27 This model of a tea clipper is similar to the real ship preserved in a maritime museum. If the length of the real clipper is 32 metres, calculate its true height from the keel to the top of the mast.

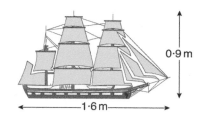

0·9 m

1·6 m

28 Prove that the following pairs of triangles are similar and hence find the values of x and y.

(a)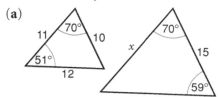

11   70°   10

51°

12

x 70°

15

59°

y

(b)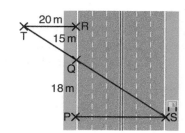

38°   35

15

120°

25

x

38° 120°

7

y

29 Errol is surveying a motorway. He wants to find the width of the road without having to close it. From a point P directly opposite a road sign, S, Errol walks along the verge for 18 metres to point Q and puts a marker pole in the ground.
He walks a further 15 metres along the verge to point R.
Errol then walks 20 metres at right angles to the road and puts another pole in the ground at T so that poles T, Q and the road sign, S, are in a straight line.
Calculate the width of the motorway.

20 m   R
T   15 m

Q

18 m

P   S

30 A postcard print of a famous painting is 15 centimetres in height.
The original painting is 75 centimetres high.
The area of the postcard is 165 cm².
Calculate the area of canvas used in the real painting.

75 cm

15 cm

31 A miniature bottle of *Famous Ptarmigan* is 8 centimetres high.
The largest sized bottle of *Famous Ptarmigan* is 28 centimetres high.
The bottles are similar and the miniature holds 35 millilitres.
What is the volume of the larger bottle?

8 cm

28 cm

Pythagoras' theorem

32 Calculate the length of the unknown side in each triangle.
Round your answers correct to one decimal place.

(**a**)
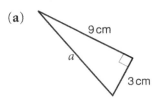
9 cm
a
3 cm

(**b**)
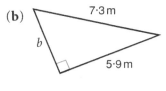
7·3 m
b
5·9 m

(**c**)
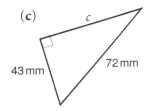
c
43 mm
72 mm

33 At a football training session Ryan has to run round the
edge of the field from corner flag *A* to corner flag *C*.
He has to try to beat team mate Steve who runs across
the field diagonally.
How much further does Ryan have to run?

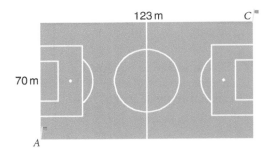

123 m
C
70 m
A

34 The diagram shows a cuboid with edges 12 centimetres, 9 centimetres
and 8 centimetres.

(**a**) Calculate the length of face diagonal *TV*.

(**b**) Calculate the length of space diagonal *TR*.

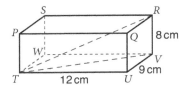

S
R
P
Q
8 cm
W
V
T
12 cm
U
9 cm

35 The vertices of a triangle are $K(4, 5)$, $L(-4, 2)$ and $M(1, -3)$.
Show that triangle *KLM* is isosceles.

36 Bobby the builder has laid the foundations for a new rectangular
building which is to be 25·8 metres long and 19·2 metres broad.
As a check, he measures the length of a diagonal and finds it to be
31 metres. Are the foundations rectangular?

37 The points $V(3, 5)$, $W(5, -4)$ and $U(-6, 2)$ are vertices of a triangle.
Is the triangle right angled?

7 Brackets and equations

7.1 Multiplying terms

Learning intentions

Remember $c \times 5 = 5 \times c = 5c$
$b \times a \times 3 = 3ab$
$2c \times 5d = 10cd$
$y \times y = y^2$

Writing algebraic expressions:
- numbers first
- letters in alphabetical order

Example

Simplify each of the following:

(a) $8g \times 4f$ (b) $-3m \times -2n \times 2b$ (c) $(-5b)^2$ (d) $(2zy)^3$

(a) $8g \times 4f$
  $= \mathbf{32fg}$

(b) $-3m \times -2n \times 2b$
  $= \mathbf{12bmn}$

(c) $(-5b)^2$
  $= (-5)^2 b^2$
  $= \mathbf{25b^2}$

(d) $(2zy)^3$
  $= 2^3 y^3 z^3$
  $= \mathbf{8\,y^3 z^3}$

Exercise 7.1

1 Simplify each of the following:

(a) $4 \times y$ (b) $w \times 7$ (c) $a \times b$

(d) $w \times v$ (e) $p \times 3r$ (f) $5s \times 4t$

(g) $4n \times 7k$ (h) $9k \times 8c$ (i) $7h \times g$

(j) $2d \times 5s \times 3b$ (k) $6q \times 2p \times 5r$ (l) $6t \times 3w \times a$

(m) $5p \times 6p$ (n) $7y \times 8y$ (o) $(2p)^2$

(p) $(4k)^2$ (q) $(5pq)^2$ (r) $(3rt)^2$

2 Simplify:

(a) $-4 \times f$ (b) $-2t \times 5$ (c) $-a \times -b$

(d) $-w \times -y$ (e) $-p \times m$ (f) $t \times -e$

(g) $3w \times -5a$ (h) $-6y \times 7t$ (i) $-5h \times -6j$

(j) $d \times -5s \times 3b$ (k) $-6y \times -2p \times 5t$ (l) $6t \times -3w \times -a$

(m) $-5p \times 10p$ (n) $-7s \times -9s$ (o) $(-2k)^2$

(p) $(-3g)^2$ (q) $(-4xy)^2$ (r) $(-5mn)^2$

3 Simplify:

(a) $(2y)^3$ (b) $(3w)^3$ (c) $(-3k)^3$

(d) $(-4m)^3$ (e) $(2zy)^3$ (f) $(3gh)^3$

(g) $(-3km)^3$ (h) $(2p^2)^2$ (i) $(-5h^2)^2$

(j) $3cd \times 2c^2d$ (k) $4wy^2 \times 5w^2y$ (l) $-2g^2h \times 7gh^2$

(m) $8s^2t \times -9st^2$ (n) $-2ab \times -4a^2b$ (o) $(-3wz)^2 \times 2wz$

7.2 Multiplying a bracket by a variable

Learning intentions

Remember

To multiply out a bracket, multiply every term inside the bracket by the term outside the bracket.

Example

Expand each expression

(a) $x(5 - x)$ (b) $-(3x - y)$ (c) $-6y(2y - 3x)$ (d) $13w^2 + 4w(2 - 5w) - 3w$

(a) $x(5 - x)$ (b) $-(3x - y)$ (c) $-6y(2y - 3x)$ (d) $13w^2 + 4w(2 - 5w) - 3w$
$= 5x - x^2$ $= -3x + y$ $= -12y^2 + 18xy$ $= 13w^2 + 8w - 20w^2 - 3w$
                                                                                    $= 13w^2 - 20w^2 + 8w - 3w$
                                                                                    $= -7w^2 + 5w$

Exercise 7.2

1 Multiply out the brackets:

(a) $y(z + 1)$ (b) $y(f - 4)$ (c) $p(q - 5)$ (d) $x(r + 8)$
(e) $t(3 - s)$ (f) $x(y + 4)$ (g) $-(z + 7)$ (h) $-(d + 6)$
(i) $-r(7 - r)$ (j) $x(x - 3)$ (k) $w(w - 4)$ (l) $t(a - t)$
(m) $-b(a - b)$ (n) $z(t - 7z)$ (o) $-(g + 2)$ (p) $-x(x + 9)$
(q) $-w(w - z)$ (r) $-(g - h)$ (s) $t(s + t)$ (t) $-(x - y)$

2 Expand:

(a) $2x(z + 2)$ (b) $3y(x - 4)$ (c) $4r(q - 7)$ (d) $2x(d + 5)$
(e) $6t(3s - 2)$ (f) $4x(2y + 4)$ (g) $-3w(z + 2)$ (h) $-3e(d - 6)$
(i) $-9r(7 - 2r)$ (j) $7x(x + 9)$ (k) $2w(3w - 4)$ (l) $8t(1 - 5t)$
(m) $7b(5a - 3b)$ (n) $5z(8y + 4z)$ (o) $-7g(2g + 2h)$ (p) $-8x(2x + 9y)$
(q) $-5w(3w - 6v)$ (r) $-2h(5g - 7h)$ (s) $9t(2s + 5t)$ (t) $-7y(7x - 6y)$
(u) $-(3x - 5y)$ (v) $-y(5s + 3y)$ (w) $-t(6t - 8h)$ (x) $-p(3p - 9q)$

3 Multiply out the brackets:

(a) $3b(b + 5)$ (b) $4x(2 + 3x)$ (c) $2y(1 - 2y)$
(d) $5w(2w - 3)$ (e) $-3z(4 - 2z)$ (f) $-5t(2t + 6r)$
(g) $3x(3x - x^2)$ (h) $-2y(4x + 3y^2)$ (i) $6z^2(4z + 3z^2)$

4 Expand and simplify:

(a) $y(3y - 6) + 3y$ (b) $2x(3x - 3) + x^2$
(c) $3z(5 - 3z) + 8z - 9$ (d) $4r(2r - s) - r^2 + 6rs$
(e) $5y(y + 9x) - 35xy + y^2$ (f) $-6y(3y^2 - 8y) + 9y^2$
(g) $-3b(6 - 4b) - 15b^2 - b$ (h) $3x^2(4x - 6) - 5x^2 + 3x$
(i) $-5z^2(3z - 1) + 6z^2 - 8z$ (j) $7t(3t - a) + 3at - 10t^2$
(k) $4z(5t - 8z) - 9tz + 16z^2$ (l) $-2r(8t + 9r) - 3r^2 + rt$
(m) $-3p(7p + 2q) - 6pq + p^2$ (n) $7y(y - 6w) + 3wy - 14y^2$
(o) $-9g(h - 5g) + 12gh - g^2$ (p) $-c(d - 3c) - 6c(d + 4c)$
(q) $a(3b - a) - 2a(5a + 3b) + a^2$ (r) $-z(2y - z) - 3y(2z + y)$

5 Find an expression for the total area of each shape. All dimensions are in centimetres.

(a)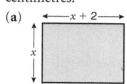

(b)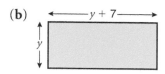

(c)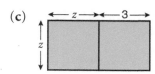

(d)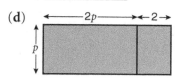

(e)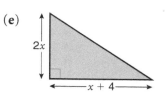

(f)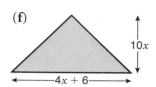

6 Simplify:

(a) $x(x^2 - 5x + 1) + 3(x^2 - 5x + 1)$

(b) $5(y^2 + 2y - 3) + y(y^2 + 2y - 3)$

(c) $z(2z^2 - 5z - 8) + 7(2z^2 - 5z - 8)$

(d) $w(3w^2 - 4w + 3) - (3w^2 - 4w + 3)$

(e) $6(2x^2 - 3x + 1) - (3x^2 - 5x + 1)$

(f) $b(3b^2 - 5b - 9) - 2(b^2 - 6b - 8)$

(g) $5y(4y^2 - 2y + 7) + y(3y^2 - 2y - 5)$

(h) $6x(2x^2 + 2x - 3) - x(5x^2 - 2x - 4)$

7.3 Expanding pairs of brackets

Learning intentions

Example

Expand the brackets

> Multiply each term in the second bracket by each term in the first bracket

(a) $(x + 2)(x + 3)$

(b) $(y - 3)(y + 9)$

(c) $(x + 5)(x - 5)$

(a) $(x + 2)(x + 3)$
$= x(x + 3) + 2(x + 3)$
$= x^2 + 3x + 2x + 6$
$= x^2 + 5x + 6$

(b) $(y - 3)(y + 9)$
$= y(y + 9) - 3(y + 9)$
$= y^2 + 9y - 3y - 27$
$= y^2 + 6y - 27$

(c) $(x + 5)(x - 5)$
$= x(x - 5) + 5(x - 5)$
$= x^2 - 5x + 5x - 25$
$= x^2 - 25$

Exercise 7.3

1 Expand the brackets:

(a) $(x + 1)(x + 2)$

(b) $(z + 3)(z + 1)$

(c) $(y + 3)(y + 4)$

(d) $(w + 2)(w + 3)$

(e) $(b - 2)(b - 4)$

(f) $(x - 2)(x - 5)$

(g) $(y - 1)(y - 5)$

(h) $(x - 3)(x - 6)$

(i) $(h - 4)(h - 2)$

2 Expand:

(a) $(a - 2)(a + 4)$

(b) $(z + 2)(z - 3)$

(c) $(y - 4)(y + 5)$

(d) $(w + 8)(w - 3)$

(e) $(y - 3)(y - 5)$

(f) $(b + 5)(b + 6)$

(g) $(x - 5)(x + 7)$

(h) $(z + 11)(z - 6)$

(i) $(12 - c)(8 + c)$

3 Expand:

(a) $(x + 2)(x - 2)$

(b) $(x + 7)(x - 7)$

(c) $(y + 3)(y - 3)$

(d) $(p - 4)(p + 4)$

(e) $(q - 6)(q + 6)$

(f) $(t - 10)(t + 10)$

7.4 More pairs of brackets

Learning intentions

Example 1

Expand $(x + 3)(x - 4)$

$$(x + 3)(x - 4)$$
$$= x^2 - 4x + 3x - 12$$

Firsts Outers Inners Lasts

$$= x^2 - x - 12$$

Brackets can be expanded more efficiently by multiplying:

- the **f**irst terms $(\bullet)(\bullet)$
- the **o**uter terms $(\bullet)(\bullet)$
- the **i**nner terms $(\bullet)(\bullet)$
- the **l**ast terms. $(\bullet)(\bullet)$

Example 2

Expand:

(a) $(x - 4)(x + 1)$

(b) $(x - 3)(x - 2)$

(a) $(x - 4)(x + 1)$
$$= x^2 + x - 4x - 4$$
$$= x^2 - 3x - 4$$

(b) $(x - 3)(x - 2)$
$$= x^2 - 2x - 3x + 6$$
$$= x^2 - 5x + 6$$

FOIL – **F**irsts **O**uters **I**nners **L**asts – is a mnemonic used to expand pairs of brackets.

A **mnemonic** is a memory aid.

Exercise 7.4

1 Expand the brackets:

(a) $(y + 5)(y + 6)$
(b) $(a + 6)(a + 4)$
(c) $(d + 3)(d + 9)$
(d) $(z + 7)(z + 7)$
(e) $(m + 9)(m + 5)$
(f) $(k + 8)(k + 7)$
(g) $(y + 9)(y + 2)$
(h) $(x + 5)(x + 3)$
(i) $(z + 4)(z + 8)$
(j) $(z + 7)(z + 6)$
(k) $(m + 9)(m + 9)$
(l) $(k + 8)(k + 8)$

2 Multiply out the brackets:

(a) $(x - 3)(x - 2)$
(b) $(y - 9)(y - 1)$
(c) $(z - 4)(z - 3)$
(d) $(b - 8)(b - 6)$
(e) $(w - 7)(w - 4)$
(f) $(x - 8)(x - 5)$
(g) $(x - 2)(x - 2)$
(h) $(y - 5)(y - 5)$
(i) $(b - 9)(b - 9)$
(j) $(z - 3)(z - 7)$
(k) $(m - 9)(m - 5)$
(l) $(k - 8)(k - 7)$

3 Expand:

(a) $(x + 3)(x + 7)$
(b) $(y + 9)(y - 2)$
(c) $(z - 5)(z + 3)$
(d) $(b - 3)(b - 6)$
(e) $(k + 7)(k - 9)$
(f) $(x - 9)(x - 8)$
(g) $(x - 11)(x + 2)$
(h) $(g - 15)(g - 2)$
(i) $(b + 9)(b - 10)$
(j) $(z - 13)(z + 4)$
(k) $(b - 10)(b - 10)$
(l) $(y + 12)(y - 12)$

4 Find an expression for the area of each shape below. All dimensions are in metres.

(a)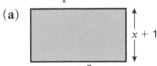

(b)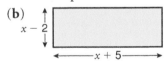

(c)

5 A garden has a rectangular lawn surrounded by a one metre wide path. The length of the lawn is $(x + 2)$ metres and the breadth is x metres.

Find an expression for the area of

(a) the lawn
(b) the lawn and path
(c) the path.

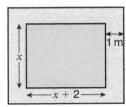

6 Find an expression for the area of the path around each lawn.

(a)
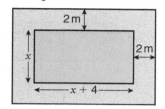

(b)
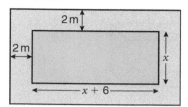

(c)
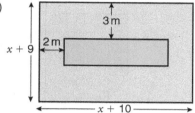

(d)
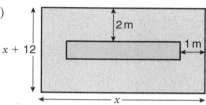

7.5   Expanding more brackets

Learning intentions

Example

Multiply out the brackets and simplify:

(a) $(2y - 3)(y - 5)$

(b) $5(2x + 3)(2x - 1)$

(a) $(2y - 3)(y - 5)$
$= 2y^2 - 10y - 3y + 15$
$= 2y^2 - 13y + 15$

(b) $5(2x + 3)(2x - 1)$
$= 5[4x^2 - 2x + 6x - 3]$
$= 5[4x^2 + 4x - 3]$
$= 20x^2 + 20x - 15$

Brackets first.

Exercise 7.5

1 Multiply out the brackets and simplify:

(a) $(2x + 1)(x + 3)$

(b) $(4y + 2)(y + 3)$

(c) $(4z + 6)(z + 1)$

(d) $(3b - 1)(2b + 5)$

(e) $(5z + 3)(3z - 8)$

(f) $(6a - 7)(2a + 3)$

(g) $(4y - 9)(3y - 2)$

(h) $(3w - 9)(5w - 6)$

(i) $(3 - 4y)(5 - 2y)$

(j) $(6m - 9)(3m + 7)$

(k) $(8x - 5)(3x - 6)$

(l) $(5y + 1)(5y - 1)$

(m) $(3k - 5)(3k + 5)$

(n) $(6z + 4)(6z - 4)$

(o) $(5b - 12)(3b - 7)$

2 Expand and simplify:

(a) $2(z + 5)(z + 3)$

(b) $4(x + 1)(x + 6)$

(c) $5(w + 2)(w - 4)$

(d) $4(k + 1)(3k - 2)$

(e) $5(2y - 3)(y - 1)$

(f) $6(z - 3)(2z - 8)$

(g) $-2(3b - 4)(2b + 3)$

(h) $-2(5 + 8m)(2 - 3m)$

(i) $-7(2k - 6)(3 + 5k)$

(j) $-5(6x - 2)(3x + 7)$

(k) $-4(8y - 5)(3y - 3)$

(l) $x(x + 1)(x + 3)$

(m) $2k(3k - 5)(3k + 5)$

(n) $-2z(6z + 4)(6z - 4)$

(o) $-5y(3y - 2)(y - 3)$

3 Find an expression for the volume of each shape below.
All dimensions are in metres.

(a)

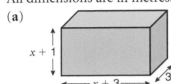

(b)

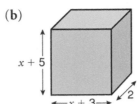

(c)

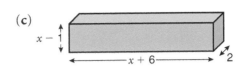

(d)

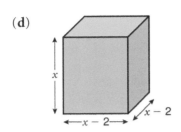

(e)

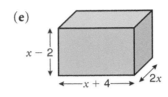

(f)

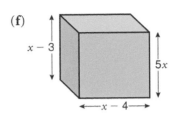

7.6 Squaring brackets

Learning intentions

Remember

y^2 means $y \times y$
$(x + 1)^2$ means $(x + 1)(x + 1)$

Example

Expand:

(a) $(x + 3)^2$

(b) $(4z - 7)^2$

(c) $(3y - 5)^2$

(a) $(x + 3)^2$
$= (x + 3)(x + 3)$
$= x^2 + 3x + 3x + 9$
$= x^2 + 6x + 9$

(b) $(4z - 7)^2$
$= (4z - 7)(4z - 7)$
$= 16z^2 - 28z - 28z + 49$
$= 16z^2 - 56z + 49$

(c) $(3y - 5)^2$
$= 9y^2 - 30y + 25$

> The middle two terms are always equal.

Square first term	$(3y)^2 = 9y^2$
Twice the product	$2 \times 3y \times -5 = -30y$
Square second term	$(-5)^2 = 25$

Exercise 7.6

1 Expand the brackets:

(a) $(x + 1)^2$
(b) $(w + 2)^2$
(c) $(k + 5)^2$
(d) $(z + 4)^2$
(e) $(x + 3)^2$
(f) $(m + 7)^2$
(g) $(y + 6)^2$
(h) $(k + 9)^2$

2 Expand the brackets:

(a) $(y - 1)^2$
(b) $(x - 3)^2$
(c) $(k - 5)^2$
(d) $(b - 4)^2$
(e) $(k - 2)^2$
(f) $(m - 9)^2$
(g) $(y - 7)^2$
(h) $(y - 12)^2$

3 Expand:

(a) $(z + 8)^2$
(b) $(w - 5)^2$
(c) $(c + 10)^2$
(d) $(d - 6)^2$
(e) $(x + 12)^2$
(f) $(m - 11)^2$
(g) $(y - 20)^2$
(h) $(x - 30)^2$

4 Expand:
- **(a)** $(3x + 2)^2$
- **(b)** $(2y + 1)^2$
- **(c)** $(5w + 3)^2$
- **(d)** $(3x - 2)^2$
- **(e)** $(2y - 5)^2$
- **(f)** $(3m + 6)^2$
- **(g)** $(8z - 1)^2$
- **(h)** $(4y + 6)^2$
- **(i)** $(9x - 8)^2$
- **(j)** $(9 + 3z)^2$
- **(k)** $(10 - 2y)^2$
- **(l)** $(20 - 2y)^2$

5 Find an expression for the area of each square.
All dimensions are in millimetres.

(a)

←$z + 1$→

(b)

←$4y - 2$→

(c)

←$7 - 3x$→

7.7 More squared brackets

Learning intentions

Example

Expand and simplify
- **(a)** $2(x + 2)^2$
- **(b)** $(y - 4)^2 - 2(3y - 7)$
- **(c)** $(z - \frac{2}{z})^2$
- **(d)** $(x + 2)(2x - 3) - (x - 1)^2$

(a) $2(x + 2)^2$
$$= 2(x^2 + 4x + 4)$$
$$= \mathbf{2x^2 + 8x + 8}$$

(b) $(y - 4)^2 - 2(3y - 7)$
$$= y^2 - 8y + 16 - 6y + 14$$
$$= y^2 - 8y - 6y + 16 + 14$$
$$= \mathbf{y^2 - 14y + 30}$$

(c) $(z - \frac{2}{z})^2$
$$= \mathbf{z^2 - 4 + \frac{4}{z^2}}$$

(d) $(x + 2)(2x - 3) - (x - 1)^2$
$$= 2x^2 - 3x + 4x - 6 - (x^2 - 2x + 1)$$
$$= 2x^2 + x - 6 - x^2 + 2x - 1$$
$$= \mathbf{x^2 + 3x - 7}$$

Exercise 7.7

1 Expand and simplify:
- **(a)** $2(w + 3)^2$
- **(b)** $4(y + 1)^2$
- **(c)** $5(x + 4)^2$
- **(d)** $5(k - 2)^2$
- **(e)** $6(z - 4)^2$
- **(f)** $2(3m + 1)^2$
- **(g)** $4(2y + 3)^2$
- **(h)** $-3(b - 2)^2$
- **(i)** $-5(y + 3)^2$
- **(j)** $-2(2x + 1)^2$
- **(k)** $-4(3y - 2)^2$
- **(l)** $-3(4 - 2z)^2$

2 Expand:
- **(a)** $(b + 3)^2 + 2b^2 - 6$
- **(b)** $(k - 6)^2 - 2(3k - 7)$
- **(c)** $10m + (m - 4)^2 + 3$
- **(d)** $6y^2 - 4(2y - 3)^2 - 9y$
- **(e)** $(3x + 2)^2 + 5(4x - 1) - 2$
- **(f)** $(4z - 5)^2 - (z + 2)^2$
- **(g)** $4(2b + 5)^2 - (5 - 3b)$
- **(h)** $-3(z - 2)^2 + (z + 1)^2$
- **(i)** $(x - 5)^2 - (x + 2)^2$
- **(j)** $(y + 3)(y - 5) - (y - 2)^2$
- **(k)** $(x - 4)^2 - (x - 1)(x + 1)$
- **(l)** $2(w + 2)^2 - 3(w + 3)^2$
- **(m)** $-2(2x + 1)^2 - 3(6 - 2x)$
- **(n)** $-4(3y - 2)^2 - 2(2y + 1)^2 - 3$

3 Simplify:
- **(a)** $(x + \frac{1}{x})^2$
- **(b)** $(z + \frac{3}{z})^2$
- **(c)** $(k - \frac{1}{k})^2$
- **(d)** $(z - \frac{2}{z})^2$
- **(e)** $(m + \frac{4}{m})^2$
- **(f)** $(2x + \frac{1}{x})^2$
- **(g)** $(3b - \frac{1}{b})^2$
- **(h)** $(5y + \frac{4}{y})^2$
- **(i)** $(\frac{5}{z} + 2z)^2$
- **(j)** $(\frac{1}{x} - 4x)^2$
- **(k)** $(\frac{3}{z} - 2z)^2$
- **(l)** $(\frac{1}{x} + \frac{1}{y})^2$
- **(m)** $(\frac{3}{x} + \frac{2}{y})^2$
- **(n)** $(\frac{1}{a} - \frac{2}{b})^2$
- **(o)** $(\frac{2}{z} - 4)^2$
- **(p)** $(5 - \frac{4}{b})^2$

4 Jasmine bought three square pictures. The picture framer mounts them with borders. What area of border was used to mount each painting?

←$2x + 5$→
Border 3 cm wide

←$3x - 1$→
Border 2 cm wide

←$5 - 2x$→
Border 5 cm wide

7.8 More complex expressions

Learning intentions

Example

Expand and simplify:

(a) $(x + a)(y + b)$

(b) $(x + 3)(5x^2 + 6x - 8)$

(a) $(x + a)(y + b)$
$= xy + xb + ay + ab$

(b) $(x + 3)(5x^2 + 6x - 8)$
$= x(5x^2 + 6x - 8) + 3(5x^2 + 6x - 8)$
$= 5x^3 + 6x^2 - 8x + 15x^2 + 18x - 24)$
$= 5x^3 + 6x^2 + 15x^2 - 8x + 18x - 24$
$= 5x^3 + 21x^2 + 10x - 24$

(c) $(2y - 3)^3$

(c) $(2y - 3)^3$
$= (2y - 3)(2y - 3)^2$
$= (2y - 3)(4y^2 - 12y + 9)$
$= 2y(4y^2 - 12y + 9) - 3(4 - y^2 - 12y + 9)$
$= 8y^3 - 24y^2 + 18y - 12y^2 + 36y - 27$
$= 8y^3 - 24y^2 - 12y^2 + 18y + 36y - 27$
$= 8y^3 - 36y^2 + 54y - 27$

Exercise 7.8

1 Expand and simplify where possible:

(a) $(x + 2)(y + b)$

(b) $(y + b)(y - 2)$

(c) $(z + x)(y + x)$

(d) $(a - b)(a + b)$

(e) $(c - d)(c - d)$

(f) $(p + q)(q - p)$

(g) $(5 - h)(g + h)$

(h) $(9 - 3x)(y - 3x)$

(i) $(3s - 2t)(5s - 2t)$

2 Expand and simplify:

(a) $(x + 1)(x^2 + 3x + 5)$

(b) $(w + 2)(w^2 - 5w + 3)$

(c) $(k + 5)(2k^2 + 3k - 4)$

(d) $(z - 2)(3z^2 + 5z + 3)$

(e) $(x - 3)(4x^2 - 5x - 9)$

(f) $(m - 7)(3m^2 + 6m + 4)$

(g) $(y + 6)(2y^2 - 5y + 8)$

(h) $(k - 9)(7k^2 - 9k + 5)$

(i) $(x + 8)(6x^2 + 8x - 7)$

(j) $(2 + z)(7z^2 - 2z + 3)$

(k) $(4 - b)(4b^2 + 5b - 6)$

(l) $(3 - x)(2x^2 + 3x - 4)$

(m) $(3y - 1)(3y^2 + 2y + 3)$

(n) $(5z + 3)(3z^2 - 5z - 3)$

(o) $(6a - 3)(7a^2 - 3a - 5)$

3 Expand and simplify:

(a) $(x + 1)(x + 2)^2$ (b) $(y + 3)(y + 1)^2$ (c) $(z + 5)(z - 2)^2$

(d) $(2w + 1)(w + 3)^2$ (e) $(x + 1)(3x - 2)^2$ (f) $(y - 1)(3y + 1)^2$

(g) $(x - 3)(2x - 1)^2$ (h) $(2m - 3)(3m + 6)^2$ (i) $(3z - 5)(8z - 1)^2$

(j) $(3 - y)(2y + 1)^2$ (k) $(2 - 3b)(3b - 4)^2$ (l) $(7 - 2x)(5x + 6)^2$

4 Expand and simplify:

(a) $(b + 2)(b + 3)(b + 1)$ (b) $(y + 1)(y + 5)(y + 2)$ (c) $(x + 1)(x + 5)(x - 3)$

(d) $(k - 2)(k + 2)(k - 3)$ (e) $(z - 4)(z - 2)(z + 3)$ (f) $(3m + 1)(m + 1)(m - 1)$

(g) $(y - 1)(2y + 3)(y - 2)$ (h) $(4b - 2)(2b + 1)(b - 3)$ (i) $(2y - 1)(y + 5)(5y + 3)$

(j) $(3 + y)(2 + y)(4 + y)$ (k) $(2 - b)(b - 4)(3 + b)$ (l) $(7 - x)(x - 6)(3 - 2x)$

5 Expand and simplify:

(a) $(x + 1)^3$ (b) $(w + 4)^3$ (c) $(k + 5)^3$

(d) $(z - 2)^3$ (e) $(x - 1)^3$ (f) $(m - 3)^3$

(g) $(2y + 1)^3$ (h) $(2k + 5)^3$ (i) $(3x - 1)^3$

(j) $(3 - y)^3$ (k) $(2 - b)^3$ (l) $(4 - 2x)^3$

6 Find an expression for the volume of each shape. All dimensions are in centimetres.

(a)

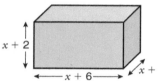

(b)

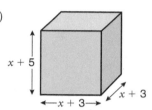

(c)
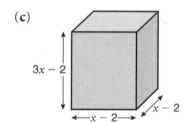

(d)

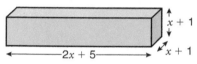

(e)

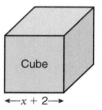

(f)
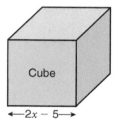

7 Expand and simplify:

(a) $2(x - 1)^3$ (b) $-3(y + 2)^3$

(c) $4(k - 5)^3 + 4k^3 - 5k^2 + 20$ (d) $3(2z - 2)^3 - 3z^3 + 5z^2 - 5z - 6$

(e) $-3(x + 2)^3 + 2x^2 - 16$ (f) $2(3y - 8)(5y^2 + 4y)$

(g) $5(2x - 1)(3x^3 + 5x)$ (h) $2(3m - 2)(2m^2 - 5m + 1)$

(i) $-3(2y + 6)(3y^2 - 2y - 1)$ (j) $(2k - 5)^2(k + 2) - 5k^2$

(k) $-2(3x + 1)^2 - 3(2x + 1)^2 + 10x$ (l) $-5(3 - 2y)^3 + 3(y - 2)^2 - 6y^3 + 15y$

7.9 Solving equations

Learning intentions

Example 1

Solve

(a) $(x + 1)^2 = x^2 + 5$

(b) $(y + 3)(y + 5) = (y - 5)^2$

(a) $(x + 1)^2 = x^2 + 5$
$$x^2 + 2x + 1 = x^2 + 5$$
$$2x + 1 = 5$$
$$2x = 4$$
$$\boldsymbol{x = 2}$$

(b) $(y + 3)(y + 5) = (y - 5)^2$
$$y^2 + 5y + 3y + 15 = y^2 - 10y + 25$$
$$y^2 + 8y + 15 = y^2 - 10y + 25$$
$$8y + 15 = -10y + 25$$
$$18y + 15 = 25$$
$$18y = 10$$
$$y = \tfrac{10}{18}$$
$$\boldsymbol{y = \tfrac{5}{9}}$$

Example 2

Form an equation and solve it to find the value of z.

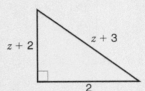

Using Pythagoras:
$$c^2 = a^2 + b^2$$
$$(z + 3)^2 = 2^2 + (z + 2)^2$$
$$z^2 + 6z + 9 = 4 + z^2 + 4z + 4$$
$$z^2 + 6z + 9 = z^2 + 4z + 8$$
$$6z + 9 = 4z + 8$$
$$2z + 9 = 8$$
$$2z = -1$$
$$\boldsymbol{z = -\tfrac{1}{2}}$$

Exercise 7.9

1 Solve the equations:

(a) $(x + 1)^2 = x^2 + 9$

(b) $(y + 2)^2 = y^2 + 13$

(c) $(z - 1)^2 = z^2 + 5$

(d) $(b + 5)^2 = (b + 1)^2$

(e) $(k + 6)^2 = (k - 1)^2$

(f) $(x + 3)(x - 4) = (x + 1)^2$

(g) $(y + 2)(y + 3) = (y + 1)^2$

(h) $(a + 2)(a - 4) = (a + 3)^2$

(i) $(x + 5)^2 = (x + 2)(x - 1)$

(j) $(2y + 3)^2 = (y + 1)(y - 3) + 3y^2$

(k) $(3z - 4)^2 = (z - 2)^2 + 8z^2$

(l) $(5m + 2)^2 - 1 = (m - 3)(m + 5) + 24m^2$

(m) $x(x + 5)^2 = (x + 1)^2$

(n) $z(z + 3) = (z - 3)^2$

(o) $(y + 1)^2 = y(y + 3)$

(p) $(2x - 3)^2 = (2x + 1)^2$

(q) $(3w - 4)^2 = (3w + 1)^2$

(r) $(2y + 5)^2 = 4(y - 1)^2$

(s) $(3z - 2)^2 = 9(z + 1)^2$

(t) $(4b + 2)^2 = 16(b - 2)^2$

2 Form an equation to find the value of x:

(a)

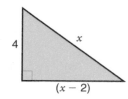

4, x, $(x - 2)$

(b)

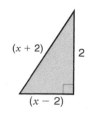

$(x + 2)$, 2, $(x - 2)$

(c)

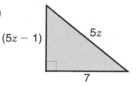

$(5z - 1)$, $5z$, 7

3 Find the value of x if the pairs of shapes are of equal area.

(a)

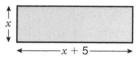

x, $x + 5$

$x + 1$, $x + 1$

(b)

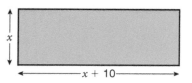

x, $x + 10$

$x + 4$

(c)

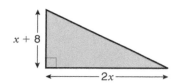

$x + 8$, $2x$

$x + 2$

4 **(a)** Write down the length of AB in triangle AOB.
   (b) Find an expression for the length of OB.
   (c) Using Pythagoras' theorem, form an equation.
   (d) Solve the equation to find the value of r.

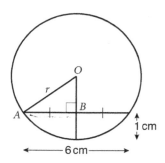

r, O, B, A, 1 cm, 6 cm

5 For each diagram below, follow the steps in question 4 to find the value of r.

(a)

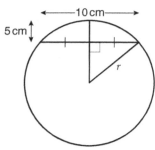

10 cm, 5 cm, r

(b)

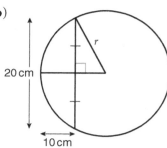

20 cm, r, 10 cm

7.10 Using fractions

Learning intentions

Example

Solve: (a) $\frac{1}{5}x = \frac{1}{2}(x - 9)$

(b) $\frac{(y + 2)}{3} = \frac{2(3y - 5)}{7}$

(a) $\frac{1}{5}x = \frac{1}{2}(x - 9)$ | Multiply by 10 |

$10 \times \frac{1}{5}x = 10 \times \frac{1}{2}(x - 9)$

$2x = 5(x - 9)$

$2x = 5x - 45$

$2x + 45 = 5x$

$45 = 3x$

$\frac{45}{3} = x$

$x = 15$

(b) $\frac{(y + 2)}{3} = \frac{2(3y - 5)}{7}$ | Multiply by 21 |

$21 \times \frac{(y + 2)}{3} = 21 \times \frac{2(3y - 5)}{7}$

$7(y + 2) = 6(3y - 5)$

$7y + 14 = 18y - 30$

$14 = 11y - 30$

$44 = 11y$

$\frac{44}{11} = y$

$y = 4$

Exercise 7.10

1 Solve the equations:

(a) $\frac{1}{2}z = (z + 5)$

(b) $\frac{1}{5}w = 2(w + 9)$

(c) $\frac{1}{3}x = \frac{1}{4}(x + 2)$

(d) $\frac{(3d)}{5} = \frac{(d - 9)}{2}$

(e) $\frac{(p + 9)}{7} = \frac{(p - 3)}{5}$

(f) $\frac{3}{4}x = 6x - 7$

(g) $\frac{1}{2}(y + 1) = \frac{1}{5}(y - 8)$

(h) $3b = \frac{b}{6} - 85$

(i) $\frac{1}{4}z + 19 = 5z$

(j) $\frac{2}{3}a = \frac{1}{4}(a + 4)$

(k) $\frac{(p - 7)}{2} = \frac{p}{5}$

(l) $\frac{1}{6}(2z - 1) = \frac{1}{2}(z - 3) - \frac{4}{3}z$

(m) $\frac{1}{4}(2w - 1) = \frac{1}{6}(w - 6) - \frac{1}{3}(w + 2)$

(n) $\frac{(3x - 1)}{15} + \frac{(x - 1)}{3} = \frac{(x + 8)}{5}$

(o) $\frac{1}{4}(y - 1) + 2y = \frac{1}{8}(3y + 2)$

(p) $\frac{3}{5}z - \frac{(z + 7)}{4} = \frac{(z - 8)}{2}$

Review exercise 7: Am I a successful learner?

1 Multiply out the brackets and simplify where necessary:

(a) $4(3z - 3)$

(b) $7(4x + 4)$

(c) $-6(2y + 5)$

(d) $-5(3 - 2w)$

(e) $3x(x + 2)$

(f) $5z(6 - 3z)$

(g) $-2t(1 - 2t)$

(h) $-6b(5 - 3b) + 5b^2$

(i) $-3x(4x + 9) - 2x + 8x^2$

2 Expand:

(a) $(y + 5)(y + 3)$

(b) $(x - 1)(x - 6)$

(c) $(z + 5)(z - 2)$

(d) $(2x - 4)(x + 5)$

(e) $(y + 2)(3y - 6)$

(f) $(4w - 5)(2w - 1)$

(g) $(5z + 5)(3z + 2)$

(h) $3(y - 5)(y + 6)$

(i) $-5(2x + 3)(3x - 2)$

3 Expand:
- **(a)** $(y + 3)^2$
- **(b)** $(z - 5)^2$
- **(c)** $(2x + 8)^2$
- **(d)** $(5k - 6)^2$
- **(e)** $4(y + 2)^2$
- **(f)** $7(w - 3)^2$
- **(g)** $10y^2 + 2(y + 1)^2$
- **(h)** $(4x - 6)^2 - 12x + 4x^2$
- **(i)** $(3z - 1)^2 + (2z + 1)^2$

4 Expand and simplify:
- **(a)** $(x - 2)(3x^2 + 5x + 4)$
- **(b)** $(y + 3)(5y^2 + 8y + 6)$
- **(c)** $(2b - 3)(3b + 5)^2$
- **(d)** $(y + 3)(y + 5)(y + 2)$
- **(e)** $(5b - 2)(2b + 4)(b - 3)$
- **(f)** $(3k - 5)^3$
- **(g)** $(2x + 7)^3$
- **(h)** $-5(2y + 2)(3y^2 - 5y - 1)$
- **(i)** $(2x - 4)^2(x + 2) - 5x^2 + 6$
- **(j)** $(3y + 5)(y - 3)^2 + y^2 + 15$

5 Solve the equations:
- **(a)** $(x + 2)^2 = x^2 + 12$
- **(b)** $(z - 3)^2 = z^2 - 24z$
- **(c)** $(k + 8)^2 = (k - 1)^2$
- **(d)** $y(y + 15) = (y + 5)^2$
- **(e)** $(x - 5)^2 = (x + 3)(x - 1)$
- **(f)** $(2y + 5)^2 = (y + 2)(y - 5) + 3y^2 - 11$

6 Form an equation and solve it to find the value of x:

(a)

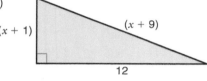

(b)

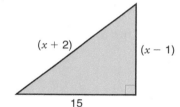

7 If the area of the square is equal to the area of the rectangle, find the value of x.

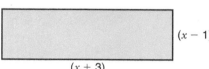

8 Solve the equations:
- **(a)** $\frac{1}{4}y = 5y - 19$
- **(b)** $\frac{2}{3}x - \frac{1}{4}(x + 6) = -(x - 7)$
- **(c)** $\frac{(x - 2)}{5} + \frac{2x}{7} = x - 4$
- **(d)** $\frac{3(2w - 2)}{4} = \frac{(w + 9)}{2} - \frac{2(4w + 3)}{3}$

Summary 7: What I learned in this chapter.

Multiplying a bracket by a variable

(a) $4x(2 + 3x)$
$= 8x + 12x^2$

(b) $3y(5 - 3y) + 11y^2 - 9$
$= 15y - 9y^2 + 11y^2 - 9$
$= 2y^2 + 15y - 9$

Expanding pairs of brackets

$(5z + 2)(3z - 8)$
$= 15z^2 - 40z + 6z - 16$
$= 15z^2 - 34z - 16$

FOIL – Firsts Outers Inners Lasts

Expand brackets more efficiently by multiplying:

- the first terms $(\bullet\ )(\bullet\ )$
- the outer terms $(\bullet\ )(\ \bullet)$
- the inner terms $(\ \bullet)(\bullet\ )$
- the last terms. $(\ \bullet)(\ \bullet)$

Squaring brackets

$(5x - 2)^2$
$= 25x^2 - 20x + 4$

Square first term	$(5x)^2 = 25x^2$
Twice the product	$2 \times 5x \times -2 = -20x$
Square second term	$(-2)^2 = 4$

Expanding more complex brackets

$(x + 3)(5x^2 + 6x - 8)$
$= x(5x^2 + 6x - 8) + 3(5x^2 + 6x - 8)$
$= 5x^3 + 6x^2 - 8x + 15x^2 + 18x - 24$
$= 5x^3 + 21x^2 + 10x - 24$

Solving equations

$(y + 3)(y + 5) = (y - 5)^2$
$y^2 + 5y + 3y + 15 = y^2 - 10y + 25$
$y^2 + 8y + 15 = y^2 - 10y + 25$
$8y + 15 = -10y + 25$
$8y + 10y = 25 - 15$
$18y = 10$
$y = \frac{10}{18}$
$y = \frac{5}{9}$

$\frac{1}{3}(y + 2) = \frac{2}{7}(3y - 5)$
$21 \times \frac{1}{3}(y + 2) = 21 \times \frac{2}{7}(3y - 5)$
$7(y + 2) = 6(3y - 5)$
$7y + 14 = 18y - 30$
$14 = 11y - 30$
$44 = 11y$
$\frac{44}{11} = y$
$y = 4$

8 Statistics 1

8.1 Pie charts

Learning intentions

On a pie chart the angle at the centre of each sector is calculated as a fraction of 360°.

The *Daily Caledonian* has a total of 30 pages.
The pages given to different types of articles are shown in the table.

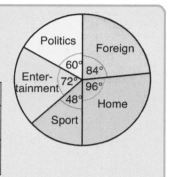

Article	Foreign news	Home news	Sport	Entertainment	Politics	Total
Number of pages	7	8	4	6	5	30
Angle	$\frac{7}{30} \times 360°$ $= 84°$	$\frac{8}{30} \times 360°$ $= 96°$	$\frac{4}{30} \times 360°$ $= 48°$	$\frac{6}{30} \times 360°$ $= 72°$	$\frac{5}{30} \times 360°$ $= 60°$	360°

Exercise 8.1

For questions 1 to 3 draw a pie chart to illustrate the information given.
Diagrams should be large enough to annotate.

1 Favourite school subject for pupils in 3C2.

Subject	Maths	English	PE	Music	Science
Number of pupils	14	3	8	2	3

2 Age at which a group of people in a survey were married.

Age range	under 20	20–24	25–29	30–34	35–39	40 and over
Number	5	26	14	7	5	3

3 A survey on methods of travelling to work.

Method of travel	Car	Bus	Train	Subway	Cycle	Walk
Percentage	35%	21%	15%	15%	9%	5%

4 The *Weekly Journal* contained 72 pages last week.

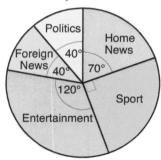

(a) Calculate the fraction of the paper for each section.

(b) Hence calculate the number of pages for each section.

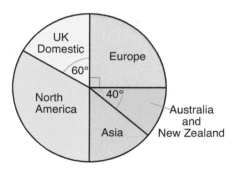

5 In a survey of 1440 travellers at Glasgow Airport, the numbers going to various destinations were noted and illustrated in the pie chart.
How many were going to each destination?

8.2 Scatter graphs

Learning intentions

The graphs below are examples of **scatter graphs**.

A scatter graph is used to investigate or display a relationship between two variables and may show a general rather than an exact relationship.

A **line of best fit** has been added to the graphs. This line may be used to estimate values.

A group of athletes recorded their weights and the distances they threw the shot.

A record was made of the weights of ten men and the number of laps of the running track they were able to run in 40 minutes·

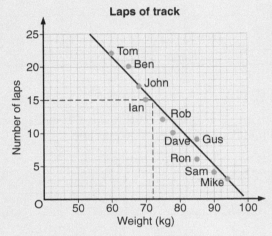

A shot putter weighing 77 kg might be expected to putt the shot about 13·5m.

A man weighing 72 kg might be expected to run about 15 laps of the track.

The first graph shows a **positive correlation** between *weight* and *distance thrown*.

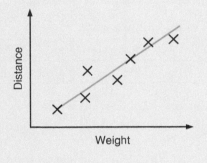

Distance increases as weight increases

The second graph shows a **negative correlation** between *weight* and *laps completed*

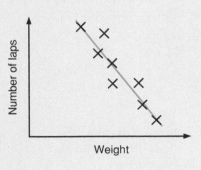

Number of laps decreases as weight increases

Exercise 8.2

1 (**a**) Use the *Shot putt* scatter graph in the teaching panel to find:
    (**i**) how many men weighed 75 kg
    (**ii**) how far Jim threw the shot
    (**iii**) who threw the shot furthest
    (**iv**) who weighed least.
  (**b**) Comment on Bob's weight and throw.
  (**c**) What distance did the heaviest man throw?

2 Use the *Laps of track* scatter graph in the teaching panel to find:
  (**a**) how many men weighed exactly 85 kg
  (**b**) who was the heaviest man
  (**c**) who completed the smallest number of laps
  (**d**) how many laps the lightest man ran
  (**e**) which two men weighed the same.

Discussion points

In which sports does height and weight play an important part?

In which sports is it less important?

3 At the Garth Sports Centre, the heights of ten women and the results of their high jump competition were recorded.

Name	Eve	Ann	Jill	Kate	Una	Dot	Fay	Sue	Usma	Jen
Height (m)	1·64	1·58	1·60	1·70	1·65	1·59	1·67	1·74	1·73	1·62
Jump (m)	1·04	0·98	1·00	1·20	1·10	1·02	1·18	1·24	1·28	1·02

  (**a**) Show this information on a scatter graph.
  (**b**) Who was the tallest woman?
  (**c**) Who jumped highest?
  (**d**) Who was the smallest woman?
  (**e**) Whose jump was lowest?
  (**f**) From your graph, is there a correlation between *Height* and *Jump*?
  (**g**) Draw a line of best fit and estimate the jump for a woman 1·66 m tall.

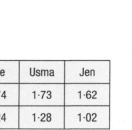

4 The weights of ten women and the distances they threw the javelin were recorded.

Name	Eve	Ann	Jill	Kate	Una	Dot	Fay	Sue	Kath	Jen
Weight (kg)	62	70	66	72	60	58	74	56	68	64
Distance (m)	25	34	28	36	24	21	38	20	33	26

Show this information on a scatter graph and make a statement about the correlation between the women's weights and the distances they threw the javelin.

5 The heights of ten women and their times for a 200 metres sprint were recorded.

Name	Jen	Lou	Jill	Pam	Ella	Sue	Kay	Eve	Amy	Sara
Height (m)	1·64	1·70	1·58	1·62	1·74	1·68	1·76	1·60	1·72	1·66
Time (s)	38	32	44	40	30	33	33	41	31	35

Show this information on a scatter graph and make a statement about the correlation between the women's heights and their times for the sprint.

6 The weights of ten men and their maximum snooker breaks were recorded.

Name	Ian	Rob	John	Tom	Jim	Ross	Said	Ihab	Ali	Ken
Weight (kg)	68	74	76	70	78	72	74	68	82	80
Break	50	32	44	46	30	34	38	32	48	36

Make a statement about the correlation between men's weights and their maximum snooker breaks.

> **Discussion points**
>
> For what other variables would you expect to find either a positive or negative correlation?
>
> Are there physical variables for which there would be no correlation?
>
> CI EC

8.3 Mean, median and mode

Learning intentions

Mean, median and **mode** are **measures of central tendency**.
All three are types of **averages** and can be used to summarise a set of data.
The most appropriate type of average depends on the nature of the data and the use to be made of it.

Mean
The mean is found by adding all the data and dividing by the number of pieces of data.

Median
The median is the middle value when the data is arranged in order.
For an even number of pieces of data, the median is midway between the middle two values.

Mode
The mode is the value which occurs most often.

Example
Here are the numbers of goals scored by the Stonebank Academy Under 16 football team in their league games last season.

$$0 \quad 5 \quad 2 \quad 0 \quad 3 \quad 4 \quad 0 \quad 1 \quad 6 \quad 7 \quad 4 \quad 5$$

Find   **(a)** the mean   **(b)** the median   **(c)** the mode.

(a) mean $= \dfrac{0 + 5 + 2 + 0 + 3 + 4 + 0 + 1 + 6 + 7 + 4 + 5}{12} = \dfrac{37}{12} = 3 \cdot 083\ldots = \textbf{3} \cdot \textbf{1 goals}$ to 1 dec. place

(b) data in order: 0 0 0 1 2 3   4 4 5 5 6 7

median is **3·5**

> Arrange data in order to help find both median and mode.

(c) mode or modal score is **0** since it is the most common score.

In this example the mean and median both describe the number of goals scored in a typical game. However, the mode is not a useful average to describe the data in this case.

Exercise 8.3

1 Calculate the mean measurement for each set:
   (**a**) Costs of items of shopping:
   £1.50, £1.05, £1.70, 75p, 34p, 36p
   (**b**) Hours of sunshine per day in Ayr during 2 weeks in April:
   3·8, 7·8, 5·7, 2·0, 3·4, 7·2, 4·1, 4·9, 6·3, 0·8, 1·3, 7·9, 7·6, 5·2
   (**c**) Temperatures, in degrees centigrade, at which car engines were tested:
   16, −15, 58, −45, 38, 55, −37, −30, −22, 37

2 Find the median of each set of numbers:
   (**a**) 12, 13, 13, 13, 14, 15, 15, 16, 17
   (**b**) 52, 46, 92, 67, 101, 123, 77, 24, 39, 86, 44
   (**c**) 2, 9, 1, 2, 5, 7, 2, 3, 1, 4, 4, 8
   (**d**) 4·9, 5·6, 3·2, 8·1, 7·3, 6·4, 9·1, 5·6, 2·5, 6·9

3 Find the modal value for each set of numbers:
   (**a**) 5, 8, 4, 5, 8, 5, 4, 8, 6, 9, 5, 4
   (**b**) 12·5, 12·6, 11·9, 12·4, 12·6, 12·5, 12·4, 11·8, 12·4
   (**c**) 240, 210, 240, 600, 240, 240, 850, 240, 220, 240

4 By putting the heights in order and finding the median of each group,
   state which set of teenagers appears to be the taller.
   Group A   120, 119, 124, 121, 118, 122, 120
   Group B   125, 122, 122, 117, 116, 123, 115

5 Billy scored these marks out of 25 in maths tests during the year:
   20, 22, 18, 21, 22, 16, 14, 19, 17
   (**a**) Find the three averages.
   (**b**) Which average would Billy use to tell his parents about his
   performance in mathematics?

6 The daily noon temperatures, in degrees centigrade, on Elie beach over a
   fourteen day period in July were recorded:
   19, 20, 19, 17, 21, 18, 19, 24, 25, 25, 28, 25, 23, 18.
   (**a**) For this distribution calculate
   (**i**) the mean   (**ii**) the median   (**iii**) the mode.
   (**b**) Which of the three averages best represents the data?
   Give reasons for your choice.

7 The scores in the final round of a golf tournament last year were:
   66, 70, 69, 68, 70, 72, 69, 71, 72, 74, 66, 63, 69, 69
   73, 73, 73, 69, 73, 69, 66, 67, 67, 70, 71, 69, 74, 80
   (**a**) What was the modal score?
   (**b**) Find the median.
   (**c**) Calculate the mean score.
   (**d**) None of these averages was in the headlines the next day.
   Which score do you think made the headlines?

8 In Rugby Union there are 8 forwards in a team. In a recent match the
   weights of the forwards were noted and the mean weight of each team
   calculated as 92·5 kg and 87·25 kg.
   What was the difference in total weight between the two sets of forwards?

9 The mean height of 4 boys in a school relay team was 152 cm.
When one boy was replaced by the reserve, the mean height changed to 154 cm.
How much taller was the reserve than the boy he replaced?

10 For the first 11 months of last year, John's bank balance was, on average, £68
overdrawn at the end of the month. At the end of December, John was £107 overdrawn.
What was his average debt per month for the year?

 11 In *Amelie's Boutique*, the sizes of the dresses sold last month were recorded.

12, 8, 10, 12, 16, 8, 12, 12,
10, 12, 12, 10, 8, 14, 12, 10,
12, 14, 8, 12, 10, 10, 12, 14

(**a**) Find the modal dress size.

(**b**) Why would the shop manager find the mode a useful average when ordering stock?

8.4 Dot plots

Learning intentions

A dot plot uses dots placed above a number line to illustrate the distribution of a data set.

Jill's scorecard recorded the
number of shots for each hole
in a round of golf.

5 6 6 5 7 4 5 4 8
5 3 7 2 7 3 6 5 4

Each score is represented by a dot placed
above the number line.

The dot plot shows that:
• the scores range from 2 to 8
• 5 is the modal score
• the distribution of scores is roughly symmetrical.

Jill's golf scores

Weekly earnings of factory workers (£)

Distribution is **skewed to the left**.

Age of patients in a surgery (years)

Distribution is **skewed to the right**.

**Number of absences last week
in class 3N1**

Distribution is **uniform**.

Exercise 8.4

1 The dot plot shows the time, in seconds,
taken by a group of students to solve a
mathematics problem.

(**a**) Find the median time

(**b**) Describe the shape of the distribution.

Time to solve a maths problem

2 On packets of tacks, the manufacturer claims each packet contains 50 tacks. To test the claim, a sample of 30 packets was chosen at random and the tacks counted.
The dot plot shows the results.

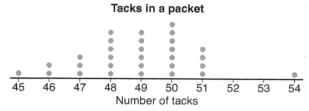

Tacks in a packet

Number of tacks

(a) Find the median.

(b) What was the modal number of tacks?

(c) Describe the shape of the distribution.

(d) Comment on the manufacturer's claim of 50 tacks in a packet.

3 A class test was marked out of 20.
The marks of the 27 pupils in the class are shown.

$$
\begin{array}{ccccccccc}
15 & 19 & 7 & 8 & 9 & 15 & 16 & 12 & 17 \\
14 & 15 & 10 & 17 & 14 & 12 & 8 & 15 & 16 \\
12 & 15 & 14 & 16 & 11 & 15 & 14 & 10 & 13 \\
\end{array}
$$

(a) Choose a suitable scale and draw a dot plot.

(b) Find   (i)   the modal mark
           (ii)   the median mark

(c) How many pupils scored less than half marks?

(d) Describe the shape of the distribution.

4 There were 21 school days last month. The numbers of S3 pupils absent in Stonebank Academy on each day was recorded.

$$
\begin{array}{ccccccc}
19 & 22 & 19 & 22 & 20 & 21 & 17 \\
19 & 21 & 16 & 20 & 19 & 18 & 18 \\
20 & 20 & 23 & 19 & 18 & 17 & 19 \\
\end{array}
$$

(a) Show these absences on a dot plot.

(b) Find the median number of absences.

(c) Describe the shape of the distribution.

5 The weights, in kilogrammes, of 20 children in the juniors at Maureen's Dance Studio were noted.

$$
\begin{array}{cccccccccc}
44 & 44 & 46 & 45 & 47 & 48 & 47 & 41 & 48 & 45 \\
45 & 44 & 42 & 43 & 44 & 46 & 46 & 43 & 49 & 45 \\
\end{array}
$$

(a) Construct a dot plot.

(b) Describe the shape of the distribution.

(c) How many children weighed at least 47 kilogrammes?

(d) Calculate the mean weight of the children.

(e) Would the median weight provide a more usful average than the mean? Explain.

8.5 Median and quartiles

Learning intentions

The **median** is the middle value of a set of data when the numbers are arranged in order.
The median splits the data into an upper and a lower group. The **quartiles** are the middle values of the groups. The median and quartiles divide the data set into four parts.

Q_1 is the **lower quartile** Q_2 is the **median** Q_3 is the **upper quartile**

For this set of 13 test marks:

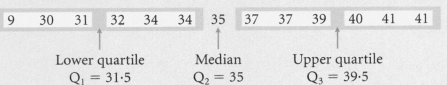

	Lower quartile	Median	Upper quartile
	$Q_1 = 31\cdot5$	$Q_2 = 35$	$Q_3 = 39\cdot5$

Example

Find the median and quartiles of this set of test marks:

28, 27, 32, 19, 37, 7, 39, 17, 23, 28, 30, 42, 37, 35

Arrange the 14 test marks in order:

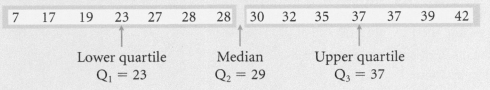

	Lower quartile	Median	Upper quartile
	$Q_1 = 23$	$Q_2 = 29$	$Q_3 = 37$

Exercise 8.5

1 As they left a supermarket, a random sample of shoppers was asked to
say how much they had just spent, to the nearest £5.
The amounts were:

    95, 30, 25, 70, 65, 55, 50, 45, 60, 35
    40, 50, 55, 45, 60, 40, 90, 70, 65

(**a**) Arrange the results in order.

(**b**) Find:
   (**i**) the median   (**ii**) the lower quartile   (**iii**) the upper quartile.

2 The pupils in class $3C_2$ were asked to record the number of times they
used the internet during a particular day. The results were:

    0, 2, 1, 2, 5, 0, 3, 7, 2, 8, 3, 4, 0, 1, 3,
    4, 6, 5, 3, 6, 5, 6, 4, 3, 7, 0, 1, 6, 5, 7

Find:

(**a**) the median   (**b**) the lower quartile   (**c**) the upper quartile.

3 The number of guests staying at the Cross Keys Hotel each day over a
period of 13 days was recorded. The numbers were:

    26, 18, 22, 36, 34, 40, 37, 40, 30, 12, 16, 23, 10

Find:

(**a**) the median   (**b**) the lower quartile   (**c**) the upper quartile.

4 The weights, in kilogrammes, of new born babies in Stonedyke Maternity Unit last Wednesday were recorded. The weights were:

3·4, 2·9, 1·8, 3·5, 4·1, 2·7, 4·6, 3·4, 2·8, 3·2, 3·6, 2·6, 3·5, 3·3

Find:

(a) the median   **(b)** the lower quartile   **(c)** the upper quartile.

5 The number of hours of sunshine was recorded on the first day of each month last year by a local weather station. The results were:

3, 1, 0, 4, 6, 9, 11, 8, 2, 5, 2, 0

Find:

(a) the median   **(b)** the lower quartile   **(c)** the upper quartile.

6 The number of third year pupils absent each school day last month was recorded. The absences were:

20, 19, 19, 20, 19, 22, 17, 20, 18, 21, 19,
22, 20, 18, 23, 17, 16, 18, 19, 21, 19

(a) Construct a dot plot for this data.

(b) Find the median and quartiles.

7 The marks out of 30 in a mathematics test were recorded for class 3N.

21, 25, 26, 22, 27, 25, 26, 27, 26, 23, 26, 25, 26, 23, 21, 27,
23, 27, 27, 23, 26, 23, 21, 26, 24, 26, 25, 27, 21, 22, 25

(a) Construct a dot plot for these marks.

(b) Find the median and quartiles.

8 The ages, in years, of patients in a doctors' surgery at 9am last Monday morning were:

1, 23, 41, 2, 76, 39, 41, 55, 7, 13,
82, 63, 60, 44, 9, 18, 36, 70, 49, 68

(a) Find the median.

(b) Find the difference in ages between the upper and lower quartiles.

8.6 Measures of dispersion

Learning intentions

The **range** and **interquartile range** are measures of dispersion or spread.

The **range** is the difference between the highest and the lowest values in a set of data.

When there are extreme values, the range can give a misleading picture. A more satisfactory measure which avoids extreme values is the **interquartile range**. It measures the range between the upper and lower quartiles .

Interquartile range $= Q_3 - Q_1$

The **semi-interquartile range** may also be used as a measure of dispersion and is simply half of the interquartile range.

Semi-interquartile range $= \dfrac{Q_3 - Q_1}{2}$

Example

These are the percentage marks for class 3L in their Mathematics examination.

35, 57, 64, 53, 62, 51, 39, 47, 54, 49, 55, 63, 70, 60, 56, 48,
83, 45, 54, 58, 64, 49, 75, 62, 58, 46, 57, 64, 81, 40, 54.

Find

(a) the range

(b) the median and quartiles

(c) the interquartile range

(d) the semi-interquartile range.

```
                          54                              64
              49          54          57  58      62      64
35  39  40  45  46  47  48  49  51  53  54  55  56  57  58  60  62  63  64  70  75  81  83
              ↑                       ↑                   ↑
              Q₁                      Q₂                  Q₃
```

(a) Range $= 83 - 35$
$= 48$

(b) Lower quartile $= 49$ Upper quartile $= 63$ Median $= 56$

(c) Interquartile range $= Q_3 - Q_1$
$= 63 - 49$
$= 14$

(d) Semi-interquartile range $= \dfrac{Q_3 - Q_1}{2}$ $= \dfrac{63 - 49}{2}$

$= \dfrac{14}{2}$

$= 7$

Exercise 8.6

1 For the following sets of data find

(i) the range   (ii) the quartiles and interquartile range   (iii) the semi-interquartile range.

(a) Marks in a test: 21, 16, 14, 15, 8, 25, 29, 18, 20, 19, 17.

(b) Weights of pupils in kilogrammes: 44, 45, 41, 42, 49, 40, 45, 44, 43, 48, 45, 47.

(c) Weekly wages in £s:
320, 416, 370, 345, 392, 650, 275, 364, 416, 385, 320, 345, 345, 710, 320, 345, 320.

(d) Weights of rugby players in pounds:
190, 145, 220, 198, 262, 165, 180, 184, 234, 268, 188, 244, 250, 210, 245, 192.

(e) Discus throws in metres:
61·0, 50·5, 40·9, 29·1, 65·1, 56·3, 49·5, 39·3, 64·8, 52·8, 45·2, 39·3, 68·8, 56·3, 47·3, 64·4, 55·0, 44·7.

2 These are the hourly wage rates in pounds of a group of workers:

8, 18, 7, 16, 19, 8, 11, 18, 22, 9, 10, 14, 11, 15, 16

Find   (a) the mean   (b) the median   (c) the range   (d) interquartile range.

3 Ten pupils scored the following marks in Chemistry and Maths examinations.

Chemistry: 45, 48, 52, 54, 55, 55, 57, 59, 60, 65
Maths: 25, 32, 40, 45, 53, 60, 61, 71, 78, 85

(a) Calculate the mean mark for each set.

(b) Show each set of marks on a dot plot.

(c) Find the range of each set.

(d) Find the interquartile range for each set.

(e) Jim scored 60 in both tests. Explain which you think was his better result.

4 Twelve pupils scored the following marks in Physics and English examinations.

Physics: 9, 18, 26, 35, 42, 50, 57, 62, 75, 80, 83, 88
English: 9, 42, 43, 46, 50, 53, 56, 57, 59, 60, 62, 88

(a) Calculate the mean mark for each set.

(b) Show each set of marks on a dot plot.

(c) Find the range of each set.

(d) Find the semi-interquartile range.

(e) Jim scored 62 in both tests. Explain which you think was his better result.

8.7 Stem and leaf diagrams

Learning intentions

A stem and leaf diagram may be used to illustrate a data set.

Example

The percentage marks for class $3M_1$ in a mathematics exam were noted.

85 45 61 63 59 41 69 70 68 52 55 62 63 57
39 48 56 68 65 70 66 68 63 59 71 64 65 63

(a) Draw an ordered stem and leaf diagram to illustrate this data.

(b) Find the median and quartiles.

(a) The tens digits will form the stem and the units digits will form the leaves.

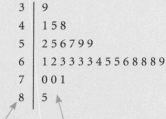

3	9
4	1 5 8
5	2 5 6 7 9 9
6	1 2 3 3 3 3 4 5 5 6 8 8 8 9
7	0 0 1
8	5

> The leaves are single digits.
> They have been put in ascending order to make an **ordered** stem and leaf diagram.

$n = 28$ Key: 6|3 represents a mark of 63%

Stem   Leaves   Number of pieces of data

(b) For 28 pieces of data the median lies between the 14th and 15th values.
Median = **63**
Lower quartile is between the 7th and 8th values. $Q_1 = $ **56·5**
Upper quartile is between 21st and 22nd values. $Q_3 = $ **68**

Exercise 8.7

1 At Stonedyke Infirmary the waiting times, in minutes, are shown on a stem and leaf diagram.

(a) What was
   (i) the longest waiting time
   (ii) the shortest waiting time?

(b) How many people were treated that evening?

(c) Find the median and upper and lower quartiles.

(d) Calculate the interquartile range.

Waiting times

0	2 3
1	4 5 6 7
2	1 4 5 5 6 7 9
3	0 1 2 2 2 3 5 8
4	0 1 2 3 4 4 5 5 6 7 9
5	1 2 3 3 4 5 6 7

$n = 40$
Key 2|4 represents 24 minutes

2 In an agricultural research laboratory a record was made of the heights, in millimetres, of 30 seedlings one week after germination.

35	42	61	45	29	62	39	37	52	41
43	48	48	46	49	51	50	53	47	60
29	52	58	36	49	44	46	54	56	53

(a) Draw an ordered stem and leaf diagram to illustrate the data.

(b) Find the median and quartiles

3 The weights, in kilogrammes, of babies born last week at Stonedyke Infirmary are shown in the stem and leaf diagram.

(a) How many babies were born?

(b) What was the range?

(c) What was the median weight?

(d) Calculate the semi-interquartile range.

Baby weights (kg)

```
1 | 7
2 | 0 3 5 6 6 7 7
3 | 0 1 2 2 3 3 4 4 5 5 6 6 6 6 8 9 9
4 | 1 1 2 4
```
n = 29
Key 2|5 represents 2·5 kg

4 In a recent survey in Glasgow on the cost of renting domestic property, a sample of people were asked to note the weekly cost, in pounds, for renting their homes. Here are some of the results.

94	136	154	185	200	125	117	135	140	100
155	125	130	110	115	128	132	145	157	165
95	106	163	190	144	135	127	115	128	135

(a) Find the range.
(b) Draw an ordered stem and leaf diagram.
(c) From this survey would you consider £175 per week to be an expensive rent?

8.8 Back-to-back stem and leaf diagrams

Learning intentions

A back-to-back stem and leaf diagram is used to compare two sets of data.

Example

The weights, in kilogrammes, of football players and rugby players was collected at Garth Sports Centre. Use a back-to-back stem and leaf diagram to compare the two sets of weights.

Football
74 68 82 90 79 88 68
75 80 74 69 76 78 81

Rugby
80 72 90 83 96 79 102 108 93
78 98 81 115 77 96 82 88 91

```
   Football    |    | Rugby
        9 8 8  |  6 |
    9 8 6 5 4 4|  7 | 2 8 7 9
        8 2 1 0|  8 | 0 1 2 3 8
              0|  9 | 0 1 3 6 6 8
               | 10 | 2 8
               | 11 | 5
       n = 14  |    | n = 18
```
Key 4|7 represents 74 kg   Key 10|2 represents 102 kg

From the diagram, rugby players seem to be generally heavier than footballers.

Exercise 8.8

1 The percentage marks for class 3C$_2$ in English and Mathematics are shown below.

English	Mathematics
42 50 61 72 80 92 88 77 62 53	65 52 70 40 82 35 90 29 38 73
49 45 52 62 75 86 95 53 62 79	41 66 53 42 53 67 42 54 68 54
79 65 54 56 58 66 68 59 68 69	45 69 55 56 47 56 49 58 59 77

(a) Draw an ordered back-to-back stem and leaf diagram for this data.

(b) In which exam did pupils generally score higher marks?

(c) Many pupils say they find one of the subjects more difficult than the other.
Which subject appears to be more difficult? Explain.

2 At the Wellbeing Medical Centre, a record was kept last year of the ages of patients who died and whether or not they were smokers.

Lifespan of smokers in years	Lifespan of non-smokers in years
82 63 75 41 52 32 38 46 56 66 56	35 42 55 68 70 82 93 71 72 69 69
33 55 76 64 45 69 68 49 58 67 66	74 76 69 89 58 75 79 85 75 78 80

(a) Draw an ordered back-to-back stem and leaf diagram.

(b) What age was the oldest smoker to die?

(c) What age was the youngest non-smoker to die?

(d) Compare the lifespans of smokers and non-smokers.

3 A survey of a group of teenagers asked "When will you marry?"
The ages, in years, for boys and girls are shown below.

Boys	Girls
30 35 27 25 28 32 40 45 30 38	25 21 27 16 30 28 18 20 45 22
28 39 44 35 39 30 40 25 26 37	18 21 25 30 26 17 29 32 35 25
50 32 38 40 27 29 36 28 45 25	33 22 21 25 30 23 27 34 27 23

(a) Draw an ordered back-to-back stem and leaf diagram for the data.

(b) What was the youngest predicted age?

(c) How many boys claimed that they expected to be over 40 when they married?

(d) Calculate the interquartile range for both sets of data. Comment on your results.

Discussion point

What kind of survey could you undertake in your mathematics class?

CI EC

8.9 Box plots

Learning intentions

A **box plot** may be used to illustrate a set of data and also to compare sets of data.
It uses five statistics: lowest value, highest value, median, lower quartile and upper quartile.

Example

Illustrate this set of test marks with a box plot.

　　　51, 46, 44, 45, 38, 55, 59, 48, 60, 29, 73

Marks arranged in order: 29, 38, 44, 45, 46, 48, 51, 55, 59, 60, 73

Lowest mark = 29　　Q_1 = 44　　Q_2 = 48　　Q_3 = 59　　Highest mark = 73

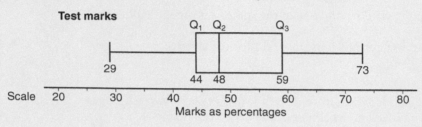

Exercise 8.9

1 This box plot illustrates the weights of a group of men attending a gym.

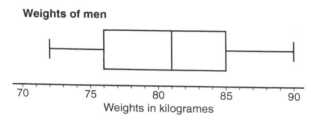

　Find　(a) the range
　　　　(b) the median weight
　　　　(c) the lower and upper quartiles
　　　　(d) the interquartile range.

2 This box plot illustrates the weekly wages of a group of office workers.

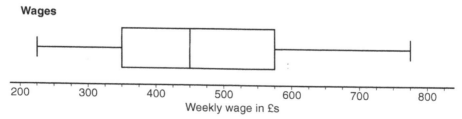

　Find　(a) the range
　　　　(b) the median and quartiles
　　　　(c) the semi-interquartile range.

3 Use a box plot to illustrate each set of data.

    (**a**) Marks in a mathematics test:

          23, 31, 35, 39, 42, 44, 44, 47, 48, 53, 54, 55, 57, 57, 69

    (**b**) Time spent per week, in minutes, by a group of pupils doing maths
        homework:

          0, 0, 10, 10, 15, 40, 65, 70, 100, 120, 125, 140, 155,
          175, 180, 195, 215, 240, 245

    (**c**) Number of children per family in a survey of first year pupils:

          2, 3, 2, 4, 5, 2, 1, 2, 3, 4, 6, 4, 3, 1, 3

    (**d**) The sizes of shoes sold yesterday at High Step Shoes::

          10, 3, 7, 4, 9, 4, 8, 10, 6, 11, 3, 12, 2, 6,
          4, 9, 4, 10, 7, 8, 6, 7, 5, 3, 4, 6, 5, 5, 9

    (**e**) Monthly rainfall, in millimetres, recorded last year:

          74, 96, 99, 299, 266, 84, 123, 274, 219, 144, 62, 304

4 These box plots have been arranged vertically
and illustrate the results of a survey on mean life
expectancy for males and females in nineteen
European countries.

    (**a**) What was the median life expectancy for males?

    (**b**) What was the maximum life expectancy
        for females?

    (**c**) Find the interquartile range for the life expectancy
        of males.

    (**d**) Calculate the difference between the median life
        expectancies for males and females.

    (**e**) Compare the life expectancy of males and females.

    (**f**) Veronique from Paris died aged 76.
        Could she be considered to have had a long life?

    (**g**) Jimmy from Glasgow lived till he was 76.
        Was this longer than expected?

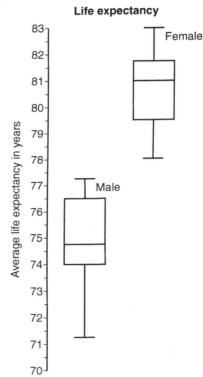

Life expectancy

5 Class $3C_1$ has 15 boys and 15 girls. Percentage marks in a
recent test are shown.

Boys: 43, 49, 75, 68, 51, 55, 60, 81, 70, 34, 45, 50, 60, 59, 51
Girls: 33, 52, 58, 78, 73, 69, 59, 67, 46, 56, 79, 77, 58, 63, 69

    (**a**) On the same diagram, set against the same scale, draw a box plot for
        each set of data.

    (**b**) In general who did better, boys or girls? Explain.

6 In a factory two types of batteries were tested by measuring and
recording the length of time in minutes during which a sample of ten of
each type of battery gave continuous light.

Battery A: 120, 122, 108, 135, 115, 126, 114, 129, 118, 123
Battery B: 115, 124, 141, 133, 125, 107, 119, 142, 140, 129

    (**a**) On the same diagram draw a box plot for each set of data.

    (**b**) Compare the batteries.

7 Class 3M's mathematics teacher wanted to know if the pupils who had attended his after-school study classes had benefited from them. He recorded their percentage test marks in the week before and in the week after the classes.

Before
32, 49, 61, 35, 47, 68, 75, 51, 42, 36, 59, 66, 87, 38, 43, 50, 39, 58, 21, 61, 40
After
37, 66, 52, 80, 47, 64, 87, 48, 44, 34, 45, 56, 42, 75, 58, 43, 73, 45, 57, 65, 68

(a) Show these results in two box plots.

(b) Karim scored 38 in the first test. Describe how this compared with other scores in that test.

(c) Karim improved his score to 52 in the second test.
Was this the sort of improvement made by most pupils?

(d) Use the range and semi-interquartile range to explain if the dispersion of marks was similar in the two tests.

(e) Would the teacher have felt that running the study class was worthwhile? Explain your answer.

Review exercise 8: Am I a successful learner?

1 A group of first year pupils was asked how they normally travel to school.

Method of travel	Walk	Bus	Car	Cycle	Taxi
Number of pupils	13	10	7	4	2

Draw a pie chart to illustrate this information.

2 The table shows the number of days absent last term for ten pupils together with their marks in the term test for maths.

Name	Kim	Eva	Ali	Khan	Ruby	Brian	Meg	Greg	Jill	Kurt
Days absent	4	20	4	0	18	16	12	20	22	9
Percentage mark	100	40	90	85	45	60	65	25	20	80

(a) Show this information on a scatter graph.

(b) Does your graph show a correlation? Explain.

3 Here is a list of charity donations, in pounds.

2, 1, 5, 1, 2, 1, 1, 10, 1, 1, 5, 20, 400,
20, 5, 1, 1, 10, 1, 1, 2, 1, 5, 1, 1

(a) Find   (i) the mean donation
         (ii) the median donation
        (iii) the modal donation.

(b) A donor was selected at random and asked about her donation.
Was her donation likely to have been above or below the mean?

4 There were 21 school days last month. The mean daily absence for class 3G was 3·2 pupils per day for the first 20 days. On the last day of the month 9 pupils were absent with flu.
Calculate the mean daily absence for the month.

5 The mean weight of 4 girls in a school relay team is 51 kg.
When the reserve is included, the mean weight of the 5 girls is 52 kg.
Calculate the weight of the reserve.

6 The weights of babies born last week at Stonedyke Maternity Unit were
recorded.

3·4, 3·5, 4·1, 2·0, 3·3, 3·9, 3·2, 3·1, 2·3, 2·6, 3·6, 3·3, 2·6, 3·6,
3·8, 1·7, 2·7, 3·2, 4·1, 3·5, 3·9, 3·0, 2·5, 3·6, 4·4, 3·6, 4·2, 1·9

(a) Construct a dot plot.

(b) Describe the shape of the distribution.

(c) Find the median weight.

7 The numbers taking dinner in Rumbold's restaurant each evening over a
two week period were recorded.

12, 14, 20, 14, 17, 52, 24, 48, 26, 52, 30, 32, 46, 30

Find:

(a) the median

(b) the range

(c) the semi-interquartile range.

8 The number of swimming costumes sold by a large department store in
Edinburgh each shopping day in July and August was noted.

July	August
12 24 30 20 30 38 37	2 10 25 31 14 31 22
33 13 42 31 21 27 33	19 4 11 26 17 28 23
45 36 39 18 35 36 38	29 28 8 12 18 19 32
33 24 23 31 50 19 32	30 29 24 8 23 27 32

(a) Draw an ordered back-to-back stem and leaf diagram for the two
sets of data.

(b) For each month, calculate the range and interquartile range.

(c) Which was the better month for sales? Why do you think this was so?

9 This box plot illustrates the lengths of a sample
of young salmon released into a fish farm.

Find:

(a) the range

(b) the values of the median and quartiles

(c) the interquartile range.

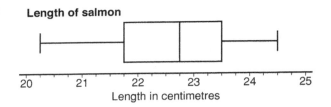

Length of salmon

Length in centimetres

10 There are two S3 credit sections studying mathematics in Stonedyke Academy.
The classes are thought to be of similar ability.

Here are percentage marks in a recent examination.

Class 3C$_A$ 62, 41, 53, 35, 49, 22, 62, 59, 80, 29, 38, 56, 91, 71,
62, 35, 54, 43, 64, 48, 62, 79, 54, 39, 56, 71, 45

Class 3C$_B$ 67, 59, 22, 46, 40, 55, 64, 62, 34, 85, 44, 89, 60, 75,
67, 40, 59, 50, 70, 51, 71, 80, 59, 44, 60, 73, 47

(a) Show these results in two box plots.

(b) Do these marks seem to show two sections of similar ability?
Explain.

Summary 8: What I learned in this chapter.

Pie charts

The size of the angle at the centre of each sector is proportional to the size of the sector and is calculated as a fraction of 360°.

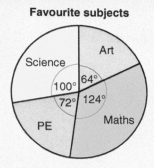

Favourite subjects

Scatter graphs

Scatter graphs may show a relationship between two variables.

There may be a **positive** or **negative correlation**.

A **line of best fit** may be used to estimate values.

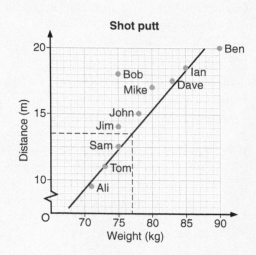

Shot putt

Measures of central tendency

The **mean** is found by adding all the data and dividing by all the pieces of data.
The **median** is the middle value when all the data is written in numerical order.
The **mode** is the value which occurs most often.

Dot plots

Dot plots use dots placed above a number line to illustrate data.

Jill's golf scores

Median and quartiles

Median and quartiles divide a set of data into four parts.
For this set of 13 test marks:

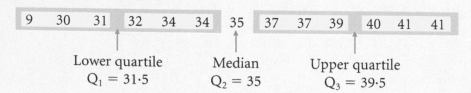

| 9 | 30 | 31 | 32 | 34 | 34 | 35 | 37 | 37 | 39 | 40 | 41 | 41 |

Lower quartile $Q_1 = 31{\cdot}5$

Median $Q_2 = 35$

Upper quartile $Q_3 = 39{\cdot}5$

Measures of dispersion

$$
\begin{array}{cccccccccccccccccccccccccc}
 & & & & & 54 & & & & & & & & 64 & & & & & \\
 & & & 49 & & 54 & & & 57 & 58 & & 62 & & 64 & & & & & \\
35\,39 & 40 & 45 & 46 & 47 & 48 & 49 & 51 & 53 & 54 & 55 & 56 & 57 & 58 & 60 & 62 & 63 & 64 & 70 & 75 & 81 & 83 \\
 & & & \uparrow & & & & & \uparrow & & & & & & & & \uparrow & & & & & \\
 & & & Q_1 & & & & & Q_2 & & & & & & & & Q_3 & & & & &
\end{array}
$$

Range is the difference between highest and lowest $= 83 - 35 = \mathbf{48}$

Interquartile range is $Q_3 - Q_1 = 63 - 49 = \mathbf{14}$

Semi-interquartile range is $\dfrac{Q_3 - Q_1}{2} = 14 \div 2 = \mathbf{7}$

Stem and leaf diagrams

Ordered stem and leaf diagram

```
3 | 9
4 | 1 5 8
5 | 2 5 6 7 9 9
6 | 1 2 3 3 3 3 4 5 5 6 8 8 8 9
7 | 0 0 1
8 | 5
```

> The leaves are single digits. They have been put in ascending order.

$n = 28$

Stem   Leaves   Number of pieces of data

Key: $6\,|\,3$ represents a mark of 63%

Back-to-back stem and leaf diagram

Football		Rugby
9 8 8	6	
9 8 6 5 4 4	7	2 8 7 9
8 2 1 0	8	0 1 2 3 8
0	9	0 1 3 6 6 8
	10	2 8
	11	5
$n = 14$		$n = 18$

Key $4\,|\,7$ represents 74 kg   Key $10\,|\,2$ represents 102 kg

Box plots

Box plots use lowest value, highest value, median and quartiles to illustrate a set of data.

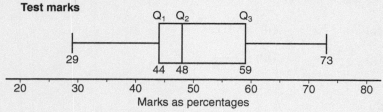

Test marks

9 Formulae

9.1 Evaluating formulae

Learning intentions

Formulae are used to make routine calculations. They are used in many different areas such as physics, chemistry, statistics, economics and medicine.

$$E = mc^2$$

$$q_n^d = D(p_n, p_1 - - - p_{n-1}, Y, T)$$

$$T = 2\pi\sqrt{\frac{1}{g}}$$

$$F = \frac{Gm_1 m_2}{d^2}$$

In the formula $k = \frac{1}{2}mv^2$, k is the **subject** of the formula
A formula is evaluated by replacing variables with numerical values.

Example 1

Evaluate $A = b + cd$
when $b = -5$, $c = -3$ and $d = 7$

$A = b + cd$
$A = -5 + (-3 \times 7)$
$A = -5 - 21$
$\mathbf{A = -26}$

Example 2

Evaluate $P = \dfrac{2s + 3q}{r}$
when $s = -5$, $q = 8$ and $r = 2$

$P = \dfrac{2s + 3q}{r}$

$P = \dfrac{(2 \times -5) + (3 \times 8)}{\cdot\, 2}$

$P = \dfrac{-10 + 24}{2}$

$\mathbf{P = 7}$

Exercise 9.1

1 Given $a = 7$, $b = 2$ and $c = 3$, evaluate:

  (**a**) abc (**b**) $ab + c$ (**c**) $a + bc$ (**d**) $(a + b)c$

  (**e**) $2a + 4b$ (**f**) $\dfrac{a + b}{c}$ (**g**) $\dfrac{4a + 2c}{b}$ (**h**) $\dfrac{2abc}{4}$

2 Given $a = 3$, $b = -4$ and $c = 5$, evaluate:

  (**a**) $-2a + 4b$ (**b**) $ab - ac$ (**c**) $bc - ba$ (**d**) $ab + c$

  (**e**) $(a + b)c$ (**f**) $\dfrac{4a + b}{2c}$ (**g**) $\dfrac{a - c}{b}$ (**h**) $\dfrac{bc}{2a - b}$

3 Given $a = 1\cdot5$, $b = 4$ and $c = 2\cdot3$, evaluate:

  (**a**) abc (**b**) $ab + c$ (**c**) $a + bc$ (**d**) $(a + b)c$

  (**e**) $a + b - 2c$ (**f**) $\dfrac{a + b}{5}$ (**g**) $\dfrac{2a + 3c}{b}$ (**h**) $\dfrac{ab + 2c}{2b}$

4 Evaluate each formula for the given values:
   (a) $V = IR$ when   (i) $I = 15$ and $R = 60$ (ii) $I = 6{\cdot}5$ and $R = -8$
   (b) $R = ab + bc$ when   (i) $a = 3, b = 7, c = 5$ (ii) $a = 3.2, b = 30, c = 18$
   (c) $P = \dfrac{x + y}{z}$ when   (i) $x = 17, y = 34, z = 2$ (ii) $x = 5{\cdot}4, y = 12{\cdot}6, z = 3$
   (d) $T = 13d - 0{\cdot}5h$ when   (i) $d = 6$ and $h = 12$ (ii) $d = 2{\cdot}5$ and $h = -2$

5 To convert a Celsius temperature (C) into Fahrenheit (F) the formula
$F = \frac{9}{5}C + 32$ is used.
Find F when C is   (a) 25   (b) 100   (c) 80   (d) 66

6 To calculate distance travelled d, the formula $d = st$ may be used where
s = average speed and t = time taken. Find the distance travelled by:
   (a) a car travelling at an average speed of 60 miles per hour for $3\frac{1}{2}$ hours
   (b) a cyclist travelling at an average speed of 25 miles per hour for 2 hours 15 minutes.
   (c) a person walking at a speed of 6 kilometres per hour for 1 hour and 54 minutes.

9.2 Powers and brackets

Learning intentions

When evaluating a formula with a power, it affects only the term to which it is attached. Brackets need to be inserted to change this priority.
$3x^2$ only the x is squared
$(3x)^2$ the 3 and the x are squared.

Example

Evaluate
(a) $s = ut + \frac{1}{2}at^2$
    when $u = 10, a = 8$ and $t = 5$

$s = ut + \frac{1}{2}at^2$
$s = 10 \times 5 + \dfrac{8 \times 5^2}{2}$
$s = 50 + \dfrac{8 \times 25}{2}$
$s = 50 + 100$
$s = \mathbf{150}$

(b) $P = \dfrac{3(a - b)^2}{5}$
    when $a = 6{\cdot}3$ and $b = -2{\cdot}5$

$P = \dfrac{3(a - b)^2}{5}$
$P = \dfrac{3(6{\cdot}3 - (-2{\cdot}5))^2}{5}$
$P = \dfrac{3 \times (8{\cdot}8)^2}{5}$
$P = \dfrac{3 \times 77{\cdot}44}{5}$
$P = \mathbf{46{\cdot}464}$

Exercise 9.2

1 Given $a = 2, b = 4$ and $c = 5$, evaluate:
   (a) a^2b (b) ab^2 (c) $(ab)^2$ (d) a^2b^2
   (e) $\dfrac{(a + b)^2}{5}$ (f) $3a^2$ (g) $(3a)^2$ (h) $3(c - b)^2$
   (i) $a^3 + c^2$ (j) $\frac{1}{2}a^2 - bc$ (k) $\dfrac{2(b + c)^2}{4}$ (l) $a^4 - 2c$

2 Given $a = -2, b = 3$ and $c = 1$, evaluate:
   (a) a^2b (b) ab^2 (c) $(ab)^2$ (d) a^2b^2 (e) $a^3 + b$
   (f) $4a^2$ (g) $(4a)^2$ (h) $3(c - b)^2$ (i) $a^3 + c^2$

3 Evaluate each formula for the given values:

(a) $A = 4d^2$ when   (i) $d = 6$ (ii) $d = 1.2$

(b) $A = (4d)^2$ when   (i) $d = 3$ (ii) $d = -2$

(c) $D = b^2 - 4ac$ when   (i) $b = 2, a = 10, c = 3$ (ii) $b = -4, a = 3, c = -2$

(d) $k = \frac{1}{2}mv^2$ when   (i) $m = 12, v = 5$ (ii) $m = 1.2, v = 4$

(e) $G = (x + 3)^2$ when   (i) $x = 20$ (ii) $x = -12$

(f) $V = \frac{4}{3}\pi r^3$ when   (i) $r = 3$ (ii) $r = 5$

(g) $s = ut + \frac{1}{2}at^2$ when   (i) $u = 20, a = 5, t = 3$ (ii) $u = 30, a = -5, t = 4.5$

4 To convert a Fahrenheit temperature (F) into Celsius (C) the formula

$C = \dfrac{5(F - 32)}{9}$ is used.

Find C when F is   (a) 212   (b) 14   (c) -13 (d) 32

5 The number of diagonals in an n sided polygon is given by the formula

$d = \dfrac{n(n - 3)}{2}$

Find the number of diagonals in a

(a) pentagon   (b) nonagon   (c) dodecagon.

$n = 5$

9.3 Square roots and further formulae

Learning intentions

Example 1

Evaluate $P = \frac{1}{a} + \frac{1}{b}$

when $a = 3$ and $b = 5$

$P = \frac{1}{a} + \frac{1}{b}$

$P = \frac{1}{3} + \frac{1}{5}$

$P = \frac{5}{15} + \frac{3}{15}$

$P = \frac{8}{15}$

Example 2

Evaluate $V = \sqrt{\dfrac{3RT}{m}}$ when $R = 12$, $T = 6.9$ and $m = 18$

$V = \sqrt{\dfrac{3RT}{m}}$

$V = \sqrt{\dfrac{3 \times 12 \times 6.9}{18}}$

$V = \sqrt{13.8}$

$V = 3.7148$

$V = \mathbf{3.71}$ to 2 d.p.

Exercise 9.3

1 Given $x = 10$, $y = 6$ and $z = 2$, find:

(a) $x + \dfrac{y}{z}$ (b) $\dfrac{x + y}{z}$ (c) $\dfrac{x}{z} + \dfrac{y}{z}$ (d) $\dfrac{(x + z)^2}{y}$

(e) $\dfrac{2x + 3z}{2y + 1}$ (f) $\dfrac{x^2}{y - z}$ (g) $\left(\dfrac{x}{z}\right)^2 + \left(\dfrac{y}{z}\right)^2$ (h) $\left(\dfrac{yz}{x}\right)^3$

2 Given $a = 2$, $b = 5$ and $c = 8$, find:

(a) $\sqrt{bc - a^2}$ (b) $2b + \sqrt{10bc}$ (c) $\dfrac{bc}{\sqrt{2c}}$ (d) $\sqrt{20abc}$

(e) $\sqrt{(ab)^2}$ (f) $\sqrt{3ab^2}$ (g) $\sqrt{(3ab)^2}$ (h) $\sqrt[3]{(a + b + 1)c}$

3 Given $a = -6$, $b = 3$ and $c = 10$, find:

(a) $\sqrt{c - a}$ (b) $2a + \sqrt{12b}$ (c) $\dfrac{bc}{\sqrt{3b}}$ (d) $\sqrt{a^2bc + b^2}$

(e) $\dfrac{a + c}{2}$ (f) $\dfrac{a}{c} + \dfrac{b}{c}$ (g) $\dfrac{4c}{a - b}$ (h) $\dfrac{(b - a)^2}{c}$

4 Evaluate each formula for the given values:

(a) $L = \dfrac{2b}{c} + 3$ when (i) $b = 16$ and $c = 8$ (ii) $b = 200$ and $c = 0\!\cdot\!2$

(b) $a = \dfrac{V^2}{r}$ when (i) $V = 14$, $r = 4$ (ii) $V = 1\!\cdot\!7$, $r = 2$

(c) $z = \sqrt{x^2 + y^2}$ when (i) $x = 6$, $y = 8$ (ii) $x = \frac{1}{2}$, $y = \frac{1}{16}$

(d) $p = \sqrt{\dfrac{ab - 4}{4}}$ when (i) $a = 13$, $b = 8$ (ii) $a = 6.4$, $b = 5$

(e) $A = \sqrt{x^2 + 15} + 5$ when (i) $x = 7$ (ii) $x = 2.7$

(f) $R = \dfrac{1}{a} + \dfrac{1}{b}$ when (i) $a = 13$, $b = 5$ (ii) $a = \frac{1}{2}$, $b = \frac{1}{4}$

(g) $A = P\left(1 + \dfrac{r}{100}\right)$ when (i) $P = 8$, $r = 5$ (ii) $P = 12$, $r = 4$

5 The time taken for a pendulum to swing once is given by $T = 2\pi\sqrt{\dfrac{l}{g}}$
where l is the length of the pendulum in centimetres and $g = 10$.
Find the time taken for a pendulum with length:

(a) 50 centimetres (b) 72 centimetres

6 The curved surface area of a cone with base radius r and height h
is given by the formula

$A = \pi r\sqrt{h^2 + r^2}$

Find the curved surface area of a cone with:

(a) height 15 centimetres and base radius 8 centimetres

(b) height 1.8 metres and base radius 45 centimetres.

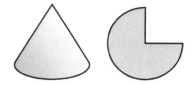

7 (a) The force in newtons between two bodies is given by $F = \dfrac{Gm_1m_2}{r^2}$
where G is the gravitational constant, 6.67×10^{-11}.
m_1 and m_2 are the masses of two bodies in kilogrammes and r is the distance
between their centres in metres.
Find the force between the Earth with a mass of 5.98×10^{24} kilogrammes
and a person weighing 80 kilogrammes who is standing at sea level
(6.37×10^6 metres from the centre of the Earth)

(b) Using the above formula calculate the force between the Earth and the Moon.

385 000 km

Earth   radius   6376 km
         mass 5.98×10^{24} kg

Moon   radius   1738 km
         mass 7.3×10^{22} kg

9.4 Finding other variables

Learning intentions

A formula may be evaluated for any variable. Substitute values and solve for the required variable.

Example

For the formula $a = bc - 2d$, find the value of b when $a = 6$, $c = 4$ and $d = 8$

$a = bc - 2d$
$6 = (b \times 4) - (2 \times 8)$ | Substitute values |
$6 = 4b - 16$
$22 = 4b$ | Solve equation |
$b = 5\frac{1}{2}$

Exercise 9.4

1 The circumference of a circle with diameter d is given by the formula $C = \pi d$. Find the diameter of a circle with circumference:

(a) 15 centimetres

(b) 2·5 metres

(c) 0·89 metres

2 The area of a circle with radius r is given by the formula $A = \pi r^2$. Find the radius of a circle with area:

(a) 400 square centimetres

(b) 1·5 square metres

3 The volume of a cylinder with radius r and height h is given by the formula $V = \pi r^2 h$.

(a) Find the height of a cylinder with volume 1 250 cubic centimetres and radius 5 centimetres.

(b) Find the radius of a cylinder with volume 3 000 cubic centimetres and height 24 centimetres.

4 Substitute the given values to form an equation and solve it to find the missing variable.

(a) $C = 6h + 17$ $C = 89$

(b) $F = ma$ $F = 30$ and $m = 1·5$

(c) $C = \dfrac{Q}{V}$ $C = 80$ and $V = 5$

(d) $P = x - yz$ $P = 3$, $x = 15$, $y = 2$

(e) $P = 2l + 2b$ $P = 46$ and $b = 12$

(f) $A = b^2 - c$ $b = 5$ and $A = 90$

(g) $I = \dfrac{V}{R}$ $I = 0·6$ and $R = 3·5$

(h) $V = \frac{4}{3}\pi r^3$ $V = 400$

5 The area of a triangle is given by the formula $A = \frac{1}{2}bh$. Find b if $A = 1·2$ square metres and $h = 95$ centimetres.

9.5 Literal equations

Learning intentions

Equations which involve letters for the coefficients and constants, instead of numbers, are called **literal equations**. These can be solved in the same way as equations:

Example 1

Solve for x:

(a) $2x - 5 = 13$

(b) $cx - a = b$

(a) $2x - 5 = 13$
$2x = 13 + 5$ Add to both sides
$x = \dfrac{13 + 5}{2}$ Divide both sides
$x = 9$

(b) $cx - a = b$
$cx = b + a$
$x = \dfrac{b + a}{c}$

Example 2

Solve for x:

(a) $2(x + 3) = 8$

(b) $a(x + b) = c$

The solutions are left as algebraic expressions.

(a) $2(x + 3) = 8$
$2x + 6 = 8$ Multiply out brackets
$2x = 2$ Subtract from both sides
$x = 1$ Divide both sides

(b) $a(x + b) = c$
$ax + ab = c$
$ax = c - ab$
$x = \dfrac{c - ab}{a}$

Exercise 9.5

1 Solve for x:
(a) $x + 5 = 16$ (b) $x + a = 16$ (c) $x + a = b$ (d) $x - 3 = 12$
(e) $x - a = 3$ (f) $x - 2 = b$ (g) $6 = 3x$ (h) $a = 3x$
(i) $p = qx$ (j) $10 = bx$ (k) $2x = 5$ (l) $5x = 2$
(m) $7x = 3$ (n) $3x = 7$ (o) $ax = b$ (p) $bx = a$

2 Solve for x:
(a) $2x + 6 = 18$ (b) $2x + a = b$ (c) $3x - 5 = 13$
(d) $3x - a = b$ (e) $2x - 3 = x + 7$ (f) $2x - z = x + y$
(g) $5x + a = 3x + b$ (h) $7x - a = 3x - 6$

3 Solve for x:
(a) $3px = 18$ (b) $4tx = 6s$ (c) $2tx = a$ (d) $5px = r$

4 Solve for x:
(a) $2(x + 5) = 8$ (b) $2(x + b) = 8$ (c) $2(x + b) = a$
(d) $3(x - 4) = 18$ (e) $3(x - a) = 18$ (f) $3(x - a) = p$
(g) $r(x - 4) = 18$ (h) $5(2x + 3) = 25$ (i) $5(2x + a) = v$
(j) $4(3x + b) = c$ (k) $p(x - 2b) = d$ (l) $a(3x - r) = 10$

9.6 More literal equations

Learning intentions

Example 1

Solve for x

(a) $\frac{x}{3} = 40$

(b) $\frac{x}{t} = g$

> Multiply both sides

$\frac{x}{3} = 40$

$x = 120$

$\frac{x}{t} = g$

$x = tg$

Example 2

Solve for x

(a) $\frac{2}{x} = 5$

(b) $\frac{a}{x} = b$

(a) $\frac{2}{x} = 5$

$2 = 5x$ > Multiply by x

$\frac{2}{5} = x$ > Divide

$x = \frac{2}{5}$

(b) $\frac{a}{x} = b$

$a = bx$

$\frac{a}{b} = x$

$x = \frac{a}{b}$

Example 3

Solve for x

(a) $4 + 6x = 9 + 2x$

(b) $a + bx = c + dx$

(a) $4 + 6x = 9 + 2x$ > Rearrange

$6x - 2x = 9 - 4$

$4x = 5$ > Simplify

$x = \frac{5}{4}$ > Divide

(b) $a + bx = c + dx$

$bx - dx = c - a$

$(b - d)x = c - a$

$x = \frac{c - a}{b - d}$

Exercise 9.6

1 Solve for x:

(a) $12 = \frac{x}{6}$ (b) $a = \frac{x}{6}$ (c) $b = \frac{x}{c}$ (d) $L = \frac{5}{x}$

(e) $r = \frac{s}{x}$ (f) $\frac{8}{x} = a$ (g) $\frac{a}{x} = 2$ (h) $\frac{a}{x} = b$

(i) $5 = \frac{40}{x}$ (j) $p = \frac{40}{x}$ (k) $p = \frac{r}{2x}$ (l) $s = \frac{4}{3x}$

2 Solve for x:

(a) $x(3 + a) = 12$ (b) $x(5 - b) = 18$ (c) $x(a - y) = b$

3 Solve for x:

(a) $5(6 + x) = -30$ (b) $5(6 + x) = -b$ (c) $d(x - 5) = -b$

4 Solve for x:

(a) $a + 5x = 3x + b$ (b) $p + 2x = 7x + q$ (c) $r + dx = s + gx$

(d) $a + bx = c - dx$ (e) $7 + ax = 12 - bx$ (f) $10 + cx = 12 + bx$

9.7 Rearranging formulae

Learning intentions

In the formula $P = a + b$, P is the subject.
The formula may be rearranged to make **a** the subject

$$P = a + b$$
$$P - b = a$$
$$a = P - b$$

This is equivalent to solving a literal equation for **a**.

Example

Change the subject of each formula to the given variable:

(a) $F = ma$ to a

(b) $y = mx + c$ to x

(c) $A = \dfrac{B}{C} - D$ to C

(a) $F = ma$ Divide

$$\frac{F}{m} = a$$

$$a = \frac{F}{m}$$

(b) $y = mx + c$ Subtract

$$y - c = mx$$

$$\frac{y - c}{m} = x$$ Divide

$$x = \frac{y - c}{m}$$

(c) $A = \dfrac{B}{C} - D$

$$AC = B - DC$$

$$AC + DC = B$$

$$(A + D)C = B$$

$$C = \frac{B}{A + D}$$

Multiply

Add

Common factor

Divide

Exercise 9.7

Change the subject of each formula in questions 1 −9 to the variable in red:

1 (a) $t = x + 3$ (b) $a = b + c$ (c) $g = P - h$ (d) $y = ax - d$

2 (a) $y = px$ (b) $y = ax$ (c) $V = IR$ (d) $p = r(s + t)$

3 (a) $g = \dfrac{t}{2}$ (b) $r = \dfrac{b}{c}$ (c) $a = \dfrac{q}{t}$ (d) $Q = \dfrac{T}{V}$

4 (a) $y = mx + c$ (b) $y = mx - d$ (c) $y = ax + d$ (d) $r = st - 2$

5 (a) $B = \dfrac{t}{2} - a$ (b) $R = \dfrac{x}{b} + f$ (c) $T = \dfrac{L}{c} + r$ (d) $V = \dfrac{P}{T} - g$

6 (a) $R = abc$ (b) $L = \dfrac{ab}{6}$ (c) $R = \dfrac{ty}{s}$ (d) $T = \dfrac{VR}{PQ}$

7 (a) $G = \dfrac{2p - x}{y}$ (b) $X = \dfrac{5y - d}{a}$ (c) $g = \dfrac{t}{4} + B$ (d) $C = \dfrac{v}{l} + g$

8 (a) $r = a - x$ (b) $r = 3 - xt$ (c) $X = \dfrac{5y - d}{a}$ (d) $G = \dfrac{1}{a}(b - c)$

9 (a) $R = c(a + b)$ (b) $Q = v(a - b)$ (c) $R = q(t - s)$ (d) $X = 2p(5t - a)$

10 Change the subject of each formula to the stated variable:

(a) $V = IR$ to I (b) $C = \pi d$ to d (c) $y = mx + c$ to c

(d) $k = \frac{1}{2}mv^2$ to m (e) $P = \dfrac{x + y}{z}$ to x (f) $P = \dfrac{x + y}{z}$ to z

(g) $L = \dfrac{2b}{c} + 3$ to b (h) $E = \dfrac{f}{q}$ to q (i) $pV = nRT$ to T

(j) $I = \dfrac{PRT}{100}$ to R (k) $A = (x + y)h$ to h (l) $A = \frac{1}{2}(a + b)h$ to h

9.8 Rearranging more complex formulae

Learning intentions

Example

Change the subject to x in each formula:

(a) $R = p(x - y)$ (b) $A = \dfrac{\sqrt{2x + 3}}{r}$ (c) $A = \dfrac{1}{x} + \dfrac{1}{y}$

(a)
$$R = p(x - y)$$
$$R = px - py$$
$$R + py = px$$
$$x = \frac{R + py}{p}$$

(b)
$$A = \frac{\sqrt{2x + 3}}{r}$$
$$Ar = \sqrt{2x + 3}$$
$$A^2r^2 = 2x + 3$$
$$A^2r^2 - 3 = 2x$$
$$x = \frac{A^2r^2 - 3}{2}$$

(c)
$$A = \frac{1}{x} + \frac{1}{y}$$
$$xyA = y + x$$
$$xyA - x = y$$
$$x(yA - 1) = y$$
$$x = \frac{y}{yA - 1}$$

Exercise 9.8

In questions 1 – 6 change the subject to the variable in red.

1 (a) $R = c(a + b)$ (b) $Q = v(a - b)$ (c) $R = q(t + s)$ (d) $X = p(5t - a)$

2 (a) $x = \dfrac{r}{ab}$ (b) $Q = \dfrac{P}{x + y}$ (c) $V = \dfrac{c}{d - e}$ (d) $r = \dfrac{g}{2t + 4}$

3 (a) $r = \sqrt{b}$ (b) $l = \sqrt{A}$ (c) $R = \sqrt{ab}$ (d) $P = \dfrac{\sqrt{xy}}{t}$

    (e) $L = \sqrt{\dfrac{ax}{b}}$ (f) $P = \sqrt{a + b}$ (g) $T = \sqrt{A} + 7$ (h) $R = a\sqrt{b}$

4 (a) $T = b^2$ (b) $A = L^2$ (c) $D = a + b^2$ (d) $R = (a + b)^2$

    (e) $X = ab^2$ (f) $X = (ab)^2$ (g) $R = \dfrac{a}{b^2}$ (h) $a = \dfrac{xt}{b^2}$

5 (a) $A = \frac{1}{2}(r + l)$ (b) $D = \dfrac{1}{a}(b - c)$ (c) $A = \dfrac{a}{x}(b - c)$ (d) $A = \frac{1}{2}(a + b)h$

6 (a) $R = am + bm$ (b) $Q = rt + rs$ (c) $A = lb + ls$

7 Change the subject of each formula to the stated variable:

(a) $a = \dfrac{V^2}{r}$ to r (b) $A = \pi r^2$ to r (c) $k = \frac{1}{2}mv^2$ to v

(d) $A = 4d^2$ to d (e) $A = (4d)^2$ to d (f) $D = b^2 - 4ac$ to b

(g) $G = (x + 3)^2$ to x (h) $z = \sqrt{x^2 + y^2}$ to x (i) $p = \sqrt{\dfrac{ab}{5}}$ to a

(j) $V = \sqrt{\dfrac{3RT}{m}}$ to m (k) $F = \dfrac{mv^2}{r}$ to v (l) $T = 2\pi\sqrt{\dfrac{l}{g}}$ to l

(m) $V = \sqrt{\dfrac{3RT}{m}}$ to T (n) $A = (x + y)h$ to x (o) $I = \dfrac{mnE}{mR + nr}$ to m

8 Change the subject of each formula to the stated variable:

(a) $A = \pi r(r + l)$ to l (b) $F = \dfrac{Gm_1 m_2}{r^2}$ to r

(c) $s = \dfrac{a}{l - r}$ to r (d) $C = \frac{5}{9}(F - 32)$ to F

(e) $A = P\left(1 + \dfrac{r}{100}\right)$ to r (f) $T = \dfrac{1}{g} + \dfrac{1}{h}$ to h

(g) $f = \dfrac{a - b}{a + b}$ to b (h) $S = 2\pi rl + 2\pi r^2$ to r

9 The focal length of a lens is given by
$\dfrac{1}{f} = \dfrac{1}{u} + \dfrac{1}{v}$ where u is the object distance
from the lens and v is the image distance
from the lens.
Rearrange to find a formula for u.

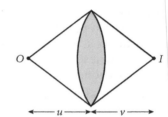

10 Total resistance is given by the formula $\dfrac{1}{R} = \dfrac{1}{r_1} + \dfrac{1}{r_2}$
Rearrange to find a formula for r_1.

9.9 Constructing formulae

Learning intentions

Example

(a) Melissa puts £20 of diesel into the empty fuel tank of her car. Diesel costs 86p per litre. Her car uses 5 litres of diesel per hour when she drives at a particular speed.
At this constant speed, how many litres of diesel will remain in the car after two hours?

(b) The following week Melissa puts £20 of diesel into the empty tank. Diesel costs c pence per litre and the car uses d litres of diesel per hour when driven at a constant speed. Find a formula for R, the amount of diesel remaining in the car after t hours.

(a) Number of litres of diesel $= \dfrac{2000}{86}$

Remaining litres of diesel $= \dfrac{2000}{86} - 5 \times 2 = \mathbf{13 \cdot 26}$

(b) $R = \dfrac{2000}{c} - dt$

Exercise 9.9

1 (**a**) A walking group have a 200 kilometre route to walk. If they walk for 18 kilometres per day, find the distance remaining after 7 days.

(**b**) A walking group have a D kilometre route to walk. If they walk for p kilometres per day, find the distance remaining after 7 days.

2 Internet use is charged at 20 pence per 15 minutes.
Find a formula for the cost £C if the internet is used for t hours.

3 (**a**) Jane makes greetings cards. She uses 30 centimetres of ribbon per card. If Jane has 20 metres of ribbon, how much will be left after she makes 40 cards?

(**b**) If Jane has L metres of ribbon, how much will be left after she makes n cards each using r centimetres of ribbon?

4 (**a**) Joanne pays £30 credit into her electricity meter. Electricity costs 2.5p per unit and she knows that the metre uses 5 units per hour. At this rate of use, how many units will be left after 100 hours?

(**b**) When the meter is emptied Joanne puts in another £40 credit. Electricity costs c pence per unit and she knows the meter uses k units per hour. How many units will be left after t hours?

5 (**a**) Adrian puts £25 of diesel into the empty fuel tank of his car. Diesel costs 86p per litre. His car uses 5 litres of diesel per hour when he drives at a particular speed.
At this constant speed, how many litres of diesel will remain in the car after two hours?

(**b**) The following week, Adrian puts £20 of diesel into the empty tank. Diesel costs c pence per litre and the car uses d litres of diesel per hour when driven at a constant speed. Find a formula for R, the amount of diesel remaining in the car after t hours.

6 A kiosk sells large coffee for 99p and small coffees for 75p.
Find a formula for the daily takings, £T, if x large coffees and y small coffees were sold.

7 Alkanes are chemical compounds made from carbon (C) and hydrogen (H) atoms.

$$
\begin{array}{cccc}
\underset{\text{Methane}}{\text{H}-\overset{\displaystyle\text{H}}{\underset{\displaystyle\text{H}}{\text{C}}}-\text{H}} &
\underset{\text{Ethane}}{\text{H}-\overset{\displaystyle\text{H}}{\underset{\displaystyle\text{H}}{\text{C}}}-\overset{\displaystyle\text{H}}{\underset{\displaystyle\text{H}}{\text{C}}}-\text{H}} &
\underset{\text{Propane}}{\text{H}-\overset{\displaystyle\text{H}}{\underset{\displaystyle\text{H}}{\text{C}}}-\overset{\displaystyle\text{H}}{\underset{\displaystyle\text{H}}{\text{C}}}-\overset{\displaystyle\text{H}}{\underset{\displaystyle\text{H}}{\text{C}}}-\text{H}} &
\underset{\text{Butane}}{\text{H}-\overset{\displaystyle\text{H}}{\underset{\displaystyle\text{H}}{\text{C}}}-\overset{\displaystyle\text{H}}{\underset{\displaystyle\text{H}}{\text{C}}}-\overset{\displaystyle\text{H}}{\underset{\displaystyle\text{H}}{\text{C}}}-\overset{\displaystyle\text{H}}{\underset{\displaystyle\text{H}}{\text{C}}}-\text{H}}
\end{array}
$$

(**a**) Draw the next two compounds, pentane and hexane, in this series.

(**b**) Octane is the alkane with 8 carbon atoms. How many hydrogen atoms does it have?

(**c**) Another alkane has 40 hydrogen atoms. How many carbon atoms will it have?

(**d**) Write down a formula for the number of hydrogen atoms, h, for an alkane with c carbon atoms.

8 The design for a high-rise building has each floor above the first supported by 8 pillars. The diagram shows three floors but the design can be used with many floors.

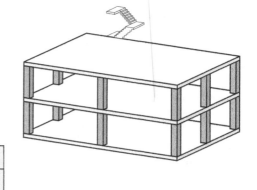

(**a**) How many pillars are needed for three floors?

(**b**) Copy and complete the table to show the number of pillars needed for different numbers of floors.

Number of floors	1	2	3	4	5	6
Number of pillars	0					

(**c**) Write a formula to find the number of pillars, P, needed for x floors.

(**d**) A new building is to be built with 11 floors. Use your formula to find the number of pillars.

9 The cost of taking a group of students to a theme park is shown below.

1 adult free for every 10 children.

Number of pupils	Cost per pupil	Cost per paying adult
Fewer than 10	£6·00	£10·00
10 – 19	£5·00	£8·00
20 – 29	£4·00	£7·00
30 – 39	£3·00	£7·00

(**a**) (**i**) Find the cost for a group of 12 pupils and 3 adults.
  (**ii**) Write a formula to find the cost, $£C$, of taking a group of p pupils and d adults, where $10 \leqslant p \leqslant 19$.

(**b**) (**i**) Find the cost for a group of 22 pupils and 4 adults.
  (**ii**) Write a formula to find the cost, $£C$, of taking a group of p pupils and d adults, where $20 \leqslant p \leqslant 29$.

(**c**) (**i**) Find the cost for a group of 36 pupils and 8 adults.
  (**ii**) Write a formula to find the cost, $£C$, of taking a group of p pupils, where $30 \leqslant p \leqslant 39$.

10 A phone company offers 2 free texts for every 10 minutes spent on calls.

Number of minutes	Cost per minute call	Cost per text
Fewer than 10	5p	10p
10 to 19	4·5p	10p
20 to 29	4p	10p
30 to 39	3·5p	10p

(**a**) (**i**) Calculate the cost of 25 minutes of calls and 20 texts.
  (**ii**) Find a formula for the cost, $£C$, of t texts and m minutes of calls where $20 \leqslant m \leqslant 29$.

(**b**) (**i**) Calculate the cost of 33 minutes of calls and 18 texts.
  (**ii**) Find a formula for the cost, $£C$, of t texts and m minutes of calls, where $30 \leqslant p \leqslant 39$.

Review exercise 9: Am I a successful learner?

1 Given $a = 3$, $b = 7$ and $c = -2$, evaluate:

(a) abc (b) $(a + b)c$ (c) $\dfrac{2a + 3c}{b}$ (d) a^2b

(e) ab^2 (f) a^2b^2 (g) $\dfrac{(a + b)^2}{5}$ (h) $3a^2$

(i) $(3a)^2$ (j) $\dfrac{4b}{a + c}$ (k) $\sqrt{3ab^2}$ (l) $\dfrac{bc}{\sqrt{7b}}$

2 Evaluate each formula for the given values:

(a) $P = \dfrac{x + y}{z}$ when $x = 3{\cdot}2$, $y = 18$, $z = 4$

(b) $A = (4d)^2$ when $d = 5$

(c) $D = b^2 - 4ac$ when $b = -3$, $a = 1$, $c = 3$

(d) $k = \frac{1}{2}mv^2$ when $m = 20$, $v = 1{\cdot}3$

(e) $G = x^2 + 3$ when $x = -16$

(f) $V = \frac{4}{3}\pi r^3$ when $r = 0{\cdot}8$

(g) $p = \sqrt{\dfrac{ab - 4}{4}}$ when $a = 7$, $b = 12$

(h) $R = \dfrac{1}{a} + \dfrac{1}{b}$ when $a = 8$, $b = 5$

3 The time taken for a pendulum to swing once is given by $T = 2\pi\sqrt{\dfrac{l}{g}}$ where l is the length of the pendulum in centimetres and $g = 10$. Find the time taken for a pendulum with length:

(a) 15 centimetres   (b) 112 centimetres

4 Solve for x:

(a) $2x - 3 = x + 7$ (b) $5x + a = 3x + b$ (c) $4tx = 6s$

(d) $2(x + b) = a$ (e) $\dfrac{8}{x} = a$ (f) $d(x - 5) = -b$

5 Change the subject of each formula to the stated variable:

(a) $y = mx + c$ to m (b) $k = \frac{1}{2}mv^2$ to v (c) $P = \dfrac{x + y}{z}$ to y

(d) $L = \dfrac{2b}{d} + a$ to b (e) $pV = nRT$ to T (f) $A = \frac{1}{2}(a + b)h$ to a

(g) $A = (3p)^2$ to p (h) $P = (a + b)^2$ to b (i) $D = b^2 - 4ac$ to b

(j) $V = \frac{4}{3}\pi r^3$ to r (k) $z = \sqrt{x^2 + y^2}$ to y (l) $p = \sqrt{\dfrac{ab}{c}}$ to c

(m) $V = \sqrt{\dfrac{3RT}{m}}$ to R (n) $F = \dfrac{mv^2}{r}$ to v (o) $T = 2\pi rl + 2\pi r^2$ to l

6 (a) Melissa puts £60 of diesel into the empty fuel tank of her car. Diesel costs 86p per litre. Her car uses 5 litres of diesel per hour when she drives at a particular speed. At this constant speed, how many litres of diesel will remain in the car after 3 hours?

(b) The following week, Melissa puts £40 of diesel into the empty tank. Diesel costs c pence per litre, the car uses d litres of diesel per hour when driven at a constant speed. Find a formula for R, the amount of diesel remaining in the car after t hours.

Summary 9: What I learned in this chapter.

Evaluating formulae

Evaluate $V = \sqrt{\dfrac{3RT}{m}}$ when $R = 12$, $T = 6{\cdot}9$ and $m = 18$

$$V = \sqrt{\frac{3RT}{m}}$$

$$V = \sqrt{\frac{3 \times 12 \times 6{\cdot}9}{18}}$$

$$V = \sqrt{\frac{248{\cdot}4}{18}}$$

$V = 3{\cdot}7$ to 1 d.p.

Literal equations

Solve for x

(a) $4 + 6x = 9 + 2x$

$6x - 2x = 9 - 4$ [Rearrange]

$4x = 5$ [Simplify]

$x = \frac{5}{4}$ [Divide]

(b) $a + bx = c + dx$

$bx - dx = c - a$

$(b - d)x = c - a$

$x = \dfrac{c - a}{b - d}$

Changing the subject of a formula

Change the subject to x.

$A = \dfrac{\sqrt{2x + 3}}{r}$ [Multiply]

$Ar = \sqrt{2x + 3}$ [Square]

$A^2 r^2 = 2x + 3$ [Subtract]

$A^2 r^2 - 3 = 2x$ [Divide]

$\dfrac{A^2 r^2 - 3}{2} = x$

Constructing formulae

Melissa puts £20 of diesel into the empty tank of her car. Diesel costs c pence per litre and the car uses d litres of diesel per hour when driven at a constant speed. Find a formula for R, the amount of diesel remaining in the car after t hours.

$$R = \frac{2000}{c} - dt$$

10 Volume and surface area

10.1 Volume of cube and cuboid

Learning intentions

Remember

The volume of a cube or cuboid may be calculated using the formula

$$\text{Volume} = \text{length} \times \text{breadth} \times \text{height}$$
$$V = lbh$$

Example 1

Calculate the volume in litres.

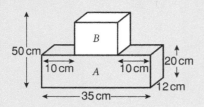

$$V_A = lbh \qquad\qquad V_B = lbh$$
$$V = 35 \times 12 \times 20 \qquad V = 15 \times 12 \times 30$$
$$V = 8400 \text{ cm}^3 \qquad\quad V = 5400 \text{ cm}^3$$

Total volume $= 8400 + 5400$
$= 13\,800 \text{ cm}^3$
$= \mathbf{13 \cdot 8}\, \boldsymbol{l}$

1 litre = 1000 cm³

Example 2

Find the length of one side.

Volume = 729 mm³

$$l^3 = V$$
$$l^3 = 729$$
$$l = \sqrt[3]{729}$$
$$l = \mathbf{9\ mm}$$

Exercise 10.1

1 Calculate the volume of each shape.

(a)

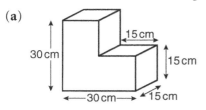

(b)

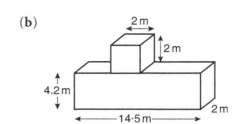

2 Find how many litres of water each fish tank could hold.

(a)

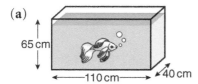

(b)

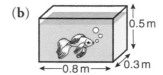

(c)

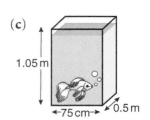

3 The volume of water in the tank is 0·144 cubic metres.
Find the height of water in this fish tank.

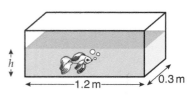

4 Find the height of each cube.

(a)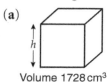

Volume 1728 cm³

(b)

Volume 0.216 m³

(c)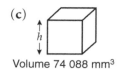

Volume 74 088 mm³

5 Ross has a locker at school which has a volume of 0·156 cubic metres.
The length and the breadth of the locker are 40 centimetres and 30 centimetres.
Find the height of the locker.

6 A television set is made from two cuboids.
Calculate the total volume of the television set.
All measurements are in centimetres.

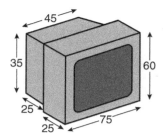

10.2 Volume of prisms

Learning intentions

Remember

A prism is a three dimensional shape which has a uniform cross-section.
A cross-section is a slice through the shape, parallel to an end face.

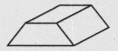

The faces at either end of this shape are identical.
It has uniform cross section and is a prism.

Cross section

Where the cross-section is an identifiable 2-D shape then it may be used to describe the type of prism.

Cube
Square prism

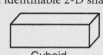

Cuboid
Rectangular prism

Traingular prism

Cylinder
Circular prism

The volume of a prism may be calculated using the formula

Volume of prism = area of base × height
$$V = A \times h$$
$$V = Ah$$

The base of a prism is equivalent to the cross-section.

Discussion point

Which real-life objects are examples of prisms?

Example

Find the volume of each prism.

(a)

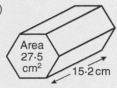

(b)

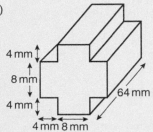

(a) . $V = Ah$
  $V = 27.5 \times 15.2$
  $V = \mathbf{418\ cm^3}$

> Base is a hexagon.

(b) Area of base
1. $A_1 = lb$
      $= 8 \times 4$
      $= 32\ mm^2$

2. $A_1 = A_2 = 32\ mm^2$

3. $A_3 = lb$
      $= 16 \times 8$
      $= 128\ mm^2$

Area of base $= 32 + 32 + 128$
        $= 192\ mm^2$
      $V = Ah$
      $V = 192 \times 64$
      $V = \mathbf{12\ 288\ mm^3}$

Exercise 10.2

1 Find the volume of each prism.

(a)

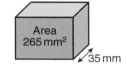

(b)

(c)

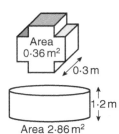

(d)

(e)

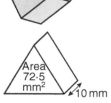

(f)

2 Calculate the volume of each prism.

(a)

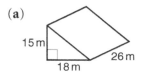

(b)

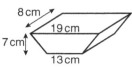

(c)

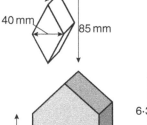

(d)

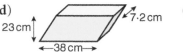

(e)

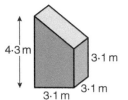

(f)

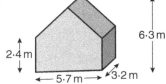

3 Tanzyla and Tommy are going camping.
Calculate the volume of their tent.

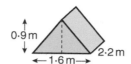

4 Calculate the volume of each cylinder.

> Volume of a cylinder
> $V = \pi r^2 h$

(a)

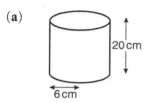

20 cm

6 cm

(b)

30 mm

135 mm

(c)

0·7 m

3·5 m

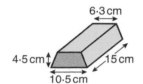

5 Find the volume of each cylinder with given dimensions.

(a) radius 7 m
height 12·5 m

(b) diameter 25 cm
height 125 cm

(c) radius 1·25 m
height 0·6 m

(d) diameter 120 cm
height 9·2 m

6 A gold bar is shown opposite.
Calculate the value of the bar if 1 gramme of gold is worth £4·99.
1 gramme = 0·125 cm³

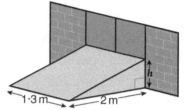

6·3 cm

4·5 cm

15 cm

10·5 cm

7 A tin of varnish has a height of 0·3 metres and holds 0·021 cubic metres.
Find the diameter of the tin.

8 A concrete ramp is made to give disabled access
to a building.
0·585 cubic metres of concrete was poured to make the ramp.
Calculate the vertical height, *h*.

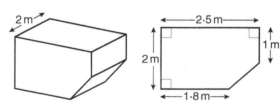

1·3 m   2 m   *h*

9 A recycling bin is prism-shaped, as shown in the
diagram opposite.
The uniform cross-section is shown in the
diagram on the right.

Find the volume of the recycling bin.

2 m

2·5 m

2 m

1 m

1·8 m

10 The barn on Mr McDonald's farm is shown on the right. It is formed
from a half cylinder and a cuboid.

(a) Calculate the volume of the barn.

(b) Mr McDonald is planning an
extension to his house like the one
shown opposite.
The volume of the extension will be
116·1 cubic metres.
Find the width of the extension.

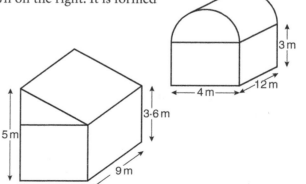

3 m

4 m   12 m

5 m

3·6 m

9 m

w m

10.3 Surface area of solids

Learning intentions

The **surface area** of a 3-D shape is the total area of all its faces.

Example 1

Find the surface area of the cuboid.

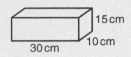

The surface of a cuboid is made from six rectangles

Top and base
$A = lb$
$A = 30 \times 10$
$A = 300 \text{ cm}^2$

Front and back
$A = lb$
$A = 30 \times 15$
$A = 450 \text{ cm}^2$

Left and right sides
$A = lb$
$A = 10 \times 15$
$A = 150 \text{ cm}^2$

Surface area $= 300 + 300 + 450$
$+ 450 + 150 + 150$
$= \mathbf{1800 \text{ cm}^2}$

Example 2

Calculate the surface area of this prism.

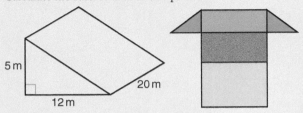

Surface area consists of three rectangles and two triangles.

$c^2 = a^2 + b^2$
$c^2 = 5^2 + 12^2$
$c^2 = 25 + 144$
$c^2 = 169$
$c = \sqrt{169}$
$c = 13$

Top
$A = lb$
$A = 13 \times 20$
$A = 260 \text{ m}^2$

Front = Back
$A = \frac{1}{2}bh$
$A = \frac{1}{2} \times 5 \times 12$
$A = 30$
$A = 30 \times 2 = 60 \text{ m}^2$

Base
$A = lb$
$A = 12 \times 20$
$A = 240 \text{ m}^2$

Left
$A = lb$
$A = 5 \times 20$
$A = 100 \text{ m}^2$

Surface area $= 260 + 60 + 240 + 100$
$= \mathbf{660 \text{ m}^2}$

Exercise 10.3

1 Find the surface area of each shape.

(a)

cube

2·5 cm

(b)

cube

7·6 m

(c)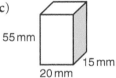

55 mm

15 mm

20 mm

(d)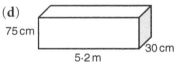

75 cm

5·2 m

30 cm

(e)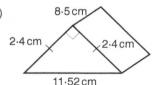

8·5 cm

2·4 cm   2·4 cm

11·52 cm

(f)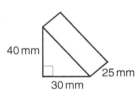

40 mm

25 mm

30 mm

2 A closed box is a cuboid made of wood 1 cm thick. Its external measurements are 80 centimetres by 50 centimetres by 42 centimetres. Calculate

(a) the internal measurements of the box.

(b) the internal volume (capacity) of the box.

(c) the total surface area of the outside of the box.

3 Tins of soup are packed into open cardboard containers which are cuboids. Each tin is identical with a diameter of 7 centimetres.

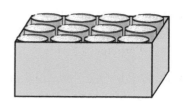

(a) What is the length and breadth of the box shown?

(b) The volume of the box is 11 760 cm³. Find the height of one tin if there are 2 layers of tins in the box.

(c) Calculate the total surface area of the cardboard box.

10.4 Surface area of a cylinder

Learning intentions

The label from this tin of beans is rectangular.

$l = C = \pi d$

$b = h$

The curved surface of a cylinder forms a rectangle when flattened out.
The length of the rectangle equals the circumference of the circular end.
The breadth of the rectangle equals the height of the cylinder.

The curved surface of a cylinder = length × breadth
= $\pi d \times h$
= πdh

Example 1

Calculate the surface area of the cylinder.

15 cm

←8 cm→

Top and base
$A = \pi r^2$
$A = \pi \times 4^2$
$A = 50.26$ cm²
Area of top and base = 100.52 cm²
Curved surface = πdh
= $\pi \times 8 \times 15$
= 376.8 cm²

Surface area = 100.52 + 376.8
= **477.06 cm²**

Example 2

A cylindrical pencil case is made from a rectangular and two circular pieces of material.

The area of the rectangular piece of material is 376.8 square cemtimetres. If the pencil case has a radius of 3 centimetres, what is its length?

3 cm   h

πdh = curved surface area
$\pi \times 6 \times h = 376.8$
$188.4 \times h = 376.8$
$h = 376.8 \div 188.4$
$h = $ **20 cm**

Exercise 10.4

1 Calculate the curved surface area of each cylinder.

(a)
←9 cm→
16 cm

(b)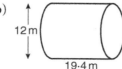
12 m
19.4 m

(c)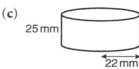
25 mm
22 mm

2 Find the curved surface area of each cylinder with the given dimensions.

   (**a**) height = 130 mm   (**b**) height = 5·7 m   (**c**) height = 36·8 cm

         diameter = 60 mm   radius = 2·4 m   radius = 12·9 cm

3 Calculate the total surface area of each closed cylinder.

   (**a**)  15 cm   3 cm   (**b**) 2·5 m   5 m   (**c**) 190 mm   70 mm

4 A metal canister to hold kitchen utensils is a
cylinder, open at the top.
The diameter of the base is 9·5 centimetres
and the height is 13 centimetres.
Calculate the total surface area of the canister.

5 Workmen are using a road roller to flatten newly laid tarmac.
The roller is a cylinder of radius 0·55 metres and length 1·45 metres.
Calculate the area of tarmac flattened during one revolution of the
roller.

6 A graphic artist is designing a new label for tins of baked beans.
Assuming that there is a two-centimetre overlap for adhesive,
calculate the area of the new label.

9·8 cm   6 cm

7 Find the diameter of the cylinders that these labels would fit round
assuming no overlap.

   (**a**) Area 628·3 m²   10 m   (**b**) Area 196 cm²   12 cm   (**c**) 0·6 m   Area 5·84 m²

8 A water tank, open at the top, is cylindrical in shape.
When full the tank holds 15 000 cubic metres of water.
Peter has been asked to repaint the outer curved surface area of
the tank.
What area does he paint?
Round your answer to 3 significant figures.

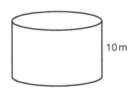

10 m

9 Find the curved surface area of each of cylinder leaving your answer as a multiple of π.

   (**a**) 5 m   4 m   (**b**) 3 cm   2 cm   (**c**) 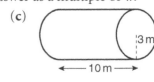 3 m   10 m

10.5 Spheres and cones

Sphere

The formula to calculate the volume of a sphere is

$$V = \tfrac{4}{3}\pi r^3$$

Cone

The formula to calculate the volume of a cone is

$$V = \tfrac{1}{3}\pi r^2 h$$

Example 1

Calculate the volume of a tennis ball with a diameter of 6 centimetres.

Answer to 3 significant figures.

$V = \tfrac{4}{3}\pi r^3$
$V = \tfrac{4}{3} \times \pi \times 3^3$
$V = 113{\cdot}0399$
$V = \textbf{113 cm}^3$

Example 2

A bag for holding treats at Halloween is in the shape of a conical witch's hat.

The bag has a one litre capacity and is 25 cm deep.

Show that the radius of the bag can be written as $\sqrt{\dfrac{120}{\pi}}$ cm.

$\tfrac{1}{3}\pi r^2 h = V$
$\tfrac{1}{3} \times \pi \times r^2 \times 25 = 1000$
$25\pi r^2 = 3000$
$r^2 = \dfrac{3000}{25\pi}$
$r^2 = \dfrac{120}{\pi}$
$r = \sqrt{\dfrac{120}{\pi}}$ cm

Exercise 10.5

1 Calculate the volume of each shape.

(a)
5 cm

(b)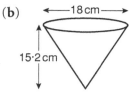
18 cm
15·2 cm

(c)
16 m

(d)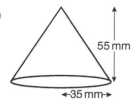
55 mm
35 mm

(e)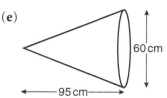
60 cm
95 cm

(f)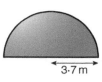
3·7 m

2 A container for a new ice cream product is formed using a hemisphere and a cone. Find the volume of ice cream the container holds.

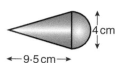
4 cm
9·5 cm

3 A vanity unit is created by removing a hemisphere from a cube. If the cube has side 50 centimetres and the hemispherical bowl has diameter 36 centimetres, calculate the volume of the vanity unit.

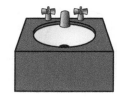

4 A baby's toy is formed by adding two identical cones
to a cylinder as shown in the diagram.
Calculate the volume of the toy.

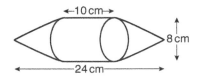

5 A block of metal in the shape of a cube of side 0·4 metres is
melted down and recast to make ball bearings. Each ball bearing
has a diameter of 2 centimetres. Calculate, to 2 significant
figures, the number of ball bearings which can be formed.

6 A plant pot is formed from a cone as shown in the diagram.
Calculate the volume of the plant pot.

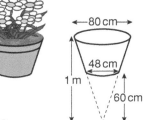

Review exercise 10: Am I a successful learner?

1 Calculate the volume of each prism.

(a)
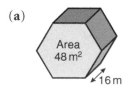

(b)
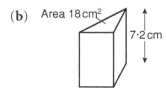

(c)
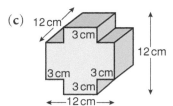

2 Calculate the volume of each cylinder.

(a)

(b)
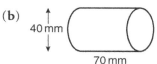

(c)
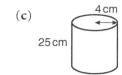

3 Naveed grows tomatoes in his greenhouse.
The greenhouse has a volume of 10·45 cubic metres
and has the dimensions shown in the diagram.
Calculate the length of the greenhouse.

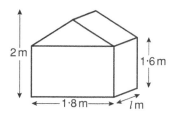

4 Calculate the surface area of each shape.

(a)
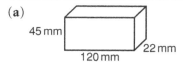

(b)
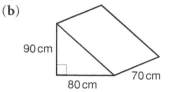

(c)
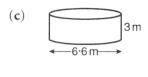

5 Calculate the volume of each shape.

(a)
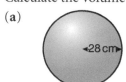

(b)
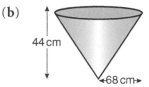

(c)
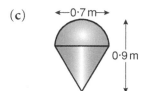

Summary 10: What I learned in this chapter.

Volume of cube and cuboid

Volume = length × breadth × height
$$V = lbh$$

Volume of a prism

Volume of prism = area of base × height
$$V = A \times h$$
$$V = Ah$$

The base is equivalent to the cross-section.

Volume of a cylinder

The formula to calculate the volume of a cylinder is $V = \pi r^2 h$

Surface area of solids

The surface area of a 3-D shape is the total area of all its faces.
The curved surface of a cylinder = length × breadth
$$= \pi d \times h$$
$$= \pi dh$$

Spheres and cones

The formula to calculate the volume of a sphere is
$$V = \tfrac{4}{3}\pi r^3$$

The formula to calculate the volume of a cone is
$$V = \tfrac{1}{3}\pi r^2 h$$

Review 2

Exercise 2A

Brackets and equations

1 Multiply out the brackets and simplify where possible:
   (**a**) $5(4x + 3)$ (**b**) $3(2x - 5)$ (**c**) $-3(6 - 2x)$
   (**d**) $2x(x - 5)$ (**e**) $2x(4 - 3x) + 3x(4x - 3)$ (**f**) $2x(5 - 3x) - 5x(3x - 4)$

2 Expand and simplify:
   (**a**) $(x + 2)(x + 5)$ (**b**) $(x - 4)(x + 5)$ (**c**) $(x - 3)(x - 8)$
   (**d**) $(2x + 3)(3x - 2)$ (**e**) $(x + 4)^2$ (**f**) $(5x - 2)^2$

3 Expand and simplify:
   (**a**) $(x + 2)(2x^2 + 3x + 1)$ (**b**) $(x - 2)(x + 3)(x + 1)$ (**c**) $5x^2 + 3(x + 2)^2$

4 Solve the equations:
   (**a**) $(x + 1)^2 = x^2 + 15$ (**b**) $(x - 2)^2 = (x + 4)(x - 3)$

5 Find the height, h, if the area of the triangle is 25 square centimetres and the length of the base is 15 centimetres.

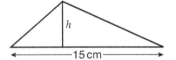

6 Find the value of x in the right angled triangle.

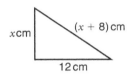

Statistics 1

7 The following data gives the scores of a class in a test.

23	56	44	67	54	87	65	34	37	28
34	95	37	28	47	58	95	23	89	56
76	98	87	56	27	39	45	76	52	45

   (**a**) Find the range.
   (**b**) Construct a stem and leaf diagram to illustrate this data.
   (**c**) Calculate the median and quartiles.
   (**d**) Construct a boxplot to display this data.

8 The boxplots display data showing the weight of rubbish, in kilogrammes, collected from households before recycling was introduced, and after.
Compare the boxplots and comment on the effect of recycling.

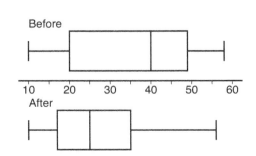

9 The table shows the type of weather recorded during June. Draw an appropriate statistical diagram to display this data. Justify why you have chosen this type of diagram.

Type of weather	No. of days
Sunny	12
Overcast	8
Windy	4
Rain	6

Formulae

10 Find the value of V if $V = 2x^2 - y^2$ when $x = 4$ and $y = -2$

11 The formula $s = ut + \frac{1}{2}at^2$ is used to calculate displacement. Find a when $s = 36$, $u = 12$ and $t = 2\cdot5$

12 Change the subject of each formula to the given variable.

   (**a**) $\frac{PV}{T} = K$ to V (**b**) $S = \frac{(t + r)}{2}$ to t (**c**) $r = \sqrt{(a^2 + b^2)}$ to a

13 The cost of hiring a mountain bike is £20 for the first 5 hours and then £2 for each additional hour.

   (**a**) Find the cost of hiring a mountain bike for 9 hours.

   (**b**) Find a formula for the cost, C, of hiring a mountain bike for h hours, where $h > 5$. Simplify your answer,

Volume

14 Calculate the volume of the storage area in this van.

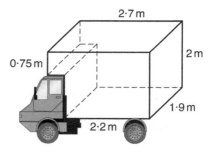

15 This skip is manufactured in the shape of a prism. The front is symmetrical.

   (**a**) Calculate its volume.

   (**b**) Garden waste weighs 250 kilograms per cubic metre on average. What is the maximum weight which the skip can hold if the waste is not allowed above the level of the top of the skip?

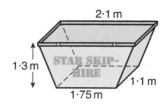

16 Calculate the volume of each shape.

   (**a**)   (**b**)   (**c**)

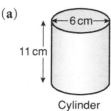
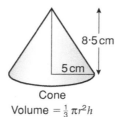
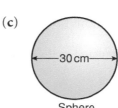

Cylinder

Cone
Volume $= \frac{1}{3}\pi r^2 h$

Sphere
Volume $= \frac{4}{3}\pi r^3$

17 Ardmore Dairy makes cheeses in the shape of regular hexagonal prisms and cylinders.

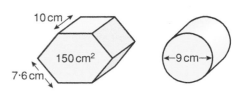

    (**a**) If the volume of the cheeses are the same, calculate the length of the cylindrical cheese.

    (**b**) If the cheeses are covered with paper, calculate the area of paper needed in each case.

    (**c**) Which is the most economic in terms of paper?

Exercise 2B (Cumulative)

1 Simplify each expression:

    (**a**) $9x - 2y + 4x - y$ (**b**) $4x^2 + 5xy - x^2 - 3x^2 - 2xy$

2 Multiply out the brackets and simplify:

    (**a**) $5(3x - 2) + 2(3 - 2x)$ (**b**) $8 - 2(3y - 1)$ (**c**) $2(5x + 3) - 3(4 - x)$

3 Solve each equation:

    (**a**) $5x - 3 = 7x + 15$ (**b**) $5x - 3(2x - 1) = 10$

    (**c**) $3(4x - 2) = 2(1 + 3x)$ (**d**) $\dfrac{2x + 3}{4} = \dfrac{x - 4}{3}$

4 Solve each inequation:

    (**a**) $4x - 5 < 2x + 4$ (**b**) $2y + 3 \geqslant 3y - 8$

    (**c**) $2(3x - 2) \leqslant 3(6 - 5x)$ (**d**) $\dfrac{3x - 1}{2} > \dfrac{2x + 1}{3}$

5 The number of bacteria present in an ill person increases at a rate of 95% every two hours. At 8 am the number of bacteria detected was 3000. How many would be expected at 2 pm?

6 The amount of a particular drug in the bloodstream decreases by 12% every hour. If a nurse administers 250 milligrams of drug at 12 noon, how much would there be in the bloodstream at 3 pm?

7 A jam producer makes a special offer on bramble jelly. It claims there is 12·5% more in a special offer jar weighing 450 grams. What was the weight of the original jar?

8 The cost of a car including VAT charged at $17\frac{1}{2}$% is £10 575. What is the price excluding VAT?

9 A high school music department hires a hall for a Christmas Concert every year. In order to break even they must sell 360 tickets at £6·25. If they managed to sell 450 tickets, how much should be charged for each ticket for the department to still break even.

10 Find the volume of this bread bin made in the shape of a prism.
The side is constructed in the shape of rectangle and quarter circle.

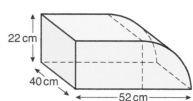

11 Change the subject in the following formula to x.
$$Z = \tfrac{1}{2}(y - x)$$

12 The diagram shows an area of a sports field used for throwing the javelin. The arcs form part of two circles. Find the area of the field between the 40 metre arc and the 60 metre arc.

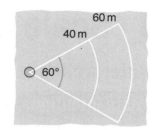

13 A satellite travels in a geosynchronous orbit which is circular. If the radius of the orbit is 4.2×10^4 kilometres, calculate the length of the orbit.

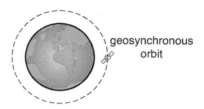

geosynchronous orbit

14 Ardmore Dairy makes cheeses in the shape of a regular hexagonal prism. The hexagon is made from 6 congruent equilateral triangles of side 4 centimetres.
Calculate

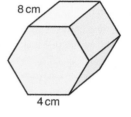

(**a**) the altitude of each triangle

(**b**) the area of each triangle

(**c**) the area of the hexagon

(**d**) the volume of cheese.

15 A crofter uses the wooden triangle to test whether the walls he builds are at right angles to each other.
He claims the triangle contains an accurate right angle.
Is his claim true?

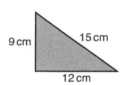

16 When Carol lies on a beach the top of a lighthouse and the top of a cliff are exactly aligned as shown. The height of the lighthouse is 24 metres and the height of the cliff is 36 metres. If the lighthouse is 120 metres from Carol, how far is the lighthouse from the foot of the cliff?

17 The logos on this brand of T–shirts are similar. If the logo on the small T-shirt is 12·5 centimetres high and covers an area of 200 square centimetres, what is the area of the large logo, given that it is 15 centimetres high?

18 These cola tins are similar in shape.

(**a**) Calculate the volume of the larger tin.

(**b**) Which gives better value for money?
Justify your answer.

11 Scale drawing and tolerance

11.1 Interpreting scale drawing

A scale drawing has all lengths reduced, or enlarged, in the same ratio. A map is an example of a scale drawing.

The scale may be expressed in several ways.

Ratio   1 cm:2·75 km

Representative fraction $\frac{1}{275\,000}$

Linear scale

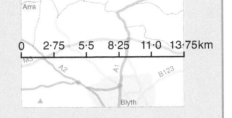

Example 1

The distance from Calais to Lille is 39 centimetres on a map with scale 1 cm : 2·75 km. What is the actual distance between Calais and Lille?

Map distance (cm)	True distance (km)
1	2·75
39	2·75 × 39 = 107·25

The actual distance between Calais and Lille is **107·25** kilometres.

Example 2

A new kitchen has been designed using a scale drawing. Each dimension has been reduced in the ratio 1:20.

(a) What are the actual dimensions of the room?

(b) The cooker is 600 millimetres wide. How wide is the cooker on the plan?

(a)
Plan length (cm)	True length (cm)
1	20
22	20 × 22 = 440
18	20 × 18 = 360

Length of room is **4·4 metres**

Width of room is **3·6 metres**

(b)
True length (mm)	Plan width (mm)
20	1
600	600 ÷ 20 = 30

Cooker width is **3 centimetres** on the plan.

Example 3

On a map with representative fraction $\frac{1}{15\,000}$ calculate:

(a) the distance on the map representing 3 kilometres

(b) the distance on the ground represented by 4·5 centimetres.

(a) $3\,\text{km} \times \frac{1}{15\,000} = 300\,000\,\text{cm} \times \frac{1}{15\,000} = \textbf{20 cm}$

(b) $4\cdot5\,\text{cm} \times 15\,000 = 67\,500\,\text{cm} = 675\,\text{m} = \textbf{0·675 km}$

Exercise 11.1

1 The diagram shows a scale drawing of a kitchen.

(a) What is the actual length of the window?

(b) A kitchen unit is 1300 millimetres long.
    How long is it on the plan?

Scale 1 : 20

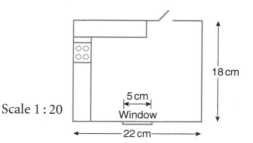

2 Rewrite each scale as
(i) a ratio, (ii) a representative fraction.

(a)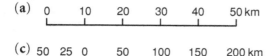

(b)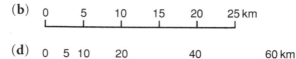

(c) 50 25 0   50   100   150   200 km

(d) 0 5 10   20   40   60 km

3 A map has scale 1 cm : 1·5 km.

(a) Convert each distance on the map to the actual distance:
    (i) 5 cm   (ii) 16·5 cm   (iii) 9 mm
(b) Convert each distance on the ground to its distance on the map:
    (i) 4·5 km   (ii) 24 km   (iii) 0·75 km
(c) Express the scale as a representative fraction.

4 On a map the representative fraction is $\frac{1}{120\,000}$.

(a) Find the distance on the ground represented by
    (i) 1·5 cm   (ii) 3·2 cm   (iii) 15 mm
(b) Calculate the distance on the map which represents
    (i) 48 km   (ii) 36·6 km   (iii) 600 m

5 On a photograph, the height of a statue is 195 millimetres.
If the photograph represents a reduction of the statue with scale 1 : 160,
what is the true height of the statue in metres?

6 A model car is 300 millimetres long and 120 millimetres high.
The real car is 4·5 metres long.

(a) By comparing lengths, find the scale of the model car.
(b) Calculate the real height of the car in metres.

7 The distance between Glasgow and Kilmarnock is 38 kilometres.
On a map this is represented as 76 millimetres.

(a) Write the scale of the map as a representative fraction.
(b) What distance on the map would represent a
    real distance of 141 kilometres?

8 The scale on this map is $\frac{1}{50\,000}$. John has planned
the orienteering course shown on the map.
Calculate the true length of each leg of the course.

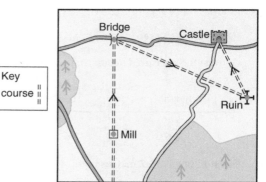

9 Deborah is using a scale diagram to plan a new bathroom. Her scale is 1:25.
On her plan she has a 5 centimetre space along one wall.
Can she fit a shower stall which is 1500 millimetres long into this space?
Explain your answer.

10 Sarah has a sheet of paper 32 centimetres by 22 centimetres.
She wishes to make a scale drawing of her garden which is 21 metres
long and 18 metres wide. Which scale should she use, 1:70 or 1:90?

11 The diagram is drawn to scale 1 cm:4·5 m.
Measure the distances on the diagram and calculate

(**a**) the width of the path

(**b**) the length of the wall.

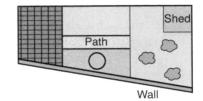

12 The plan for Carole's new carport has a scale 1:60.
(**a**) The proposed height of the carport is 2·4 metres.
What height will this be on the plan?
(**b**) The plan shows a drop in roof height from front to rear of
3·6 millimetres. What is the true drop in height?

11.2 Scale drawing

Learning intentions

Remember
Scale drawings may be used to calculate distances which are difficult to measure.

Example
Use a scale drawing to calculate the height
of the building.

Choose a suitable scale.   1 cm to 2 m or 1:200

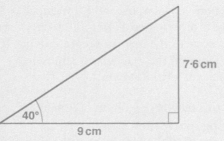

True distance (m)	Plan distance (cm)
2	1
18	9

or

True distance	Plan distance
18 m	18 ÷ 200 = 0.09 m = 9 cm

Make the scale drawing.

First draw a 9 centimetre line

Then draw a 40° angle

Finally draw the vertical height and measure it.

Convert the measured height to the actual height.

Plan height (cm)	True height (m)
1	2
7·6	7·6 × 2 = 15·2

or

Plan height	True height
7·6 cm	7·6 × 200 = 1520 cm = 15·2 m

The building is **15·2 metres** high.

Exercise 11.2

For this exercise you need a ruler and protractor.

1 Make a scale drawing for each diagram, choosing a suitable scale for
each. Find the required height.

(a) 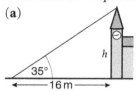   **(b)** 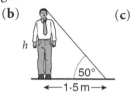   **(c)** 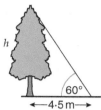   **(d)**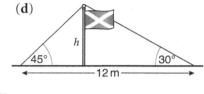

2 From the top of a tower, a manhole cover is clearly visible.
Make a scale drawing and find the distance between the manhole
cover and the tower.

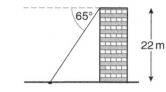

3 From the top of a cliff two buoys can be seen.
Use a scale diagram to find the distance between the buoys.

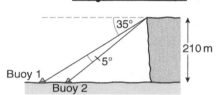

4 Sakina and Omar observe the top of a spire from
opposite sides.
Use a scale diagram to find the height of the spire.

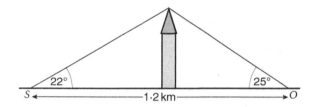

5 A wall mounted spotlight illuminates points A and B as shown in
the diagram.
Use a scale diagram to find the distance between A and B.

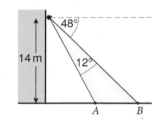

6 Tom is rowing across the river but is pushed downstream by the
current. Make a scale drawing and find how far he travels.

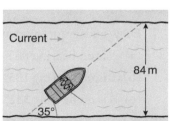

7 From ground level the angle of elevation of the base and top of a
telephone mast is 45° and 58° respectively.
Use a scale drawing to calculate the length of the mast.

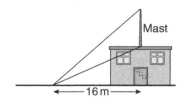

11.3 Bearings

Learning intentions

Remember

Directions may be defined by three figure bearings.
These are angles measured clockwise from north.

```
        000°
         N
315°           045°

270° ───────── 090°

225°           135°
        180°
```

Example

A ship is observed from point X on bearing 075°,
and from point Y on a bearing of 320°.
If X is 20 kilometres due west of Y, use a scale
drawing to find how far the ship is from X and from Y.

Select a suitable scale, possibly 1:200 000 or 1 cm : 2 km

True distance (km)	Map distance (cm)
2	1
20	10

The map distance is **10 cm**.

Make a scale drawing and measure required distances.

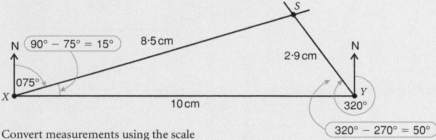

Convert measurements using the scale

Plan distance (cm)	True distance (km)
1	2
8·5	8·5 × 2 = 17
2·9	2·9 × 2 = 5·8

Ship is **17 km** from X and **5·8 km** from Y.

Exercise 11.3

1 Draw a diagram to calculate the required bearing.

 (a) P is on bearing 065° from Q. What is the bearing from P to Q?

 (b) L is on bearing 135° from M. What is the bearing of M from L?

 (c) S is on bearing 342° from T. What is the bearing from S to T?

2 From X, the bearing of Y is 075° and Z is on bearing 142°.
What is the size of $\angle YXZ$?

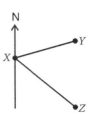

3 From the lighthouse L, ship M is on bearing 038°.
From M, the bearing of ship N is 195°.
Find the size of $\angle LMN$.

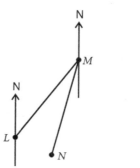

4 Point P is 7·5 kilometres due west of Q. A ship, S, is on
bearing 080° from P and bearing 290° from Q.
Use a scale drawing to find the distance of the ship
from P and from Q.

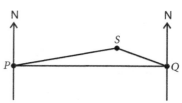

5 From two air traffic control centres, C_1 and C_2, a plane P is on bearing 110° and 035°.
If the first centre is 80 kilometres due north of the second, calculate
how far the plane is from each centre.

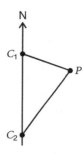

6 You need a pair of compasses for this question.

Three radio stations, Buffalo (B), Horse (H)
and Steer (S), are situated in California.

Buffalo is 240 kilometres due south of Horse.
Horse is 400 kilometres from Steer.
Steer is on a bearing of 125° from Buffalo.
Find the distance between Buffalo and Steer.

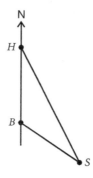

7 Observation station A is 48 kilometres west of station B.
From the stations the bearing of a ship is measured at 038° and 315°
respectively.
Use a scale drawing to find the distance of the ship from both stations.

8 Two yachts sail from Stonehaven.
Yacht P sails for 25 kilometres on bearing 085°.
Yacht Q sails for 45 kilometres on bearing 168°.
How far apart are the yachts?

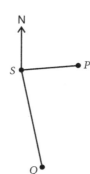

11.4 Tolerance

Measurements cannot be exact. In every measurement there is an element of error.

A measurement of 5 centimetres with an error of 0·2 centimetres may be written as 5±0·2 cm.
This means that any measurement between 4·8 cm and 5·2 cm is acceptable.
The **tolerance** is the difference between the **upper** and **lower bounds**, in this case 0·4.

Example 1

Find the upper and lower bound of each measurement.

(a) 70 ± 3 cm

(b) 8·3 ± 0·01 kg

(a)
70 cm
73 cm upper bound
67 cm lower bound

(b)
8·3 kg
8·31 kg upper bound
8·29 kg lower bound

If the error is not specified, it is assumed to be half of the smallest unit of measurement.

A measurement of 18 kilometres has an assumed error of 0·5 kilometres.
This may be written as 18 ± 0·5 km.
This means that any measurement between 17·5 km an 18·5 km is acceptable.

Example 2

Find the upper and lower bound of each measurement.

(a) 81 kg

(b) 15·25 sec

(a)
81 kg
81·5 kg upper bound
80·5 kg lower bound

(b)
15·25 sec
15·255 sec upper bound
15·245 sec lower bound

Exercise 11.4

1 Find the upper and lower bound for each measurement.

(a) 7 ± 1 cm
(b) 3·5 ± 0·2 kg
(c) 2·9 ± 0·03 ml
(d) 2·58 ± 0·01 m
(e) 7·65 ± 0·001 cm³
(f) 8·04 ± 0·005 g
(g) 6·9 ± 0·02 l
(h) 4·83 ± 0·05 g
(i) 9·2 ± 0·5 sec

2 State the assumed error in each measurement.

(a) 15 m
(b) 4·8 cm
(c) 16·9 kg
(d) 7·09 sec
(e) 5·67 min
(f) 0·034 mm
(g) 32·00 km
(h) 1008 g
(i) 1·0035 s
(j) 50 m
(k) 25·05 cm
(l) 3·3 ml

3 Write the assumed error for each measurement and hence give the maximum and minimum values.

(a) 4 sec
(b) 21 cm
(c) 6·75 m
(d) 0·9 kg
(e) 45·80 m
(f) 1·00 mm
(g) 120·5 km
(h) 0·001 g
(i) 32·005 h
(j) 4500 kg
(k) 30·775 ml
(l) 0·5560 mg

4 The upper and lower measurements are given in the table.
For each pair, write the measurement in the form $a \pm b$.

	(a)	(b)	(c)	(d)
Upper limit	7 cm	6·5 km	8·4 mm	0·57 ml
Lower limit	5 cm	6·3 km	8·0 mm	0·51 ml

5 (a) An engineering firm manufactures bolts with lengths specified
as 6·5 ± 0·3 cm. Which of the following bolt lengths meet the
specification?

6·52 cm, 6·31 cm, 6·15 cm, 6·78 cm, 6·84 cm, 6·07 cm

(b) The diameter of the bolts was specified as 1·20 ± 0·002 cm.
Which of the following diameters meet the specification?

1·213 cm, 1·201 cm, 1·194 cm, 1·199 cm, 1·198 cm, 1·203 cm

6 The gap between the electrodes of a car's spark plugs needs to be
1·25 ± 0·015 mm to work efficiently. Which of the following gaps would
cause the spark plugs to work inefficiently?

1·261 mm, 1·234 mm, 1·321 mm, 1·266 mm

7 Find the assumed maximum and minimum possible values for each area.

(a)
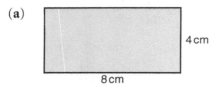
4 cm
8 cm

(b)
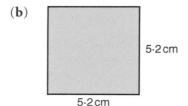
5·2 cm
5·2 cm

(c)
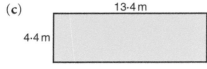
13·4 m
4·4 m

(d)
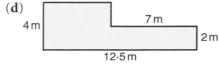
4 m
7 m
2 m
12·5 m

(e)
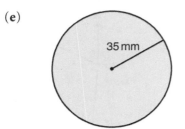
35 mm

(f)
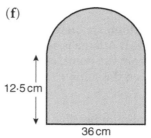
12·5 cm
36 cm

8 Calculate the assumed maximum and minimum possible values for each volume.

(a)
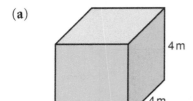
4 m
4 m
4 m

(b)
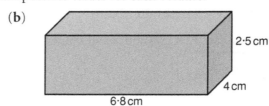
2·5 cm
4 cm
6·8 cm

(c)

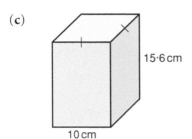

15·6 cm

10 cm

(d)

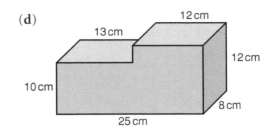

12 cm

13 cm

10 cm

12 cm

25 cm

8 cm

Review exercise 11: Am I a successful learner?

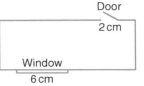

Door

2 cm

Window

6 cm

1 From the scale plan of Susan's kitchen, find:
  (**a**) the true length of the window
  (**b**) the true width of the door

Scale 1:60

2 Derek is building a scale model ship, using the scale 1:15.
The actual dimensions of the ship are height 6·5 metres, length 23 metres
and width 4·23 metres. Calculate the dimensions of his model.

3 The scale of a map is 1 cm:2·5 km. Write this as a representative fraction.

4 A map has scale $\frac{1}{15\,000}$.
  (**a**) What distance on the ground is represented by 2·1 centimetres on the map?
  (**b**) What distance on the map represents an actual distance of 1·32 kilometres?

5 Paul and Heather can be seen from the top of a tower.
The angles of depression are as shown on the diagram.
Use a scale drawing to find the distance between
Paul and Heather.

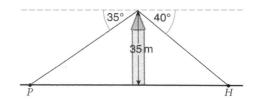

35° 40°

35 m

P   H

6 Draw a diagram to find the required bearing.
  (**a**) The bearing from A to B is 056°. Find the bearing of A from B.
  (**b**) The bearing from X to Y is 280°. What is the bearing from Y to X?

7 HMS Atlanta and HMS Loudoun are on bearings of 065° and 175°
from an observation point P. If Atlanta is 42 kilometres and
Loudoun is 48 kilometres from the point, use a scale drawing to
calculate the distance between the ships.

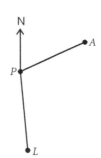

N

A

P

L

8 Find the maximum and minimum possible values for each measurement.
  (**a**) 4·5 ± 0·2 m   (**b**) 16·55 ± 0·001 g   (**c**) 0·045 ± 0·003 km

9 State the assumed error in each measurement.
  (**a**) 14 km   (**b**) 20·55 cm   (**c**) 40·000 kg

10 Calculate the assumed maximum and minimum values of each area.
  (**a**)

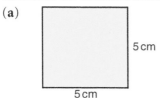

5 cm

5 cm

  (**b**)

4·2 mm

12·1 mm

Summary 11: What I learned in this chapter.

Interpreting scale drawing

A scale may be expressed in several ways.

Ratio   1 cm:2·75 km

Representative fraction $\frac{1}{275\,000}$

Linear Scale

0   2·75   5·5   8·25   11·0   13·75km

A new kitchen has been designed using
a scale drawing. Each dimension has been reduced
in the ratio 1:20.

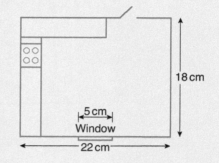

Plan length (cm)	True length (cm)
1	20
22	20 × 22 = 440 Length of room is **4·4 metres**
18	20 × 18 = 360 Width of room is **3·6 metres**

Scale drawing

Choose a suitable scale.   1 cm to 2 m or 1:200
Convert distances to scale distances.

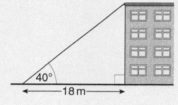

True distance (m)	Plan distance (cm)
2	1
18	9

or

True distance	Plan distance
18 m	18 ÷ 200 = 0.09 m
	= 9 cm

Make the scale drawing.

First draw a 9 centimetre line

Then draw a 40° angle

Finally draw the vertical height and measure it.

Convert the measured height to the actual height.

7·6 cm

40°

9 cm

Plan height (cm)	True height (m)
1	2
7·6	7·6 × 2 = 15·2

or

Plan height	True height
7·6 cm	7·6 × 200 = 1520 cm
	= 15·2 m

The building is **15·2 metres** high.

Tolerance

If the error is not specified the assumed error in a measurement is half the smallest unit of measure.

5 ± 0·2 cm has an upper limit of 5·2 cm and a lower limit of 4·8 cm.

12 Trigonometry

12.1 Investigating triangles

Learning intentions

Is it possible to calculate the height of this building?

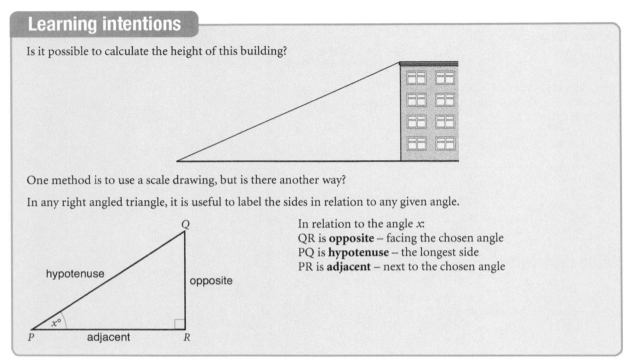

One method is to use a scale drawing, but is there another way?

In any right angled triangle, it is useful to label the sides in relation to any given angle.

In relation to the angle x:
QR is **opposite** – facing the chosen angle
PQ is **hypotenuse** – the longest side
PR is **adjacent** – next to the chosen angle

Exercise 12.1

1 In each triangle, name the opposite side to angle $x°$.

(a) 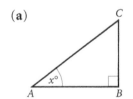 (b) (c) 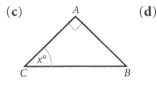 (d)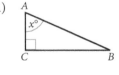

2 Copy each triangle below and mark on the opposite, adjacent and hypotenuse.

(a) 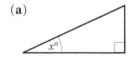 (b) 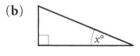 (c) 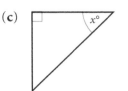 (d)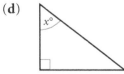

3 (**a**) Measure the sides of each triangle and copy and complete the table.

Triangle	opposite	adjacent	$\dfrac{opposite}{adjacent}$
P			
Q			
R			
S			

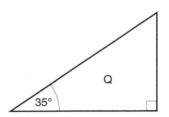

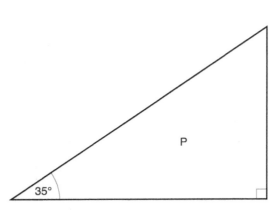

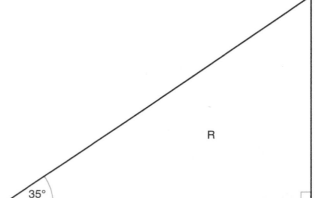

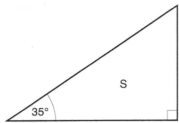

(**b**) Draw three more right angled triangles with a 35° angle and calculate $\dfrac{opposite}{adjacent}$ for each.

(**c**) What do you notice about your answers? Why do you think this happens?

4 The take-off path of a jet is shown below

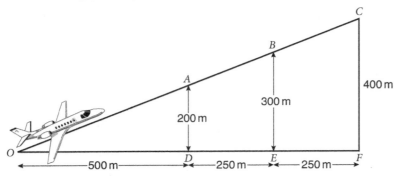

(**a**) What can you say about the triangles *OAD*, *OBE*, *OCF*?

(**b**) Calculate $\dfrac{AD}{OD}, \dfrac{BE}{OE}, \dfrac{CF}{OF}$

(**c**) What do you notice about your answers? Why do you think this happens?

12.2 The tangent ratio

Learning intentions

The ratio $\dfrac{\text{opposite}}{\text{adjacent}}$ gives the same value for all similar triangles.

In any right angled triangle, this ratio, $\dfrac{\text{opposite}}{\text{adjacent}}$, is called the **tangent** of the angle x.

$$\text{tangent of } x° = \frac{\text{opposite}}{\text{adjacent}}$$

$$\tan x° = \frac{\text{opposite}}{\text{adjacent}}$$

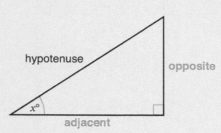

The $\boxed{\text{TAN}}$ button on the calculator may be used to find the tangent of an angle

$\boxed{\text{TAN } 35° = 0.7002075382}$ $\boxed{\text{TAN } 70° = 2.747474}$

tan 35° = 0·700 to 3 d.p. **tan 70° = 2·747 to 3 d.p.**

The ratio $\tan x°$ may be used to calculate the length of sides of triangles.

Example 1

Calculate the height of the building

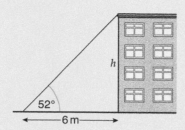

- draw a right angled triangle

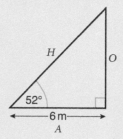

- write ratio $\tan x° = \dfrac{\text{opposite}}{\text{adjacent}}$

- substitute $\tan 52° = \dfrac{h}{6}$

- solve $6 \times \tan 52° = h$
  $$h = 6 \times 1·27994$$
  $$h = 7·6796$$

  $h = \mathbf{7·68}$ **metres to 3 s.f.**

Example 2

The angle of depression of a boat from the top of a cliff is 15°. If the boat is 240 metres from the base of the cliff how high is the cliff?

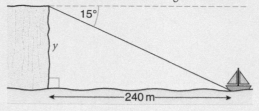

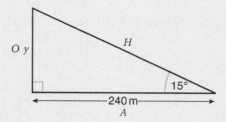

$\tan x° = \dfrac{\text{opposite}}{\text{adjacent}}$

$\tan 15° = \dfrac{y}{240}$

$240 \times \tan 15° = y$
$$y = 240 \times 0·26794$$
$$y = 64·3078$$
$$y = \mathbf{64·3} \text{ m to 3 s.f.}$$

Exercise 12.2

1 Use a calculator to find to 3 decimal places:

(**a**) tan 32° (**b**) tan 76° (**c**) tan 45° (**d**) tan 18° (**e**) tan 62°

2 Calculate the length of *h* in each triangle below.

(**a**)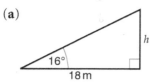

(**b**)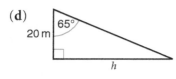

(**c**)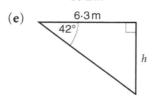

(**d**) (**e**)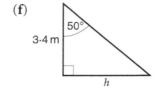

(**f**)

3 The end of a ladder is placed 1·7 metres from a wall. The angle between the ladder and the ground is 35°. Find how high up the wall the ladder will reach.

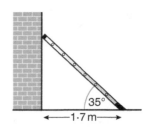

4 Jake is standing 5 metres from the base of a tree. The angle of elevation of the tree top is 64°. Calculate the height of the tree.

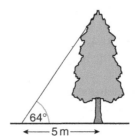

5 Captain Ford sails from Rutherston to an oil rig. He leaves Rutherston and sails on a bearing of 155°. Findry is 38 kilometres due south of Rutherston. How far east of Findry is the oil rig?

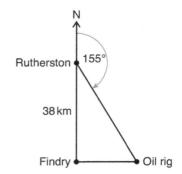

6 The angle of depression from the top of a waterfall to a boat on the river below is 30°. If the boat is 14 metres from the base of the waterfall, calculate the height of the waterfall.

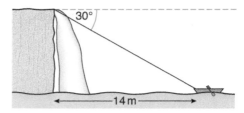

7 Calculate the height of each isosceles triangle.

(a)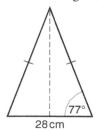

28 cm

77°

(b)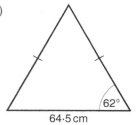

64·5 cm

62°

(c)

30·4 cm

80°

8 (a) Use Pythagoras' theorem to calculate the value of *a*.

(b) Hence calculate *b*.

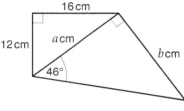

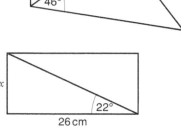

16 cm
12 cm
a cm
46°
b cm

9 (a) Calculate the length of the side *x* in this rectangle.

(b) Hence calculate the length of the diagonal.

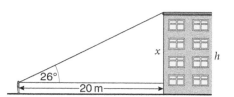

x
26 cm
22°

10 (a) Ailsa stands 20 metres away from her school building and uses a theodolite to measure the angle of elevation as 26°. Calculate *x*.

(b) If Ailsa is 1·72 metres tall, calculate the height of the school building.

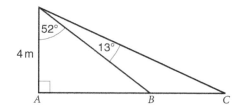

26°
20 m
x
h

11 Graeme stands 13 metres away from his block of flats and measures the angle of elevation to be 57°. If Graeme is 1·87 metres tall, calculate the height of the block of flats.

12 Calculate the length of:

(a) *AC*

(b) *AB*

(c) *BC*

52°
4 m
13°
A
B
C

13 Olivia and Bob stand on a riverside path 6 metres apart. Morven and Darren stand in line with Bob on either bank of the river. As Olivia turns from Bob to Morven, she measures an angle of 60°. As she turns from Morven to Darren, she measures an angle of 16°. Calculate the width of the river.

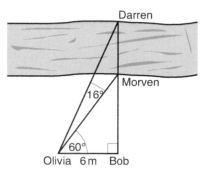

Darren
16°
Morven
60°
Olivia 6 m Bob

12.3   Using the tangent ratio to find an angle

Learning intentions

The tan button $\boxed{\text{TAN}}$ on a calculator gives the tangent of an angle.

The inverse tan button $\boxed{\text{TAN}^{-1}}$ gives the angle if the tangent is known.

$\boxed{\text{TAN}^{-1}}\ \boxed{(0{\cdot}2)}\ \boxed{=}\ \boxed{11{\cdot}30993247}$

So the angle with a tangent of $0{\cdot}2$ is $11{\cdot}3°$

Example 1

Find the angle $x°$ to the nearest degree.

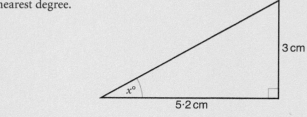

3 cm

5·2 cm

Sketch diagram and mark sides

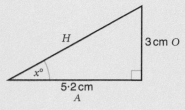

H

3 cm O

$x°$

5·2 cm

A

Write ratio $\tan x° = \dfrac{\text{opp}}{\text{adj}}$

Substitute values $\tan x° = \dfrac{3}{5{\cdot}2}$

$\tan x° = 0{\cdot}576923$

Use inverse tan $x° = \tan^{-1}(0{\cdot}577)$ $\boxed{\text{TAN}^{-1}}\ \boxed{(}\ \boxed{3}\ \boxed{\div}\ \boxed{5{\cdot}2}\ \boxed{)}$

$x° = 29{\cdot}98°$

$x° = \mathbf{30°}$ to the nearest degree

Example 2

Robert is lying 15 metres from a building, that is 12·2 metres high. Find the angle of elevation $x°$, of the top of the building.

12·2 m

15 m

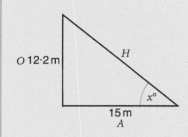

O 12·2 m

H

$x°$

15 m

A

$\tan x° = \dfrac{\text{opp}}{\text{adj}}$

$\tan x° = \dfrac{12{\cdot}2}{15}$

$x° = \tan^{-1}\left(\dfrac{12{\cdot}2}{15}\right)$

$x° = \mathbf{39°}$ to the nearest degree

Exercise 12.3

1 Find each angle, to the nearest degree:

(a) $\tan x° = 0{\cdot}5$ (b) $\tan y° = 0{\cdot}34$ (c) $\tan z° = 1$ (d) $\tan p° = 1{\cdot}7$ (e) $\tan q° = 12$

2 Use the ratio $\tan x^\circ = \dfrac{\text{opposite}}{\text{adjacent}}$ to calculate x in each triangle.

(a)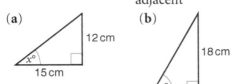

(b)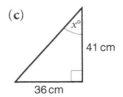

(c)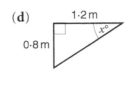

(d)

3 Find the size of the marked angles:

(a)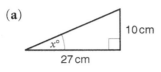

(b)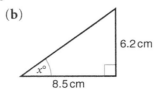

(c)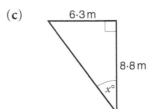

(d)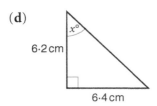

(e)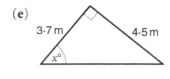

(f)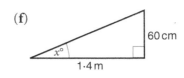

4 Calculate the angle the ladder makes with the wall.

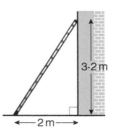

5 Find the angle of elevation of each building.

(a)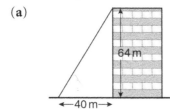

(b)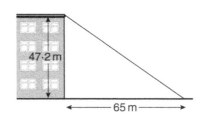

6 Find the angle of depression of each boat from the cliff top.

(a)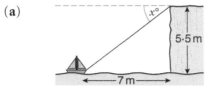

(b)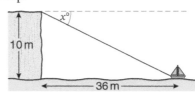

7 Find the angle of elevation of the hot air balloon.

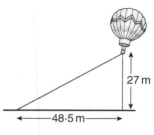

27 m

←——48·5 m——→

8 An underground tunnel should have an angle of depression of no more than 30°.
Does this plan meet requirements?

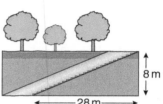

8 m

←——28 m——→

12.4 Investigating triangles further

Exercise 12.4

1 (**a**) Measure the sides of each triangle. Copy and complete the table below.

Triangle	opposite	hypotenuse	$\dfrac{\text{opposite}}{\text{hypotenuse}}$
P			
Q			
R			
S			

Q

30°

P

30°

R

30°

S

30°

(**b**) Draw three more right angled triangles with a 30° angle and calculate the ratio $\dfrac{\text{opposite}}{\text{hypotenuse}}$ for each.

(**c**) What do you notice about your answers? Why do you think this happens?

12.5 The sine ratio

Learning intentions

The ratio $\dfrac{\text{opposite}}{\text{hypotenuse}}$ gives the same value for all similar triangles.

In any right angled triangle the ratio, $\dfrac{\text{opposite}}{\text{hypotenuse}}$, is called the **sine** of the angle x.

sine of $x° = \dfrac{\text{opposite}}{\text{hypotenuse}}$

$\sin x° = \dfrac{\text{opposite}}{\text{hypotenuse}}$

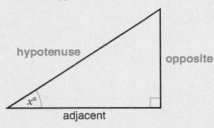

The $\boxed{\text{SIN}}$ button on the calculator may be used to find the sine of an angle

$\boxed{\text{SIN } 36° = 0.58778523}$ $\boxed{\text{SIN } 70° = 0.9396926208}$

sin 36° = 0·588 to 3 d.p.   **sin 70° = 0·940** to 3 d.p.

The ratio $\sin x°$ may be used to calculate the lengths of sides and size of angles in triangles.

Example 1

Calculate the length of side b

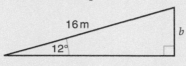

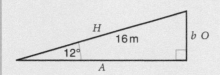

$\sin x° = \dfrac{\text{opposite}}{\text{hypotenuse}}$

$\sin 12° = \dfrac{b}{16}$

$16 \times \sin 12° = b$

$b = 3.326587$

b = 3·33 centimetres to 3 s.f.

Example 2

Calculate the size of angle $x°$

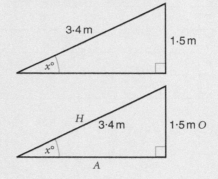

$\sin x° = \dfrac{\text{opposite}}{\text{hypotenuse}}$

$\sin x° = \dfrac{1.5}{3.4}$

$x° = \sin^{-1}\left(\dfrac{1.5}{3.4}\right)$ $\boxed{\text{SIN}^{-1}}\ \boxed{(}\ \boxed{1.5}\ \boxed{\div}\ \boxed{3.4}\ \boxed{)}$

$x° = 26.2°$ to 3 s.f.

Exercise 12.5

1 Find the length of y in each triangle.

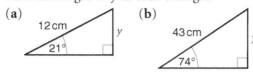

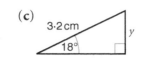

(d)

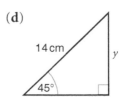

(e)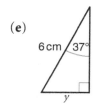

(f)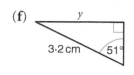

(g)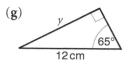

(h)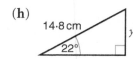

2 Calculate the size of angle x in each triangle.

(a) 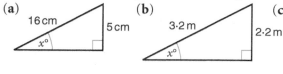 **(b)** **(c)** 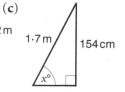 **(d)**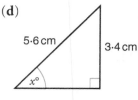

(e) 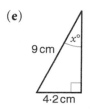 **(f)** 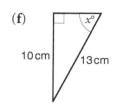 **(g)** 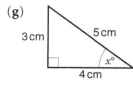 **(h)**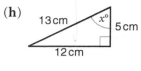

3 An aircraft takes off at an angle of 32°.
After the aircraft has travelled 1 kilometre,
how high above the ground will it be?

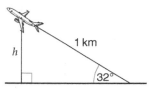

4 Calculate the sizes of all three angles in this triangle.

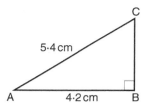

5 Mr Archer has a rectangular piece of wood.
He needs to cut a right angled triangle which
has one angle less than 35°. If he cuts along
the diagonal of the rectangle, will he have a
suitable triangle?

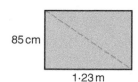

6 A guy rope 1·7 metres long is used to secure a tent. If the
angle between the guy rope and tent is 50°, calculate the
distance, d, from the tent to the tent peg.

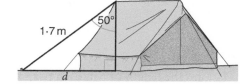

7 Paterson's Paper plan to build a ramp at their main
door. Local regulations state that the ramp should
be at an angle of no more than 18° to the horizontal.
Does this ramp meet regulations?
Give a reason for your answer.

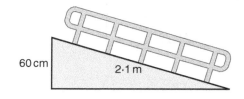

12.6 The cosine ratio

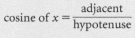

The ratio $\dfrac{\text{adjacent}}{\text{hypotenuse}}$ gives the same value for all similar triangles.

In any right angled triangle the ratio, $\dfrac{\text{adjacent}}{\text{hypotenuse}}$, is called the **cosine** of the angle x.

cosine of $x = \dfrac{\text{adjacent}}{\text{hypotenuse}}$

$\cos x = \dfrac{\text{adjacent}}{\text{hypotenuse}}$

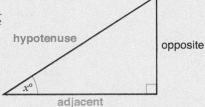

Example 1

Calculate the length of side b

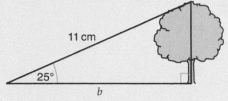

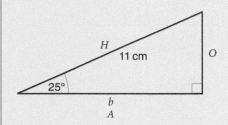

$\cos x^\circ = \dfrac{\text{adjacent}}{\text{hypotenuse}}$

$\cos 25^\circ = \dfrac{b}{11}$

$11 \times \cos 25^\circ = b$

$b = 9 \cdot 96938$

$b = \mathbf{9 \cdot 97}$ **centimetres** to 3 s.f.

Example 2

Calculate the size of angle x°

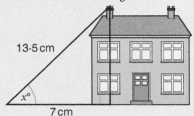

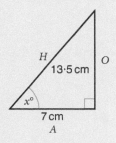

$\cos x^\circ = \dfrac{\text{adjacent}}{\text{hypotenuse}}$

$\cos x^\circ = \dfrac{7}{13 \cdot 5}$

$x^\circ = \cos^{-1}\left(\dfrac{7}{13 \cdot 5}\right)$ $\boxed{\cos^{-1}}\ \boxed{(}\ \boxed{7}\ \boxed{\div}\ \boxed{13 \cdot 5}\ \boxed{)}$

$x^\circ = 58 \cdot 76707$

$x^\circ = \mathbf{59^\circ}$ to the nearest degree

Exercise 12.6

1 Find the length of b in each triangle.

(a)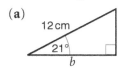

(b)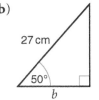

(c)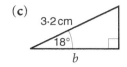

(d)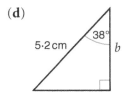

(e) 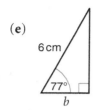 6 cm, 77°, b

(f) 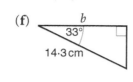 b, 33°, 14·3 cm

(g) 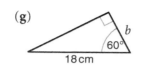 b, 60°, 18 cm

(h) b, 22°, 14·8 cm

2 Calculate the angle x in each triangle.

(a) 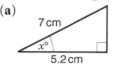 7 cm, $x°$, 5.2 cm

(b) 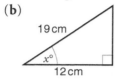 19 cm, $x°$, 12 cm

(c) 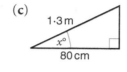 1·3 m, $x°$, 80 cm

(d) 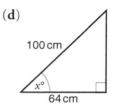 100 cm, $x°$, 64 cm

(e) 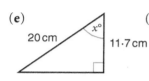 20 cm, $x°$, 11·7 cm

(f) 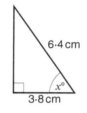 6·4 cm, $x°$, 3·8 cm

(g) 7 cm, $x°$, 15 cm

(h) 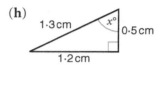 1·3 cm, $x°$, 0·5 cm, 1·2 cm

3 Guy ropes of a marquee are 4·1 metres long. They are to be pegged 2·9 metres away from the marquee.
What angle do the guy ropes make with the ground?

4 (a) Calculate the length of AC.
(b) Calculate the length of CB.
(c) Hence find the length of AB.

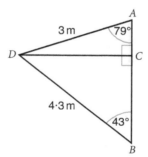

5 Calculate the length of *AB* in each triangle:

(a)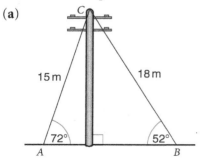

(b)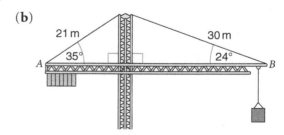

6 Calculate the length *AB* in the following triangles:

(**a**)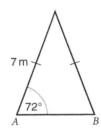

(**b**)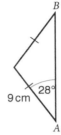

(**c**)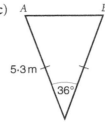

12.7 Choosing a ratio

$$\sin x° = \frac{\text{opposite}}{\text{hypotenuse}} \qquad \cos x° = \frac{\text{adjacent}}{\text{hypotenuse}} \qquad \tan x° = \frac{\text{opposite}}{\text{adjacent}}$$

This can be remembered using the mnemonic $\textrm{SOHCAHTOA}$

Example 1

Find the horizontal length of this ramp.

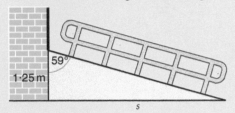

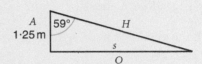

Choose ratio   SOH CAH **TOA**

$$\tan x° = \frac{\text{opp}}{\text{adj}}$$

$$\tan 59° = \frac{s}{1·25}$$

$$1·25 \times \tan 59° = s$$

$$s = 2·0803$$

$$s = \textbf{2·08 metres} \text{ to 3 s.f.}$$

Example 2

Find the size of the angle *x*.

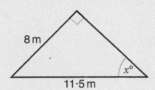

Choose ratio   SOH **CAH** TOA

$$\sin x° = \frac{\text{opp}}{\text{hyp}}$$

$$\sin x° = \frac{8}{11·5}$$

$$x° = \sin^{-1}\left(\frac{8}{11·5}\right)$$

$$x° = 44·0792°$$

$$x° = \textbf{44°} \text{ to the nearest degree}$$

Exercise 12.7

1 Choose the appropriate ratio and find the marked length in each triangle.

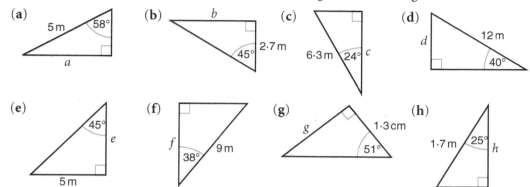

(a)   5 m   58°   a

(b)   b   45°   2·7 m

(c)   6·3 m   24°   c

(d)   d   12 m   40°

(e)   45°   e   5 m

(f)   f   38°   9 m

(g)   g   1·3 cm   51°

(h)   1·7 m   25°   h

2 Calculate the angle *x* in each triangle.

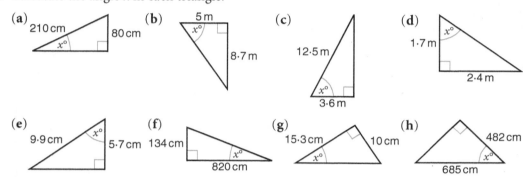

(a)   210 cm   80 cm   x°

(b)   5 m   x°   8·7 m

(c)   12·5 m   x°   3·6 m

(d)   1·7 m   x°   2·4 m

(e)   9·9 cm   x°   5·7 cm

(f)   134 cm   x°   820 cm

(g)   15·3 cm   x°   10 cm

(h)   482 cm   x°   685 cm

3 Calculate *k* in each triangle.

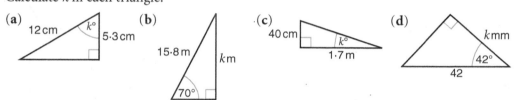

(a)   12 cm   k°   5·3 cm

(b)   15·8 m   k m   70°

(c)   40 cm   k°   1·7 m

(d)   k mm   42°   42

4 Calculate the height of each building:

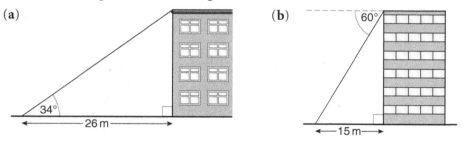

(a)   34°   26 m

(b)   60°   15 m

5 A piece of equipment 3·5 metres high is to be carried through
a corridor with a ceiling height of 3 metres. The equipment
should not be tilted any further than 30° from the vertical.
Is it possible to carry the equipment along the corridor?

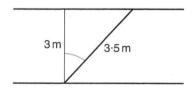

3 m   3·5 m

6 Calculate the length of base *AC* in this isosceles triangle.

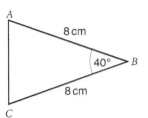

7 In the isosceles triangle shown, calculate:
(**a**) the base *AC*
(**b**) the height *BD*
(**c**) the area of the triangle.

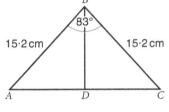

8 (**a**) Calculate the length of side *h*.
(**b**) Use Pythagoras' theorem to calculate the length of the hypotenuse.

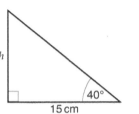

9 Calculate the missing lengths in this triangle.

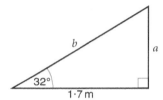

10 A boat leaves Peterhead and travels 35 kilometres East and 87 kilometres North.
Calculate:
(**a**) the bearing of the boat from Peterhead
(**b**) the bearing of Peterhead from the boat.

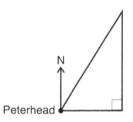

11 A regular pentagon is inscribed in a circle, centre *O*, of radius 10 centimetres.

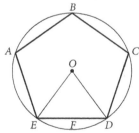 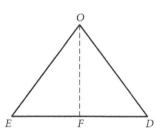

Calculate:
(**a**) the angle *EOD*
(**b**) the length of *OF*, where *F* is the midpoint of *ED*
(**c**) the length of *ED*
(**d**) the area of the pentagon.

12.8   Finding the denominator

Learning intentions

In a right angled triangle, given 1 side and 1 angle, it is possible to calculate any side.

Example

(a) Find the length of side p

(b) Find the length of side r

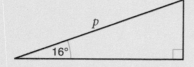

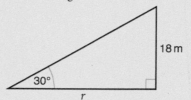

Choose ratio   SOH CAH TOA

$$\cos x° = \frac{adj}{hyp}$$

$$\cos 16° = \frac{5}{p}$$

$$p \cos 16° = 5$$

$$p = \frac{5}{\cos 16°}$$

$$p = 5 \cdot 201497$$

$$p = \mathbf{5 \cdot 20\,m} \text{ to 3 s.f.}$$

Choose ratio   SOH CAH TOA

$$\tan x° = \frac{opp}{adj}$$

$$\tan 30° = \frac{18}{r}$$

$$r \tan 30° = 18$$

$$r = \frac{18}{\tan 30°}$$

$$r = 31 \cdot 1769$$

$$r = \mathbf{31 \cdot 2\,m} \text{ to 3 s.f.}$$

Exercise 12.8

1 Calculate the length of x in the following triangles.

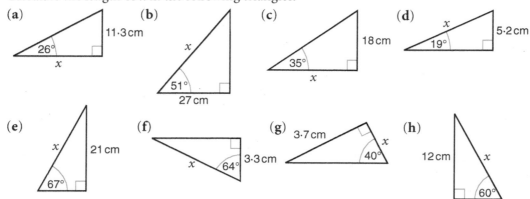

2 Calculate the length of AB in each triangle.

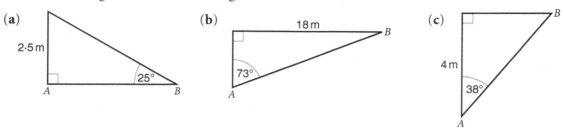

3 A ladder is needed to reach a window 4 metres above ground. For safety reasons, the angle between the ladder and the ground should be no more than 64°. Calculate the minimum length of the ladder needed.

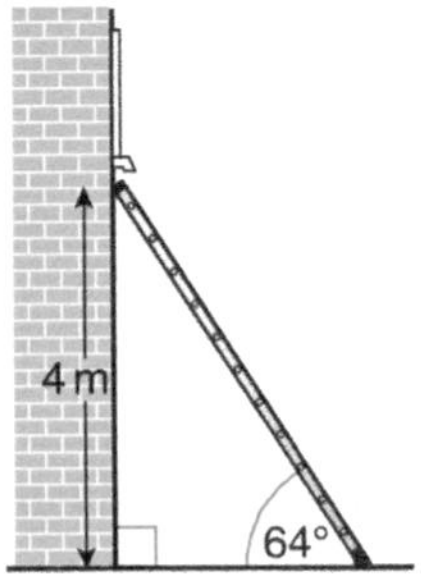

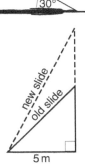

4 Joe is 1·85 metres tall. He estimates the angle of elevation of the sun to be 30°. Calculate the length of his shadow.

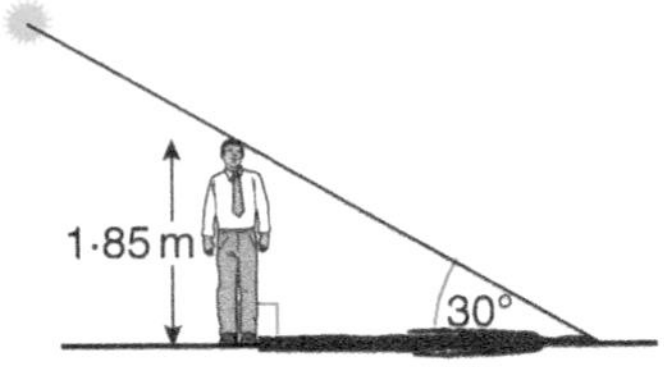

5 Ben Verbie outdoor activity centre has a children's slide. It is decided to increase the incline of the slide from 45° to 62°. How much longer will the slide be?

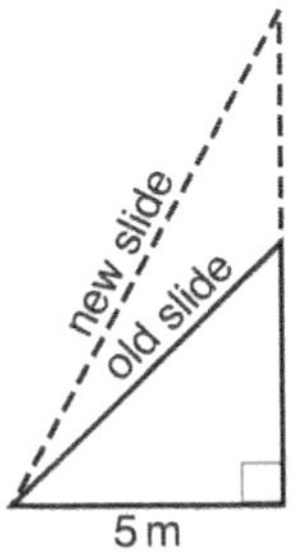

6 A pedestrian bridge is to be built over the River Inver. A safety barrier is to be installed on both sides of the footpath. Calculate the total length of barrier needed.

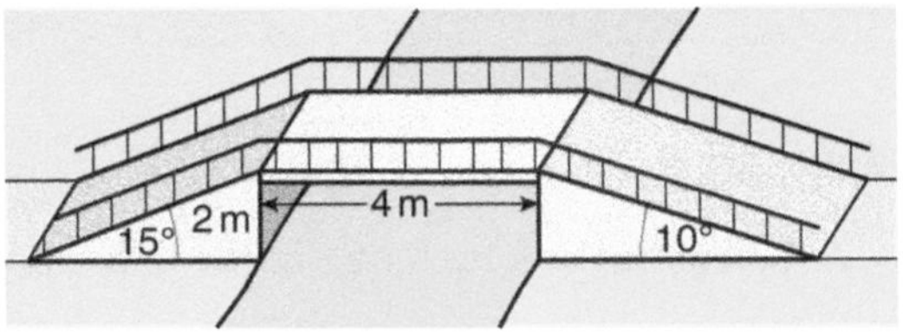

12.9 Problem solving

Learning intentions

To solve trigonometric problems:

1 make a sketch
2 mark on relevant data
3 choose a ratio
4 substitute values
5 solve equation

Example 1

A hydraulic ladder is placed 4 metres away from a building. If it is raised to an angle of elevation of 51°, how long must the ladder be to reach the building?

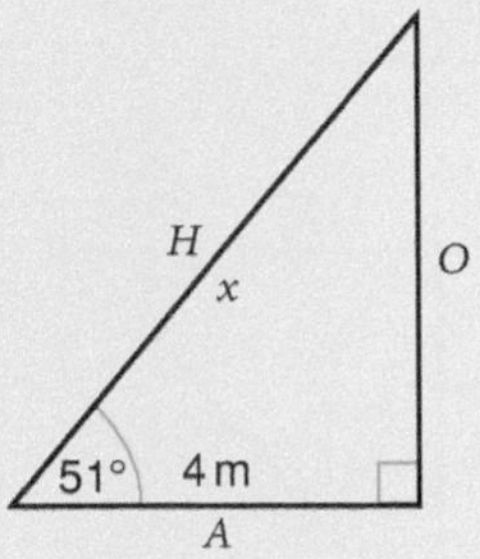

Choose ratio SOH CAH TOA

$$\cos 51° = \frac{\text{adj}}{\text{hyp}}$$

$$\cos 51° = \frac{4}{x}$$

$$x \cos 51° = 4$$

$$x = \frac{4}{\cos 51°}$$

$$x = 6{\cdot}35606 \text{ m}$$

$\boldsymbol{x = 6{\cdot}36}$ **m** to 3 s.f.

Example 2

A ramp 4·7 metres long rises vertically 1·5 metres. Calculate the angle of incline of the ramp.

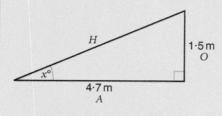

Choose ratio   SOH CAH TOA

$$\tan x° = \frac{\text{opp}}{\text{adj}}$$

$$\tan x° = \frac{1·5}{4·7}$$

$$x = \tan^{-1}(1·5 \div 4·7)$$
$$x = 17·7004°$$
$$\boldsymbol{x = 17·7° \text{ to 3 s.f.}}$$

Exercise 12.9

1 A boat sails 87 kilometres on a bearing of 029°. Calculate how far north of its original position it will be.

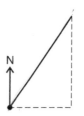

2 A ship sails 30 kilometres on a bearing of 027°, then 83 kilometres on a bearing of 054°. Calculate how far east the ship is from its starting point.

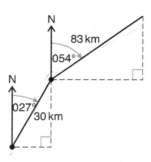

3 A ship sails 75 kilometres north east and then 120 kilometres on a bearing of 030°.
Calculate how far north the ship is from its starting point.

4 Calculate the length of *a* and hence find the length of *b*.

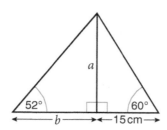

5 Calculate the missing lengths *x* and *y*.

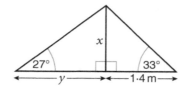

6 For each triangle calculate
(**i**) the base, b (**ii**) the height   (**iii**) the area.

(**a**)   (**b**)   (**c**)

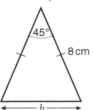
45°
8 cm
b

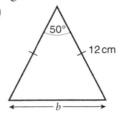
50°
12 cm
b

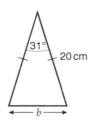
31°
20 cm
b

7 Regulations state that for safe use of a computer the viewing area of the monitor should be between 15° and 50° below horizontal eye level.
Linda sits 70 centimetres from her desk and the viewing distance to her monitor is 80 centimetres. Does the viewing angle meet regulations?

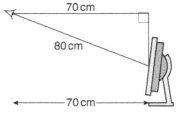

8 Blackburn Engineering need to measure the size of a damaged section of rock face . Calculate the height of this section.

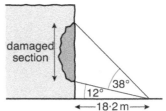

9 From where Adam stands on the mountain, he sees base camp at an angle of depression of 21°. Three hours later he sees the camp on an angle of depression of 15°. How far has he descended vertically?

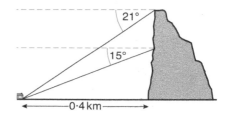

10 Tahna crosses the road, perpendicular to the pavement. Joanna crosses at an angle of 50° to the pavement. If the road is 6 metres wide, how much further does Joanna have to walk?

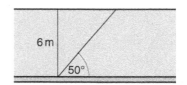

11 (**a**) Calculate the length of AB
(**b**) Prove that triangles ABE and EDC are similar.
(**c**) Hence calculate the length of CD.

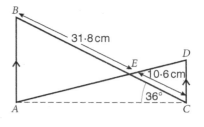

12 $ABCD$ is a kite.
The diagonals intersect at E.
$AC = 24$ centimetres
$BE = 17$ centimetres
$ED = 44$ centimetres
Calculate the sizes of all the angles and lengths of all the sides of the kite.

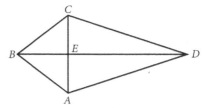

Review exercise 12: Am I a successful learner?

1 Calculate *a* in each triangle below.

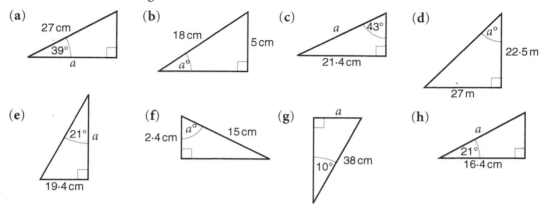

2 Iwan stands 4 metres away from his school and measures the angle of elevation of the roof to be 67°. If Iwan is 1·7 metres tall, calculate the height of the school.

3 A guy rope 2·25 metres long is used to secure a tent. If the angle between the guy rope and tent is 67°, calculate the distance from the tent to the tent peg.

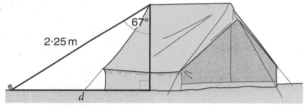

4 A ship sails on a bearing of 039° for 54 kilometres. Calculate how far east it is from its starting position.

5 A ladder is needed to reach a window 5·8 metres above ground. For safety reasons the angle between the ladder and the ground should be no more than 74°. Calculate the minimum length of ladder needed.

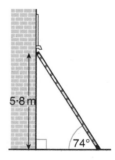

6 Calculate the distance *AB* of this triangle.

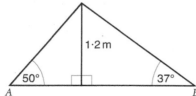

Summary 12: What I learned in this chapter.

Trigonometric ratios

$$\sin x° = \frac{\text{opposite}}{\text{hypotenuse}} \qquad \cos x° = \frac{\text{adjacent}}{\text{hypotenuse}} \qquad \tan x° = \frac{\text{opposite}}{\text{adjacent}}$$

This can be remembered using the mnemonic **SOHCAHTOA**

To solve trigonometric problems:
1 make a sketch
2 mark on relevant data
3 choose a ratio
4 substitute values
5 solve equation

To find x:

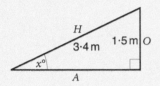

Choose ratio   SOH CAH TOA

$$\sin x° = \frac{\text{opp}}{\text{hyp}}$$

$$\sin x° = \frac{1\cdot5}{3\cdot4}$$

$$x° = \sin^{-1}\left(\frac{1\cdot5}{3\cdot4}\right)$$

$$x° = 26\cdot2° \text{ to 3 s.f.}$$

To find b:

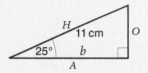

Choose ratio   SOH CAH TOA

$$\cos x° = \frac{\text{adj}}{\text{hyp}}$$

$$\cos 25° = \frac{b}{11}$$

$$11 \times \cos 25° = b$$

$$b = 9\cdot96938$$

$$b = 9\cdot97 \text{ cm to 3 s.f.}$$

To find r:

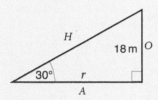

Choose ratio   SOH CAH TOA

$$\tan x° = \frac{\text{opp}}{\text{adj}}$$

$$\tan 30° = \frac{18}{r}$$

$$r\tan 30° = 18$$

$$r = \frac{18}{\tan 30°}$$

$$r = 31\cdot1769$$

$$r = 31\cdot2 \text{ m to 3 s.f.}$$

13 Statistics 2

13.1 Relative frequency

Learning intentions

Gwen rolled a die 24 times and recorded her results.

```
6  2  3  5  6  1  5  4
2  2  4  5  1  1  6  3
1  3  4  6  1  6  4  4
```

Gwen finds she has rolled a 5 three times

For this experiment, the **relative frequency** of 5 is $\frac{3}{24} = \frac{1}{8}$

Relative frequency $= \dfrac{\text{number of times an event occurs}}{\text{number of repetitions}}$

Example

Jill has recorded her results for rolling a die 30 times.

```
4  5  5  6  1  2  2  4  3  5
1  1  6  3  4  5  5  5  3  6
2  4  2  3  5  6  2  1  4  2
```

Find the relative frequency of

(a) a 6   (b) an even number   (c) not a 3

(a) $\frac{4}{30} = \frac{2}{15}$ (b) $\frac{15}{30} = \frac{1}{2}$ (c) $\frac{26}{30} = \frac{13}{15}$

Exercise 13.1

1 A die was rolled 40 times and the results recorded. Find the relative frequency of:

(a) a 1   (b) a 6

(c) an odd number   (d) a number less than 3

```
5  5  6  4  3  2  2  1  1  1
6  2  3  2  3  5  4  4  6  6
5  4  4  1  2  4  6  3  3  2
3  4  1  3  5  6  2  3  4  4
```

2 Sue measured the width of nuts in millimetres in her toolbox.

(a) How many nuts were there?

(b) What is the relative frequency of a width of:

(i) 7   (ii) even   (iii) greater than 10?

```
7  8  7  9  9  8 11
9  9 11 11 10 12  8
7  9  8 10 11  9  7
8  7  7  7  8  9  7
```

3 Patrick has recorded the number of left-handed pupils in each class. Calculate the relative frequency of

(a) 5   (b) odd   (c) even   (d) prime

```
5  5  4  3  3  3  1  1  5  5  4
2  2  3  4  5  2  2  1  3  4  5
```

4 Alistair tossed a coin 50 times.
He calculated the relative frequency of a head was $\frac{3}{5}$.
How many heads occurred?

5 Keir tossed two coins simultaneously and recorded the results.
Find the relative frequency of:

(a) two heads   (b) two tails

```
HH  HH  HT  HT  TT  TT  HH
HT  TT  HT  HT  TT  HH  HT
HH  HT  HT  HH  HT  HH  HT
HH  HT  HH  HH  TT  HT  HT
```

6 Using the 16 high cards from a pack, Drew picked a card at random and recorded the results.

K	Q	Q	J	A	A	A	J	J	Q	Q
Q	J	A	J	Q	Q	J	J	A	A	Q
K	Q	Q	J	Q	A	J	Q	K	A	A

(a) Calculate the relative frequency of:
  (i) a king   (ii) a queen.

(b) Drew removed all the aces from the set of cards. Recalculate the relative frequency of
  (i) a king   (ii) a queen.

7 Mr Partridge drew up a table of information about S3 pupils.

Gender	Left handed	Right handed	Height over 1.5m	Height under 1.5m
Male	18	62	56	24
Female	14	70	72	12

(a) How many pupils are in S3?

(b) What is the relative frequency of
  (i) right handed girls
  (ii) boys under 1.5 metres tall
  (iii) left handed pupils?

8 Mr Stewart completed a check on the school computers. His results are shown in the table.

	Age of computer in years					
	1	2	3	4	5	More than 5
Laptops	4	6	12	5	1	0
PCs	40	42	36	44	12	6

(a) How many laptops are less than 4 years old?

(b) How many PCs does the school own?

(c) What is the relative frequency of:
  (i) 1 year old laptops
  (ii) 3 year old PCs
  (iii) machines older than 4 years?

9 In Deborah's boutique, a stocktaking check yields the following results.

	Size					
	10	12	14	16	18	20
Dresses	2	8	17	15	9	4
Skirts	3	5	9	9	2	1
Trousers	5	6	4	11	6	6

(a) Find the total number of each type of garment.

(b) Calculate the relative frequency of size 14 for dresses and skirts.

(c) Calculate the relative frequency of trousers in sizes greater than 12.

13.2 Probability

Learning intentions

The **probability** of an event is a measure of the likelihood of the event occurring.

Probability is the relative frequency of an event when the experiment is repeated sufficiently often.

$$\text{Probability (event)} = \frac{\text{number of times an event can occur}}{\text{total number of possible outcomes}}$$

Roll a die $\quad\quad\quad\quad P(3) = \frac{1}{6} \quad\quad\quad P(\text{even}) = \frac{3}{6} = \frac{1}{2}$

Toss a coin $\quad\quad\quad P(\text{head}) = \frac{1}{2}$

Pack of cards $\quad\quad P(\text{ace}) = \frac{4}{52} = \frac{1}{13}$

Probability ranges from 0 to 1.

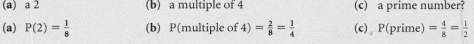

0	$\frac{1}{2}$	1
Event not possible	Equally likely events	Certain event

The total probability of all possible outcomes is 1.

Toss a coin $\quad\quad\quad\quad\quad\quad\quad\quad\quad$ Throw a die

$\quad\quad P(\text{head}) \;+\; P(\text{tail}) \quad\quad\quad\quad\quad P(1) \;+\; P(2) \;+\; P(3) \;+\; P(4) \;+\; P(5) \;+\; P(6)$

$=\quad\quad \frac{1}{2} \quad\;+\quad \frac{1}{2} \quad\quad\quad\quad\quad\; = \quad \frac{1}{6} \;+\; \frac{1}{6} \;+\; \frac{1}{6} \;+\; \frac{1}{6} \;+\; \frac{1}{6} \;+\; \frac{1}{6}$

$=\quad\quad 1 \quad\quad\quad\quad\quad\quad\quad\quad\quad\quad\; = \quad 1$

Example

For an eight sided spinner, what is the probability of

(**a**) a 2 $\quad\quad\quad\quad\quad\quad$ (**b**) a multiple of 4 $\quad\quad\quad\quad\quad$ (**c**) a prime number?

(**a**) $P(2) = \frac{1}{8}$ $\quad\quad\quad\quad$ (**b**) $P(\text{multiple of } 4) = \frac{2}{8} = \frac{1}{4}$ $\quad\quad$ (**c**) $P(\text{prime}) = \frac{4}{8} = \frac{1}{2}$

Exercise 13.2

 1 For each event listed, state whether its probability is nearer 0, $\frac{1}{2}$ or 1.

(**a**) winning the lottery $\quad\quad\quad\quad\quad\quad\quad\quad$ (**b**) a baby being a girl

(**c**) leaving school with an examination certificate $\quad\quad$ (**d**) a month without rain in Scotland

(**e**) the roulette ball lands on an even number.

2 Copy the diagram below and place each event at the appropriate place on the line.

Winning the toss

Being left handed

Throwing a six

Probability
$\frac{1}{2}$

0 $\quad\quad\quad\quad\quad\quad\quad\quad\quad\quad\quad\quad\quad\quad\quad\quad$ 1

Scotland winning the World Cup

The name of a month that has an *r* in it

3 When a six-sided die is rolled, what is the probability of:

(**a**) a 5 $\quad\quad\quad\quad\quad\quad\quad\quad\quad$ (**b**) an odd number

(**c**) a multiple of 3 $\quad\quad\quad\quad\quad\quad$ (**d**) a number less than 5?

4 Graham sold 100 raffle tickets for an Easter egg.
Jenny bought four tickets.

What is the probability that Jenny will win the egg?

5 A bag contains 1 black, 3 white and 5 red counters.

   (**a**) A counter is taken from the bag.
   What is the probability it will be white?

   (**b**) The counter is replaced in the bag and 3 blue ones added.
   If a counter is taken now, what is the probability it will be red?

6 A car dealership sold 8 white, 12 silver, 6 red and 3 black cars last month.
Myra bought one of these cars.
What is the probability she bought a car which is neither red nor black?

7 A lottery game uses red, white and blue balls, numbered from 1 to 10 in
each colour.

   (**a**) If a ball is drawn out what is the probability it will be
   (**i**) a 5   (**ii**) a red 5   (**iii**) a white even number?

   (**b**) Four balls are removed – white 2, white 3, red 5 and blue 6.
   Recalculate the probabilities in part (**a**).

8 The school sold 1200 raffle tickets and Elaine bought 20 of them. John
told her that her chance of winning the prize was less than 0·015. Was he
correct? Explain your answer.

9 Woganair airline recorded the following results for its planes.

Arrivals				
Early	On time	Up to 1 hour late	Up to 2 hours late	More than 2 hours late
25	123	32	14	24

   (**a**) On a Woganair flight, what is the probability of arriving on or before
   the expected arrival time?

   (**b**) What is the probability of arriving late?

   (**c**) Woganair claims that 70% of its planes are on time.
   Do you agree with this? Explain your answer.

10 In a survey of 400 tourists in a Spanish holiday resort, the following
results were obtained.

Nationality	On holiday for 1 week	On holiday for 2 weeks
Spanish	12	8
British	124	86
German	55	27
Dutch	16	72

On the basis of this survey what is the probability that:

(**a**) a tourist is (**i**) Spanish (**ii**) German?

(**b**) a tourist is on holiday for 2 weeks?

(**c**) a British tourist is on holiday for 1 week?

13.3 Combined probabilities

Learning intentions

Example

Michael has a white, a blue and a striped shirt. He has jeans, cords and chinos.
If he selects his clothes at random, calculate the probability that he will wear a white shirt with cords.

Tree diagram

W — J, C, Ch

B — J, C, Ch

St — J, C, Ch

Ordered list

WJ	WC	WCh
BJ	BC	BCh
StJ	StC	StCh

Random selection means all choices are equally likely.

There are 9 possible combinations.
The probability of a white shirt with cords is $\frac{1}{9}$.

Exercise 13.3

1 In Dorothy's wardrobe she has four dresses – red, white, blue and yellow. She has three pairs of shoes – black, brown and white.
Use a tree diagram to find the probability she will wear
(**a**) the red dress with black shoes
(**b**) the blue dress with either black or white shoes
(**c**) the white or yellow dress with black or brown shoes.

2 Tom rolls two dice. Use an ordered list to find the probability of rolling:
(**a**) two even numbers   (**b**) a 6 with an odd number
(**c**) an even number with a 1   (**d**) a total score greater than 8
(**e**) a total score between 5 and 10 (**f**) two prime numbers.

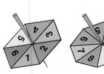

3 Carol has two spinners, one numbered 1 to 6 and the other 1 to 8. Find the probability of obtaining:
(**a**) an even and an odd number   (**b**) a total score less than 7
(**c**) a total score which is a multiple of 5 (**d**) two equal numbers.

4 To set the table for dinner Jim has a choice of bamboo, plastic or linen table mats, white or blue china, and glass, crystal or plastic glasses. Use a tree diagram to find the probability of:
(**a**) bamboo place mats, white china and crystal glasses
(**b**) plastic or linen place mats, blue china and plastic glasses
(**c**) crystal or plastic glasses

(**d**) nothing being plastic.

5 Elaine tosses three coins one after another.
Find the probability of:

(**a**) three heads   (**b**) two heads then a tail

(**c**) two tails and a head in any order.

6 Linda is making Christmas tree decorations. She has silver and gold ribbon, polystyrene shapes in the shape of a sphere, a pyramid and a cone, and red, white and blue glitter. Choosing each item at random, find the probability she will use:

(**a**) silver ribbon, a sphere and white glitter

(**b**) gold ribbon with red glitter

(**c**) a pyramid with red or white glitter.

7 In the flower shop bouquets are wrapped in paper or cellophane, tied with straw or ribbon, and labelled with a sticker, a tag or a card. If all items are selected at random, what is the probability that a bouquet will be wrapped with:

(**a**) paper and a tag

(**b**) cellophane, straw and either a sticker or a tag

(**c**) paper, ribbon and a card?

13.4 Expected frequency

Learning intentions

Example 1

Lesley tossed a coin fifty times.
How many times should she expect a head?

$P(\text{head}) = \frac{1}{2}$
Expected number of heads $= \frac{1}{2} \times 50 = 25$ She would expect **25** heads.

Example 2

For new drivers, the probability of having an accident in the first year of driving is 0·12 for males and 0·05 for females. For 300 male and 300 female drivers, how many accidents would be expected in the first year?

Males   0·12 × 300 = **36** accidents
Females   0·05 × 300 = **15** accidents

Expected value = probability × number of repetitions

Exercise 13.4

1 How many tails would you expect if you toss a coin

(**a**) 60 times   (**b**) 124 times   (**c**) 3000 times?

2 How many sixes would you expect if you roll a die:

(**a**) 12 times   (**b**) 60 times   (**c**) 420 times?

3 For a spinner numbered 1 to 5:

(**a**) What is the probability of obtaining an odd number?

(**b**) If the spinner is used 100 times, how many times would you expect

> Each number is equally likely.

an odd number?

4 The probability of a male baby is 0·51. For 2500 births, how many boys are expected?

5 Rutgers Football Club estimates the probability it will get a draw is 0·3. How many draws do they expect if they play:

(**a**) 10 games   (**b**) 30 games?

6 In the social subjects department last session, pupils picked subjects as follows:

    History   50   Modern studies   80   Geography   70

(**a**) Calculate the probabilities of pupils selecting each subject.

(**b**) If there are 180 pupils in the year group this session, how many are expected to choose each subject?

7 At Kirkdale High School, the probability of S4 pupils returning to S5 is 0·9, and for S5 returning to S6 it is 0·6.
If the current number in S4 is 190, and in S5 is 110, what numbers are expected next session in S5 and S6?

8 For a formal dinner, the chef uses the listed probabilities to make his preparations.

How many of each meal should he prepare for 60 people?

Menu choice	Probability
Steak	0·6
Fish	0·25
Pork	0·1
Vegetarian	0·05

Review exercise 13: Am I a successful learner?

1 A die was rolled 30 times and the results recorded.
Find the relative frequency of

(**a**) a 5   (**b**) a 2   (**c**) a 4 or 5   (**d**) a number less than 4

4	3	4	4	2	1
6	6	5	3	2	4
4	2	2	1	5	5
2	6	3	1	5	6
1	3	3	4	6	4

2 Sarah has the 13 clubs from a pack of cards.
What is the relative frequency of:

(**a**) odd numbers

(**b**) a face card

(**c**) a multiple of four?

3 Mr Murdoch has checked the contents of his jotter cupboard.

(**a**) How many jotters does he have in total?

(**b**) What is the relative frequency of A4 squared jotters?

(**c**) What is the relative frequency of plain jotters?

	A5	A4
Plain	22	15
Squared	42	33
Graph	6	12

4 Copy the probability scale below and place each event at the appropriate place on the line.

Probability

0              $\frac{1}{2}$ 1

| A number less than 3 on a die | | Losing the toss |

| Snow at the equator | | Leaving school |

5 Gus sold 120 raffle tickets for a cuddly toy. Aileen bought 8 tickets.
What is the probability she will win the toy?

6 A bag contains 6 blue, 5 red and 4 white marbles.
  (**a**) If a marble is pulled out of the bag, what is the probability it will be
      (**i**) blue   (**ii**) red or white   (**iii**) not white?
  (**b**) Two white marbles are removed from the bag.
      Recalculate the probabilities in part (**a**).

7 At Northern Railways, departure times are recorded.

Departures			
On time	Up to 5 minutes late	Up to 10 minutes late	More than 10 minutes late
84	26	32	48

  (**a**) What is the probability that a train departs on time?
  (**b**) What is the probability that a train leaves within 10 minutes of the departure time?
  (**c**) Northern Railways had a record of 34% of trains being more than ten minutes late. Has its record improved?

8 Tommy rolls two dice and records the combined results.
What is the probability of:
  (**a**) two equal numbers   (**b**) an even and an odd number
  (**c**) a total more than 9   (**d**) a 3 followed by an even number?

9 Denise's baby has a pink, a white and a yellow jacket, and a white and a yellow hat. If Denise selects her clothes at random, what is the probability she will wear:
  (**a**) a white jacket and hat
  (**b**) a yellow or pink jacket with a white hat?

10 If you roll a die 120 times, how often would you expect:
  (**a**) a 5   (**b**) an even number   (**c**) a number greater than 2?

11 At the Burns Supper, the probabilities for each choice of meal are

    Haggis   0·65
    Steak pie   0·3
    Quiche   0·05

If 120 tickets have been sold, how many of each meal should the cook prepare?

Summary 13: What I learned in this chapter.

Relative frequency

$$\text{Relative frequency} = \frac{\text{number of times an event occurs}}{\text{number of repetitions}}$$

A die is rolled 20 times

1 3 2 2 6 5 6 4 2 3
4 5 6 6 1 1 2 3 4 4

The relative frequency of an even number is $\frac{12}{20} = \frac{3}{5}$

Probability

$$\text{Probability} = \frac{\text{number of times an event can occur}}{\text{total number of possible outcomes}}$$

For an eight sided spinner the probability of a multiple of 4 is
P(multiple of 4) $= \frac{2}{8} = \frac{1}{4}$

Combined probabilities

Michael has a white, a blue and a striped shirt. He has jeans, cords and chinos.

Tree diagram

Ordered list

WJ	WC	WCh
BJ	BC	BCh
StJ	StC	StCh

If he selects his clothes at random, the probability that he will wear a white shirt with cords is $\frac{1}{9}$.

Expected frequency

$$\text{Expected value} = \text{probability} \times \text{number of repetitions}$$

Lesley tossed a coin 50 times.

P(head) $= \frac{1}{2}$
Expected number of heads $= \frac{1}{2} \times 50 = 25$ She would expect **25** heads.

Review 3

Exercise 3A

Scale drawing and tolerance

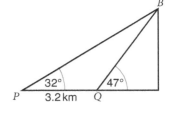

1 The scale of a map is 1 cm:3·5 km.
Write this as a representative fraction.

2 A weather balloon is spotted from two points P and Q on the ground.
P and Q are 3·2 kilometres apart. If the angles of elevation from each
point are 32° and 47° respectively, make a scale drawing and calculate the
height of the balloon.

3 A cargo ship is on a bearing of 298° from Colmais and 039° from
Borlogne. Colmais is 24 kilometres due east of Borlogne.
Use a scale drawing to calculate its distance from Borlogne.

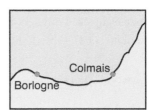

4 Find the maximum and minimum possible values for each
measurement.

(**a**) $7 \pm 0{\cdot}5$ m   (**b**) $18{\cdot}3 \pm 0{\cdot}1$ kg   (**c**) $0{\cdot}02 \pm 0{\cdot}003$ tonnes

Trigonometry

5 Calculate the value of x in each triangle.

(**a**) 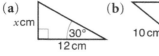   (**b**) 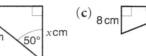   (**c**) 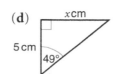   (**d**)   (**e**)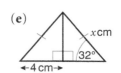

6 Calculate the value of x in each triangle.

(**a**) 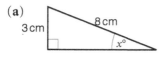   (**b**) 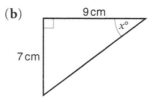   (**c**)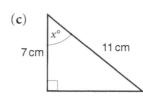

7 From a ground level observation point, the top of a flag pole has an
angle of elevation of 62°. If the observation point is 88 metres from the
base of the pole, what is the height of the pole?

8 A ship sails on a bearing of 064° for 75 kilometres.
How far east is the ship from its starting point?

9 Calculate the length of the base of this triangle.

Statistics 1

10 For an eight sided spinner, calculate the probability of
   (**a**) a 6   (**b**) an even number   (**c**) a multiple of 3.

11 A bag contains 3 red, 4 white and 5 blue marbles.
   (**a**) One marble is drawn at random. What is the probability it is blue?
   (**b**) If a blue marble is drawn out, what is the probability the next one drawn is white?

12 The pupils in 3W collate these results for the class.

Number in family	2	3	4	5	6	7
Number of pupils	4	7	9	6	3	1

What is the relative frequency of
(**a**) a family of 5
(**b**) a family smaller than 4
(**c**) a family with an even number of members?

13 Sarah rolls a die and spins a 5 sided spinner.
What is the probability of
(**a**) a 6 and a red   (**b**) an even and a green
(**c**) a prime and purple or blue?

14 For 12 year old girls the probability of size 3 shoe is 0·28. In a year group which has 75 girls of this age, how many would you expect to have size 3 shoes?

Review exercise 3B (cumulative)

1 Given that $p = -2$, $q = 6$ and $r = 1$, calculate the value of each expression.
   (**a**) $5p - 4q$ (**b**) $\dfrac{pqr}{p^2}$ (**c**) $\dfrac{2p^2 - 6r}{r^2}$ (**d**) $\dfrac{3pq^2}{q - p}$

2 Simplify:
   (**a**) $4x + 5y - x$ (**b**) $2x^2 - 3x + 5x^2 + 7$
   (**c**) $5pq - 2p + pq - p$ (**d**) $3x^3 + x^2 - x^3 + 3 - x^2 - 1$

3 Multiply out the brackets and simplify:
   (**a**) $4(y - x) - 3(y + 2x)$ (**b**) $10 - 2(4 - 2y)$

4 Solve each equation:
   (**a**) $2x - 3 = 13$ (**b**) $15 = 5 - 10y$
   (**c**) $2q - 1 = 3q + 5$ (**d**) $6 - 4m = 10 + 8m$

5 Solve:
   (**a**) $5(x - 3) + 2 = 12$ (**b**) $17 - 2(4 - y) = 15$
   (**c**) $2(3x + 1) = 5 + 3(3x - 1)$ (**d**) $23 - 3(2m + 1) = 4(9 - m) - 30$

6 Solve:
   (**a**) $\frac{1}{6}x = 2(26 - x)$ (**b**) $\dfrac{x - 5}{7} = \dfrac{x + 3}{11}$

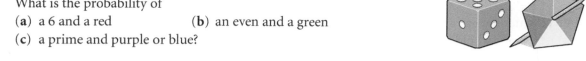

7 The perimeter of the rectangle is 46 centimetres.
Find the value of x.

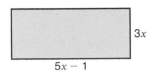

8 Solve:
  (**a**) $3m - 1 < m + 7$ (**b**) $4(p + 6) > 2(14 - 3p)$

9 Find the possible values of x if the area of the rectangle is greater than or equal to the area of the square.

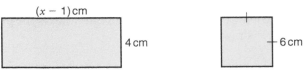

10 Find:
  (**a**) 6% of £16   (**b**) $33\frac{1}{3}$% of 72·3 kg   (**c**) 17·5% of £104

11 Sue's chicken gained 54 grammes in one week. If the chicken weighed 1·32 kilogrammes to begin with, what is its percentage weight gain?

12 In a sale all prices were reduced by 15%. Calculate the original price of each item if the sale prices were:
  (**a**) Purse £21.25   (**b**) Bag £66.30

13 Michael changed £75 into euros and received 105€.
What was the rate of exchange?

14 A 6 kilogramme bag of cat food will feed 3 cats for 12 days.
  (**a**) How long would the food last if there are 4 cats?
  (**b**) How much food is required for 9 cats to last 18 days?

15 For each pair of similar shapes, calculate the scale factor and the value of x.
  (**a**)

  (**b**)

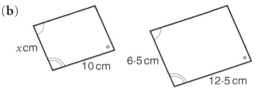

16 (**a**) Prove that these triangles are similar.
   (**b**) Find the values of x and y.

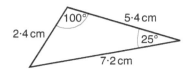

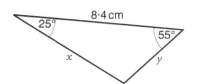

17 Find the values of x and y.
  (**a**)

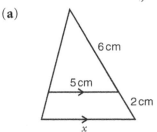

  (**b**)

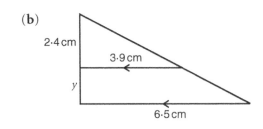

18 This pair of photographs is similar. Find the area of the larger.

4 cm

5 cm

8 cm²

19 Two carafes are similar. The smaller carafe has diameter 15 centimetres and volume 810 millilitres.
If the larger carafe has diameter 20 centimetres, what is its volume?

20 Calculate the value of *d* in each triangle.

(**a**)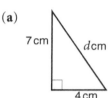

7 cm

d cm

4 cm

(**b**)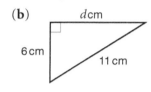

d cm

6 cm

11 cm

(**c**)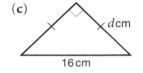

d cm

16 cm

21 The vertices of a triangle are $P(2, 2)$, $Q(7, 7)$ and $R(4, 10)$.
Prove that triangle PQR is right angled at Q.

22 In the cuboid, calculate the length of the space diagonal OQ.

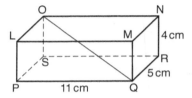

O   N

L   M   4 cm

S   R

5 cm

P   11 cm   Q

23 Find the mean, median and mode of each set of data.
(**a**) 6, 7, 9, 3, 3, 4, 6, 6, 8   (**b**) 14, 14, 24, 16, 9, 14, 11, 10

24 The number of pupils absent from each class on the worst
day of a flu epidemic was recorded.
(**a**) Draw a dot plot for this data.
(**b**) How many classes had more than 10 absent pupils?

5	11	6	8	10	12
11	7	7	10	9	2
9	12	3	5	9	9
5	9	8	12	12	7
10	8	15	3	7	8
8	7	12	4	5	6

25 The stem and leaf diagram shows the ages of
22 people attending a wedding in a hotel.
The figures below show the ages of another
group attending a birthday party.

30	42	50	36	50	38	44
31	39	56	42	40	31	39
35	44	29	42	49	37	49

(**a**) Copy and complete the diagram to form a
back to back stem and leaf diagram.
(**b**) Find the median age of each group.
(**c**) Find the quartiles of each group.
(**d**) Compare the two groups.

Ages

3	0 1 1 5 7
4	2 6 3
5	3 3 8 8
6	0 1 2 3 4 5 5
7	1 5 9

6 | 0 represents age 60 $n = 22$

26 Expand and simplify:

(a) $2b(3 - 4b) + 4b^2$

(b) $(5x - 2)(3x + 5)$

(c) $3(2m - 5)^2$

(d) $(4x + 1)^2 - (3x - 2)^2$

(e) $4(2y + 1)(2y^2 - y + 3)$

27 Solve:

(a) $(x + 2)^2 = x^2 + 7x - 5$

(b) $(p - 3)^2 = (p + 4)^2 + 21$

28 Evaluate each formula.

(a) $w = xy - v^2$ when $x = 5, y = -3$ and $v = -4$

(b) $m = \dfrac{n^2 - k}{p}$ when $n = 4, k = -5$ and $p = 1\cdot2$

29 Change the subject of each formula to the required variable.

(a) $V = IR,$ to R

(b) $v = u + at,$ to a

(c) $s = ut + \frac{1}{2}at^2,$ to a

(d) $r = s + \dfrac{t^2}{q},$ to q

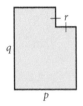

30 (a) Find a formula for the area of this shape.

(b) Evaluate the formula if $p = 8$ cm, $q = 11$ cm and $r = 2$ cm.

31 A lighthouse is on bearing 205° from HMS Arran and 305° from HMS Islay. HMS Arran is 120 kilometres due north of HMS Islay. Use a scale drawing to find the distance from the lighthouse to HMS Arran.

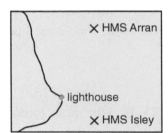

32 Calculate the value of d in each triangle.

(a)

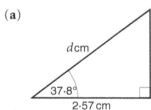

(b)

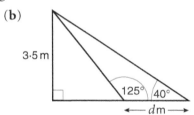

33 In an experiment tossing a 50p coin, the relative frequency of a head was found to be $0\cdot52$.
If the coin is now tossed 300 times more, how many tails would you expect?

34 In her car showroom Miranda has 4 silver, 2 black and 6 red cars.

(a) If a customer picked a car at random, what is the probability it would be
(i) silver   (ii) not black?

(b) If the bought car was silver, what is the probability that the next car bought was
(i) also silver   (ii) red?

14 Circle geometry

14.1 Diameters and chords

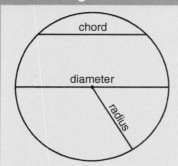

A **chord** is a straight line which joins two points on the circumference of a circle.

A diameter of a circle is a chord which passes through the centre. It is an axis of symmetry.

A radius is a straight line from the centre to any point on the circumference.

Exercise 14.1

You need compasses and a ruler.

1 (a) Draw a circle with centre O and radius 3 centimetres.
   (b) Draw an axis of symmetry on your circle and label it AB.
   (c) Draw a chord MN so that AB is **still** an axis of symmetry.
   (d) If MN and AB intersect at P,
       (i) name a line equal in length to MP
       (ii) what size is angle MPA?

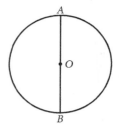

2 (a) Draw a circle with centre O and radius 3 centimetres.
   (b) Draw a chord RS on your circle.
   (c) Draw a line XY which is an axis of symmetry for your diagram.
   (d) If RS and XY intersect at T (i) what is the image of point R?
                                          (ii) name a line equal in length to TS
                                          (iii) what type of angle is XTR?

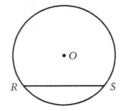

3 (a) Draw a circle with centre O and radius 3 centimetres.
   (b) Draw a diameter GH.
   (c) Draw a chord AB so that your diagram is **still** symmetrical.
   (d) Draw the radii OA and OB.
   (e) If AB and GH intersect at M,
       (i) name a line equal to OA
       (ii) name a line equal to AM
       (iii) what type of triangle is OAB?
       (iv) name an angle equal to angle AOM
       (v) what size is angle HMB?

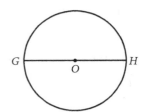

4 Draw a circle, centre O, radius 3 centimetres with a chord AB equal in length to the radius.
   Draw the radii OA and OB. What type of triangle is OAB?

14.2 Perpendicular bisectors of chords

Learning intentions

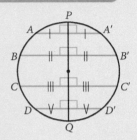

Diameter PQ is an axis of symmetry.

Points A,B,C and D have images A', B', C' and D' under reflection in PQ.

Chords AA', BB', CC' and DD' are perpendicular to the diameter and are **bisected** by the diameter.

If a chord is drawn so that the diameter is an axis of symmetry then:

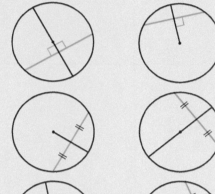

- a diameter or radius which is perpendicular to a chord bisects it

- a diameter or radius which bisects a chord is perpendicular to it

- the **perpendicular bisector** of a chord passes through the centre.

Exercise 14.2

For this exercise you need a ruler and a set square or protractor.

1 Chord GH is perpendicular to diameter EF.

(a) Name a line equal in length to GK.

(b) If EG is 5 centimetres, what length is EH?

(c) If $\angle GEH = 42°$, what size is $\angle KEH$?

(d) What type of quadrilateral is $EGFH$?

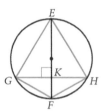

2 O is the centre of the circle and D is the mid-point of chord AB. Find the size of   (a) $\angle ODB$ (b) $\angle AOB$

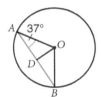

3 In the diagram, chord RS is perpendicular to diameter JK. $JS = 7$ centimetres, $RT = 5$ centimetres, $TK = 1.5$ centimetres and $\angle JST = 44°$.
Sketch the diagram and mark on it the length of each side and the size of each angle.

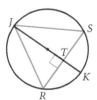

4 In the diagram, chord FE is bisected by diameter CD.
$\angle FCE = 78°$ and $\angle FDE = 102°$.
Sketch the diagram and mark on it the size of each angle.

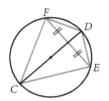

5 Draw a circle, centre O.
Draw two parallel chords in the circle, VW and XY, as shown.
Draw the axis of symmetry on your diagram.

(a) Name a chord equal in length to VX.

(b) Name an angle equal to $\angle VXY$.

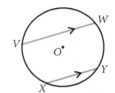

6 Draw a circle of radius 5 centimetres.
Draw any two chords in the circle.
Draw the perpendicular bisector of each chord.
Mark T, the point of intersection of the perpendicular bisectors.
Describe where you think T is located.

7 Draw around a circular object. Do not use a pair of compasses.
Draw two chords in approximately the positions shown.
Use perpendicular bisectors to find the exact position of the centre of the circle.

14.3 Pythagoras and chords

Learning intentions

Example 1

Find the length of EB

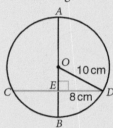

In triangle ODE
$OD^2 = OE^2 + ED^2$
$10^2 = OE^2 + 8^2$
$100 = OE^2 + 64$
$36 = OE^2$
$OE = 6\,cm$
So $EB = 10 - 6$
$= 4\,cm$

Example 2

The diagram shows the cross section of an oil tanker.
The surface of the oil measures 2·8 metres across.
Find the depth of the oil.

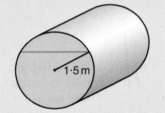

$OD^2 = OE^2 + ED^2$
$1·5^2 = OE^2 + 1·4^2$
$2·25 = OE^2 + 1·96$
$0·29 = OE^2$
$OE = 0·54$
$EB = OE + OB$
$= 0·54 + 1·5$
$= 2·04$
The depth is **2·04 m**

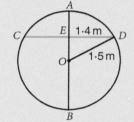

Exercise 14.3

For each question in this exercise sketch and annotate a diagram.

1 The circle with centre O has a chord $MN = 24$ cm
MN meets the diameter AB at K and is perpendicular to it.
The radius is 13 cm.
Calculate the length of   (**a**) OK (**b**) KB.

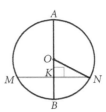

2 In the circle with centre O the diameter PQ bisects the chord XY.
The radius is 20 centimetres and the chord is 32 centimetres long.
Calculate

(**a**) the distance of the chord from the centre

(**b**) the length of PR.

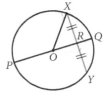

3 A circle, centre O, has diameter $EF = 30$ centimetres.
The chord GH is 9 centimetres from the centre and perpendicular to EF.
Calculate the length of chord GH.

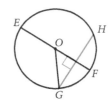

4 In the diagram, if $OT = 25$ mm and $TU = 24$ mm, calculate:
(**a**) the length of OV
(**b**) the length of VR
(**c**) the area of triangle RTU.

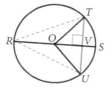

5 In the diagram, chord CD is 48 metres long and bisected by diameter AB.
The chord is 5 metres from the centre O.
Calculate the length of diameter AB.

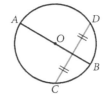

6 In the diagram diameter PQ is perpendicular to chord RS.
The radius of the circle is 2 metres and RT is 1·6 metres
Calculate the lengths of:
(**a**) OT (**b**) PT (**c**) PR.

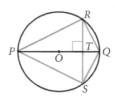

7 A chord AB is 28 centimetres long and 6 centimetres from the centre of
a circle.
Calculate the length of the radius of the circle.

8 In a circle centre O, the radius is 10 centimetres.
Chord KL is 3 centimetres from O and chord MN is 5 centimetres
from O.
Calculate, to three significant figures, the lengths of   (**a**) KL (**b**) MN.

9 The cross-section of a cylindrical
tanker shows fuel partly filling the tank.
The surface of the fuel is 3 metres wide
and the radius of the tank is 2 metres.
Calculate the depth of fuel in the tank.

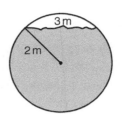

10 A flower bed is a rectangle with curved ends.
It has a total length of 17·4 metres with the rectangular part 12·8 metres long.
Each curved end is an arc of a circle with radius 4·8 metres and centre *C*.
Calculate the breadth of the flower bed.

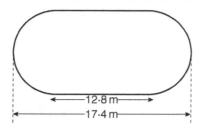
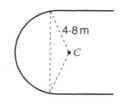

11 A large rubber ball, used for exercising in the gym, has lost
some air and is now sitting with a flat section on the floor.
When inflated the radius of the ball was 54 centimetres but
it has now shrunk to 39 centimetres with the length of the
flat part on the floor 25 centimetres.
By how much has the height of the ball gone down?

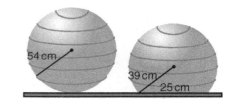

12 A table cut from a circular piece of wood is fixed to a
wall by a hinge 96 centimetres long.
It is supported by a leg which can be removed to allow
the table top to swing down and lie flat against the wall
when not in use.
The radius of the circular part is 52 centimetres.
How high up the wall does the hinge have to be fixed so
that the top can lie against the wall without catching on
the floor?

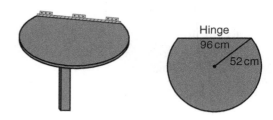
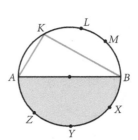

14.4 Measuring angles

Exercise 14.4

1 (a) Draw a circle of radius 5 centimetres.

   (b) Mark a diameter *AB*.

   (c) Mark the parts *K*, *L*, *M*, *X*, *Y* and *Z* on the circumference as shown.

   (d) Draw angles *AKB*, *ALB*, *AMB*, *AXB*, *AYB* and *AZB*.

   (e) Measure each of these angles.
       Record your answers in the table.

   (f) Copy and complete this statement.
       The angle in a semi-circle is ☐ degrees.

   (g) Draw three circles of your own to test your conjecture.

Angle	Size
$A\hat{K}B$	
$A\hat{L}B$	
$A\hat{M}B$	

14.5 Angles in a semi circle

Learning intentions

Every angle in a semicircle is a right angle.

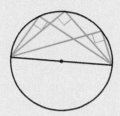

This may be proved as follows:

Triangles AOC and COB are isosceles.

Let $\angle AOC = x^\circ$

So $\angle BOC = (180 - x)^\circ$

and $\angle OCB = \dfrac{180 - (180 - x)^\circ}{2}$

$= \dfrac{x^\circ}{2}$

$\angle OCA = \dfrac{180^\circ - x^\circ}{2}$

$\angle ACB = \angle OCB + \angle OCA$

$= \dfrac{x^\circ}{2} + \dfrac{180^\circ - x^\circ}{2}$

$= \dfrac{x^\circ + 180^\circ - x^\circ}{2}$

$= \dfrac{180^\circ}{2} = \mathbf{90^\circ}$

Hence every angle in a semicircle is a right angle.

Example

Calculate the size of angle m°.

$ADB = 90^\circ$ (angle in a semicircle)

$DAB = (180 - 90 - 54)^\circ$

$m^\circ = \mathbf{36^\circ}$

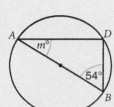

Exercise 14.5

1 Calculate the size of the marked angle in each triangle.

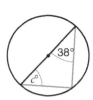

2 In each diagram, O is the centre of the circle.
Copy each diagram and mark the sizes of all the angles.

(a)

(b)

(c)

(d)

(e)

(f)

3 Draw two diameters *POQ* and *ROT* in a circle.
What shape is *PTQR*? Explain your answer.

4 Calculate the marked angle in each figure.

(a)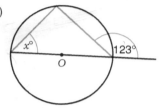

(b)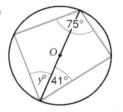

(c)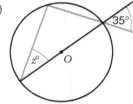

(d)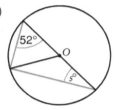

(e)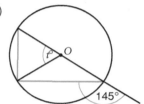

(f)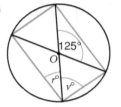

14.6   Tangents and diameters

Learning intentions

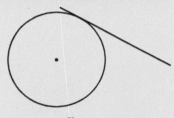

A **tangent** to a circle is a straight line which touches the circle at only one point.

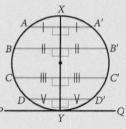

If diameter *XY* is an axis of symmetry: and tangent *PQ* is parallel to the bisected chords then the tangent is perpendicular to the diameter at the point of contact

The angle between a tangent and the radius at the point of contact is 90°.

Example

MN is a tangent to the circle meeting the
radius *OL* at *L*.
Find the size of

(a) ∠*NOL*   (b) ∠*OML*.

Since radius *OL* is perpendicular to tangent *MN*
angles *OLN* and *OLM* are right angles.

(a) ∠*NOL* = (180 − 90 − 25)°
            = **65°**

(b) ∠*OML* = (180 − 90 − 60)°
            = **30°**

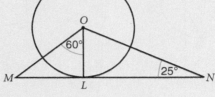

Exercise 14.6

1 *PQ* is a tangent to the circle meeting the radius *OR* at *R*.
Find the size of:

(a) ∠*OQR*   (b) ∠*POR*   (c) ∠*POQ*

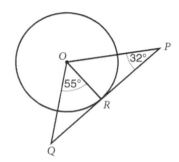

2 *XY* and *XZ* are tangents to the circle.
OY and *OZ* are radii.

(a) What type of quadrilateral is *XYOZ*?

(b) Find the sizes of these angles:
      (i) ∠*YXO*   (ii) ∠*OYZ*   (iii) ∠*ZOX*

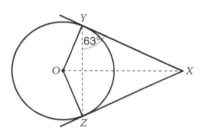

3 *PR* and *QS* are tangents at opposite ends of diameter *QP*.
Find *a*, *b* and *c*.

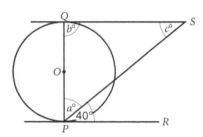

4 Find the size of all the missing angles.

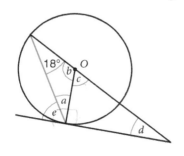
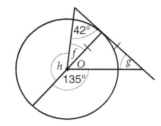
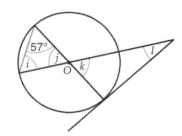

5 The circle with diameters AB and CD
has tangents PQ, QR, RS and SP.
Explain why $PQRS$ is a rhombus.

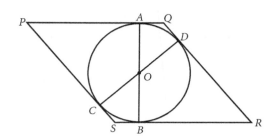

14.7 Pythagoras' theorem and circles

Learning intentions

Example 1
Find the length of RT

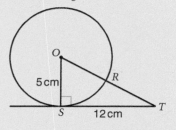

In triangle OST
$OT^2 = OS^2 + ST^2$
$OT^2 = 5^2 + 12^2$
$OT^2 = 25 + 144$
$OT^2 = 169$
$OT = 13$ cm
So **RT = 13 − 5 cm = 8 cm**

Example 2
Calculate the radius of the circle

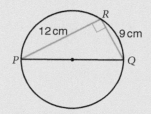

In triangle PQR
$PQ^2 = PR^2 + RQ^2$
$PQ^2 = 12^2 + 9^2$
$PQ^2 = 144 + 81$
$PQ^2 = 225$
$PQ = 15$ cm
So **radius = 7·5 cm**

Exercise 14.7

1 Tangent PQ meets the circle with centre O at T.
OT and PT are both 7 centimetres.
Calculate the length of OP.

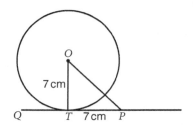

2 XY and XZ are tangents to the circle with centre O
and Y and Z are the points of contact.
The radius is 9 centimetres and the length of XY is
14 centimetres.

(**a**) What shape is $XYOZ$?

(**b**) Calculate the length of diagonal OX.

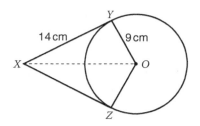

3 *ST* is a common tangent to the circles.
The circles touch at *T*, which is the point of contact
for both circles. *OS* = 7·5 cm, *CS* = 8·9 cm
and *ST* = 6 cm.
Calculate the distance between the centres of
the circles.

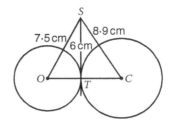

4 The circles with centres *M* and *N*
both have a radius of 11 centimetres.
P and *Q* are the points of contact
for *PQ*, which is a tangent to both circles.

(**a**) What shape is *PQNM*?

(**b**) Calculate the length of diagonal *MQ*.

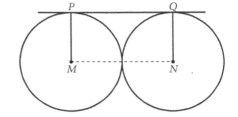

5 *PQ* is a diameter of the circle with *R* and *S* points
on the circumference so that *PS* = *QS*.

(**a**) Calculate the length of *PQ*.

(**b**) Hence calculate the length of *PS*.

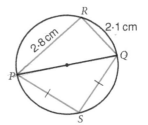

6 *DEFG* is a square with its vertices on the
circumference of a circle.
If the length of a side of the square is 15 centimetres,
Calculate the radius of the circle.

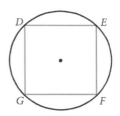

7 The semicircular arch of an old bridge is under repair and has to be
supported by a triangular construction of metal girders.
Calculate the length of the horizontal girder if both sloping girders are
4·5 metres.

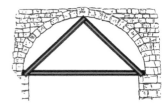

8 A strip of this pattern has been used as a border for a light shade.

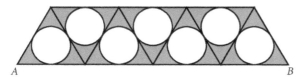

The sides of the equilateral triangles are tangents to the circles.
The radius of each circle is 2·4 centimetres and the distance
from the centre to a vertex of the triangle is 5·1 centimetres.
Calculate the length of the strip from *A* to *B*.

14.8 Trigonometry and circles

Learning intentions

Since some of the properties of circles involve right angled triangles, trigonometry may be used to calculate lengths of sides and sizes of angles.

Example

(a) Find the length of EB

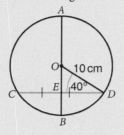

(b) Find the length of RT

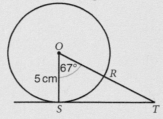

(c) Calculate angle RPQ

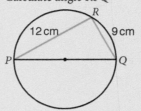

(a) $\angle OED = 90°$

$\sin 40° = \dfrac{OE}{10}$

$OE = 10 \sin 40°$

$OE = 6{\cdot}4\,\text{cm}$

$EB = 10 - 6{\cdot}4$

$\mathbf{EB = 3{\cdot}6\,cm}$

(b) $\angle OST = 90°$

$\cos 67° = \dfrac{5}{OT}$

$OT \cos 67° = 5$

$OT = \dfrac{5}{\cos 67°}$

$OT ≈ 12{\cdot}8$

$RT = 12{\cdot}8 - 5$

$\mathbf{RT = 7{\cdot}8\,cm}$

(c) $\angle PRQ = 90°$

$\tan \angle RPQ = \dfrac{9}{12}$

$= 0{\cdot}75$

$\mathbf{\angle RPQ = 37°}$

Exercise 14.8

1 Calculate the length of:

(a) OM

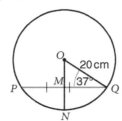

(b) VW

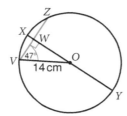

(c) OT

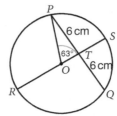

2 Calculate the length of:

(a) BD

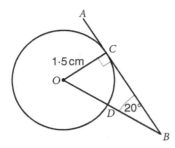

(b) RQ

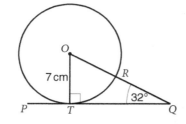

(c) QN

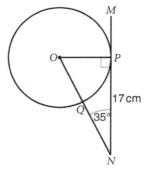

3 Calculate the length of:

(a) *CB*

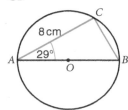

(b) *PQ*

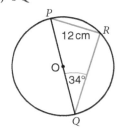

(c) *ZY*

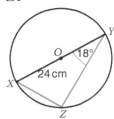

4 Calculate :

(a) angle *OQR*

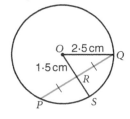

(b) angle *OST*

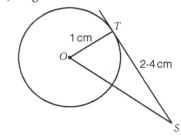

(c) angle *BAC*

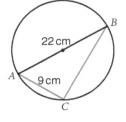

5 The circle with centre *O* has radius 12 centimetres.
PQ is a diameter.
R and *S* are points on the circumference so that *RQ* is parallel to *OS* and
$\angle PQR = 60°$.

(a) Find the length of *QS*.

(b) Calculate the length of *PR*.

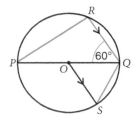

6 *PR* is a diameter of the circle with centre *O*
and radius 9 centimetres.
OM is perpendicular to chord *PQ*.
Calculate the length of

(a) *PQ*   (b) *OM*

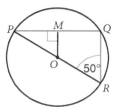

Coursework task

Presentation Pack of Golf Balls

A company is considering various ways of packaging one dozen golf balls. Your task in parts **1** to **4** is to calculate the dimensions of the box required for each design. In each case give your answer to the nearest necessary millimetre. The diameter of each golf ball is taken to be 44 mm for a comfortable fit.

1 Rectangular design (plan view)

Find the internal dimensions of the box required.

2 Equilateral triangular design

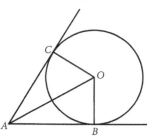

Golf ball at
bottom left vertex.

(a) Write down the size of angle *BAC*.

(b) Calculate the length of *AB*.

(c) Find the internal dimensions of the box required.

3 Rhombic design (made up of two equilateral triangles)

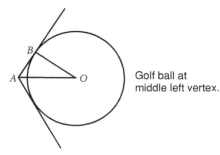

Golf ball at
middle left vertex.

(a) Write down the size of angle *OAB*.

(b) Calculate the length of *AB*.

(c) Find the internal dimensions of the box required.

4 Circular design

Two touching golf balls with centres *A* and *B*.

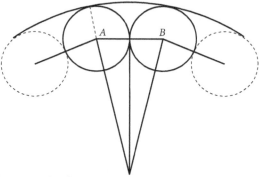

(a) Find the size of angle *AOB*.

(b) Calculate the length of *OA*.

(c) Find the internal dimensions of the box required.

5 The company decides on the circular design. As an introductory
offer they decide to put an inner ring of free balls. Find how
many balls could fit in this inner ring.

Review exercise 14: Am I a successful learner?

1 In the diagram, the chord *MN* is perpendicular to diameter *KL*.

(a) Find the length of: (i) *PN*   (ii) *MK*

(b) Find the size of: (i) ∠*KMP*   (ii) ∠*MKP*

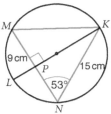

2 *O* is the centre of the circle.
M is the mid-point of chord *PQ*.
Find the size of   (a) ∠*OMQ*   (b) ∠*POQ*

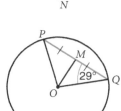

3 Calculate the sizes of the marked angles in each diagram.

(a) 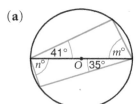   (b) 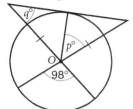   (c)

4 *AB* and *CD* are tangents to the circle with centre *O*.
A and *C*, the points of contact, are the ends of a diameter.
Find the sizes of angles *a*, *b* and *c*.

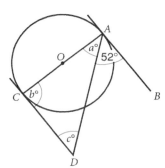

5 The circles with centres *O* and *C* touch at *T*.
TP is a common tangent.
PO = 2·6 centimetres, *PT* = 2·4 centimetres and
PC = 3 centimetres.
Calculate the distance between the centres of the circles.

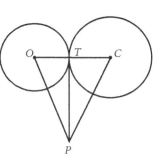

6 The sides of the square are tangents to the circle with
centre *O*.
If the radius of the circle is 7 centimetres calculate
the length of the diagonals of the square.

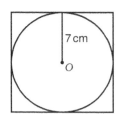

7 While under construction, a semicircular arch is supported by wooden beams.

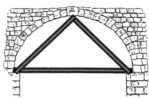

If the sloping beams are 5·6 metres and 6·2 metres
Calculate

(**a**) the length of the horizontal beam

(**b**) the angles between the beams.

8 In a circle, chord *PQ* is 34 centimetres long and 9 centimetres from the centre.
Calculate the radius of the circle.

9 Find the length of *EB*.

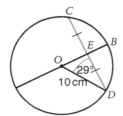

10 *ST* is a tangent to the circle.
Calculate the length of *RT*.

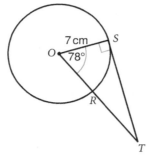

11 *PQ* is a diameter of the circle.
Calculate $\angle RPQ$.

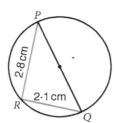

Summary 14: What I learned in this chapter.

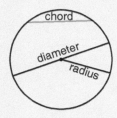

chord – joins two points on the circumference
diameter – passes through the centre
radius – line from the centre to any point on the circumference

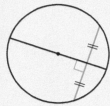

The perpendicular bisector of a chord passes through the centre.

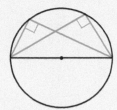

Every angle in a semicircle is a right angle.

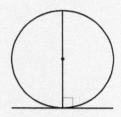

A tangent is perpendicular to a diameter or radius at the point of contact.

With right angled triangles, Pythagoras' theorem and trigonometry can be used to find lengths of sides and sizes of angles.

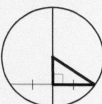

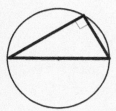

15 Simultaneous equations

15.1 Simultaneous events

Exercise 15.1

1 (a) Eilidh bought a CD and a DVD for an overall cost of £10.
Copy and continue the list of possible costs for each item.

CD cost	DVD cost	Total cost
£1	£9	£10
£2		£10

(b) Is it possible to state with certainty the cost of a CD and the cost of a DVD? Explain your answer.

(c) In the same shop, the total cost of a CD and two DVDs was £14.
Copy and continue the list of possible costs for each item.

CD cost	DVD cost	Total cost
£1	£6.50	£14
		£14

(d) Examine the lists in **(a)** and **(c)**.
Which are the only costs which match both lists?

(e) What was the cost of a **(i)** a CD **(ii)** a DVD?

2 (a) The cost of 2 calculators and 2 geometry sets is £12.
Copy and continue the list of possible costs for each item.

Calculators cost	Geometry sets cost	Total cost
£1	£5	£12
		£12

(b) Alastair paid £20 for 4 calculators and 2 geometry sets.
Copy and continue the following list of the possible cost of each.

Calculators cost	Geometry sets cost	Total cost
£3	£4	£20
		£20

(c) Examine both lists. What was the cost of
(i) a calculator **(ii)** a geometry set?

3 The cost of entry to a leisure centre for 1 adult and 2 children is £7.
The cost of entry for 1 adult and 3 children is £9.
Find the cost for 1 child and for 1 adult.

4 For each of the following different leisure centres find the cost for 1 adult and for 1 child.

(a)

Total cost £9

Total cost £8

(b)

Total cost £9

Total cost £10

(c)

Total cost £9

Total cost £12

(d)

Total cost £15

Total cost £14

15.2 Solving by elimination

Learning intentions

At a leisure centre, the cost for 1 adult and 2 children is £7. If this is the only information given, it is impossible to find a unique answer.

A list of possible costs is shown.

$a + 2c = 7$		
a	c	total
7	0	7
6	0·50	7
5	1	7
4	1·50	7
3	2	7
...	...	7

Total cost £7

If the cost for 1 adult and 3 children is £9, it is again impossible to find a unique answer.

A list of possible costs is shown.

$a + 3c = 9$		
a	c	total
9	0	9
...	...	9
6	1	9
...	...	9
3	2	9
...	...	9

Total cost £9

However, notice that there is only one value for a and one value for c which make both statements true at the same time: adult cost = £3 and child cost = £2

Solving two equations at the same time is called solving **simultaneous equations**.
Any pair of simultaneous equations can be solved by making lists in this manner.
Making and examining lists can be very time-consuming.

However, subtracting equations may eliminate one variable.

Example 1

Solve these equations simultaneously to find the adult cost and the child cost.

$$a + 3c = 9$$
$$a + 2c = 7$$

$$a + 3c = 9 \qquad ①$$
$$a + 2c = 7 \qquad ②$$

Subtract $\qquad c = 2$ $\boxed{a \text{ is eliminated}}$

Substitute for c in equation ①
$$a + 3c = 9$$
$$a + 6 = 9$$
$$a = 3$$

Check using equation ②
$$\text{L.H.S.} = a + 2c$$
$$= 3 + 4$$
$$= 7 = \text{R.H.S.}$$

Adult cost is **£3**, child cost is **£2**

Example 2

Solve these equations simultaneously.

$$4x + 3y = 11$$
$$x + 3y = 5$$

$$4x + 3y = 11 \qquad ①$$
$$x + 3y = 5 \qquad ②$$

Subtract $\quad 3x \quad = 6$ $\boxed{y \text{ is eliminated}}$
$$x \quad = 2$$

Substitute for x in equation ②
$$x + 3y = 5$$
$$2 + 3y = 5$$
$$3y = 3$$
$$y = 1$$

Check using equation ①
$$\text{L.H.S.} = 4x + 3y$$
$$= 8 + 3$$
$$= 11 = \text{R.H.S.}$$

$$x = 2 \text{ and } y = 1$$

Exercise 15.2

Solve the following simultaneous equations by elimination.

1 $2a + 3c = 9$
   $2a + 2c = 8$

2 $2a + 2c = 10$
   $2a + c = 9$

3 $4a + 3c = 15$
   $4a + 2c = 14$

4 $2a + 5c = 22$
   $a + 5c = 16$

5 $2x + y = 9$
   $x + y = 5$

6 $2x + 2y = 16$
   $2x + y = 13$

7 $4x + 2y = 12$
   $x + 2y = 6$

8 $3x + y = 15$
   $x + y = 7$

15.3 Elimination: adding

Learning intentions

Subtracting may not always eliminate a variable. Try adding.

Example

Solve each pair of simultaneous equations algebraically.

(**a**) $x + y = 12$
   $x - y = 2$

(**b**) $3a + 2b = 5$
   $2a - 2b = 10$

(**a**)
$$\begin{aligned} x + y &= 12 \quad ① \\ x - y &= 2 \quad ② \end{aligned}$$

Add $\begin{aligned} 2x &= 14 \\ x &= 7 \end{aligned}$ y is eliminated

Substitute for x in equation ①
$$\begin{aligned} x + y &= 12 \\ 7 + y &= 12 \\ y &= 5 \end{aligned}$$

Check using equation ②
$$\begin{aligned} \text{L.H.S.} &= x - y \\ &= 7 - 5 \\ &= 2 = \text{R.H.S.} \\ x &= \mathbf{7} \text{ and } y = \mathbf{5} \end{aligned}$$

(**b**)
$$\begin{aligned} 3a + 2b &= 5 \quad ① \\ 2a - 2b &= 10 \quad ② \end{aligned}$$

Add $\begin{aligned} 5a &= 15 \\ a &= 3 \end{aligned}$ b is eliminated

Substitute for a in equation ①
$$\begin{aligned} 3a + 2b &= 5 \\ 9 + 2b &= 5 \\ 2b &= -4 \\ b &= -2 \end{aligned}$$

Check using equation ②
$$\begin{aligned} \text{L.H.S.} &= 2a - 2b \\ &= 6 - (-4) \\ &= 10 = \text{R.H.S.} \\ a &= \mathbf{3} \text{ and } b = \mathbf{-2} \end{aligned}$$

Exercise 15.3

Solve each pair of simultaneous equations algebraically.

1 $a + b = 4$
   $a - b = 2$

2 $a + c = 6$
   $a - c = 0$

3 $e - 3f = 9$
   $e + 3f = 3$

4 $p + 4q = 13$
   $p - 4q = -3$

5 $2x + y = 4$
   $-2x - 3y = -4$

6 $x - 2y = -8$
   $x + 2y = 2$

7 $5x + 4y = -13$
   $6x - 4y = 2$

8 $-3x + 4y = 7$
   $3x + y = -2$

9 $2a + 3b = 16$
   $4a - 3b = 14$

10 $5x - 2y = 11$
   $2x + 2y = -4$

11 $4y + 3x = -21$
   $2y - 3x = 3$

12 $2y + 3x = -1$
   $y - 3x = 4$

15.4 Elimination: multiplying

Learning intentions

Adding or subtracting may not always eliminate a variable.
Try multiplying one of the equations first.

Example

Solve simultaneously.

(a) $4x + y = 9$
$3x - 2y = 15$

(b) $3x + 4y = 6$
$2x + y = -1$

(a) $4x + y = 9$ ①
                $3x - 2y = 15$ ②

$2 \times$ ① $8x + 2y = 18$
② $3x - 2y = 15$

Add $11x = 33$ [*y* is eliminated]
               $x = 3$

Substitute for x in equation ①
       $4x + y = 9$
       $12 + y = 9$
           $y = -3$

Check using equation ②
     L.H.S. $= 3x - 2y$
           $= 9 - (-6)$
           $= 15 =$ R.H.S.
        $x = \mathbf{3}$ and $y = \mathbf{-3}$

(b) $3x + 4y = 6$ ①
                $2x + y = -1$ ②

$4 \times$ ② $8x + 4y = -4$
① $3x + 4y = 6$

Subtract $5x = -10$ [*y* is eliminated]
               $x = -2$

Substitute for x in equation ②
       $2x + y = -1$
       $-4 + y = -1$
           $y = 3$

Check using equation ①
     L.H.S. $= 3x + 4y$
           $= -6 + 12$
           $= 6 =$ R.H.S.
        $x = \mathbf{-2}$ and $y = \mathbf{3}$

Exercise 15.4

Solve each pair of simultaneous equations algebraically.

1 $2a + 3b = 5$
     $a + b = 2$

2 $2a + 5c = 16$
     $a - c = 1$

3 $2x + y = 5$
     $x + 2y = 7$

4 $3p + 4q = -7$
     $2p + q = -3$

5 $x + y = 0$
     $4x + 3y = 3$

6 $3x + 4y = 25$
     $x - 2y = 5$

7 $5x + y = 4$
     $x - 2y = 3$

8 $2x + y = 1$
     $x + 2y = -1$

9 $3a - 2b = 11$
     $7a + 8b = 51$

10 $7y + 3x = 22$
      $2y + x = 7$

11 $3x + 2y = 43$
      $x + y = 17$

12 $3p + 4q = 14$
      $p - 2q = 3$

15.5 Elimination: further multiplying

Learning intentions

Both equations may require to be multiplied.

Example

Solve simultaneously.

(a) $2x + 3y = 5$
      $3x - 2y = 14$

(b) $5x - 4y = 22$
      $2x - 3y = 13$

(a) $2x + 3y = 5$ ①
                       $3x - 2y = 14$ ②

$2 \times$ ① $4x + 6y = 10$
$3 \times$ ② $9x - 6y = 42$
Add $13x \quad\quad = 52$ [y is eliminated]
                      $x \quad = 4$

Substitute for x in equation ①
                      $2x + 3y = 3$
                      $8 + 3y = 5$
                      $3y = -3$
                      $y = -1$

Check using equation ②
                      L.H.S. $= 3x - 2y$
                              $= 12 - (-2)$
                              $= 14 = $ R.H.S.
                      $x = 4$ and $y = -1$

(b) $5x - 4y = 22$ ①
                       $2x - 3y = 13$ ②

$3 \times$ ① $15x - 12y = 66$
$4 \times$ ② $8x - 12y = 52$
Subtract $7x \quad\quad = 14$ [y is eliminated]
                      $x \quad = 2$

Substitute for x in equation ①
                      $5x - 4y = 22$
                      $10 - 4y = 22$
                      $-4y = 12$
                      $y = -3$

Check using equation ②
                      L.H.S. $= 2x - 3y$
                              $= 4 - (-9)$
                              $= 13 = $ R.H.S.
                      $x = 2$ and $y = -3$

Exercise 15.5

Solve each pair of simultaneous equations algebraically.

1 $5a + 4c = 18$
     $4a - 3c = 2$

2 $2a + 5c = 15$
     $3a - 2c = 13$

3 $4e - 5f = 22$
     $7e + 3f = 15$

4 $2x + 3y = 6$
     $5x + 2y = -7$

5 $3x + 2y = 0$
     $2x + 3y = -5$

6 $5x + 6y = 16$
     $2x - 9y = -5$

7 $2x + 5y = 21$
     $11x + 3y = -7$

8 $3x + 5y = 23$
     $5x + 2y = 13$

9 $7a + 4b = 36$
     $2a + 3b = 14$

10 $3x - 2y = -5$
      $4x - 3y = -8$

11 $2a - 5b = 11$
      $4a - 3b = 1$

12 $2a + 4c = 7$
      $4a - 3c = 3$

15.6 Rearranging simultaneous equations

Learning intentions

To eliminate a variable, equations may first need to be rearranged.

Example
Solve each pair of simultaneous equations algebraically.

(a) $4x = 3y + 10$
$4y = 20 - 3x$

(b) $a = -2b - 2$
$5b + 4a + 1 = 0$

(a)
$$4x = 3y + 10 \quad \text{①}$$
$$4y = 20 - 3x \quad \text{②}$$

Rearrange
$$4x - 3y = 10 \quad \text{③}$$
$$3x + 4y = 20 \quad \text{④}$$

$4 \times$ ③ $\quad 16x - 12y = 40$
$3 \times$ ④ $\quad 9x + 12y = 60$

Add $\quad 25x \quad = 100$
$\quad x \quad = 4$

Substitute for x in equation ①
$$4x = 3y + 10$$
$$16 = 3y + 10$$
$$6 = 3y$$
$$y = 2$$

Check using equation ④
L.H.S. $= 3x + 4y$
$= 12 + 8$
$= 20 =$ R.H.S.
$x = \mathbf{4}$ and $y = \mathbf{2}$

(b)
$$a \quad = -2b - 2 \quad \text{①}$$
$$5b + 4a + 1 = 0 \quad \text{②}$$

Rearrange
$$a + 2b = -2 \quad \text{③}$$
$$4a + 5b = -1 \quad \text{④}$$

$4 \times$ ③ $\quad 4a + 8b = -8$
④ $\quad 4a + 5b = -1$

Subtract $\quad 3b = -7$
$\quad b = \frac{-7}{3}$

Substitute for x in equation ①
$$a = -2b - 2$$
$$a = -2 \times \frac{-7}{3} - 2$$
$$a = 2\frac{2}{3}$$

Check using equation ④
L.H.S. $= 4a + 5b$
$= 10\frac{2}{3} + (-11\frac{2}{3})$
$= -1 =$ R.H.S.
$a = \mathbf{2\frac{2}{3}}$ and $b = \mathbf{-2\frac{1}{3}}$

Exercise 15.6

Solve each pair of simultaneous equations algebraically.

1 $2a + 3b - 8 = 0$
$3a + 2b - 17 = 0$

2 $2c - 3a = 0$
$a - c + 1 = 0$

3 $7e + 4f - 1 = 0$
$5e + 2f + 1 = 0$

4 $p - 2q + 2 = 0$
$5p - 4q + 1 = 0$

5 $3x = 4y + 12$
$y = x - 1$

6 $4x = 12 - 6y$
$4y + 14 = -10x$

7 $3x = 5y + 2$
$3y = 12 - 7x$

8 $3x = -2y - 4$
$3y = -4x + 5$

9 $2a = 7b + 24$
$2b + 19 = 3a$

10 $x = y - 7$
$3y - 19 = 5x$

11 $y = x + 1$
$5x - 3y = 1$

12 $3x = 5y + 4$
$8x - 7 = 6y$

15.7 Simultaneous equations involving fractions

Learning intentions

Equations which involve fractions may be simplified before solving.

Example

Solve these simultaneous equations algebraically.

(a) $\frac{1}{2}x + \frac{1}{3}y = \frac{1}{2}$

$\frac{1}{3}x + \frac{2}{3}y = -5$

(b) $\frac{2x - y}{3} = \frac{1}{3}$

$\frac{3x - y}{5} = 1$

(a)

$$\frac{1}{2}x + \frac{1}{3}y = \frac{1}{2} \quad \text{①}$$

$$\frac{1}{3}x - \frac{2}{3}y = -5 \quad \text{②}$$

$6 \times \text{①} \quad 3x + 2y = 3 \quad \text{③}$

$3 \times \text{②} \quad x - 2y = -15 \quad \text{④}$

Add $\quad 4x \quad\quad = -12$

$\quad\quad x \quad\quad = -3$

Substitute for x in equation ③

$3x + 2y = 3$

$-9 + 2y = 3$

$2y = 12$

$y = 6$

Check using equation ④

L.H.S. $= x - 2y$

$= (-3) - 2 \times 6$

$= -15 = $ R.H.S.

$x = -3$ and $y = 6$

(b)

$$\frac{2x - y}{3} = \frac{1}{3} \quad \text{①}$$

$$\frac{3x - y}{5} = 1 \quad \text{②}$$

$3 \times \text{①} \quad 2x - y = 1 \quad \text{③}$

$5 \times \text{②} \quad 3x - y = 5 \quad \text{④}$

Subtract $\quad x \quad\quad = 4$

Substitute for x in equation ③

$2x - y = 1$

$8 - y = 1$

$y = 7$

Check using equation ④

L.H.S. $= 3x - y$

$= 12 - 7$

$= 5 = $ R.H.S.

$x = 4$ and $y = 7$

Exercise 15.7

Solve each pair of simultaneous equations algebraically.

1 $\frac{1}{2}x - y = 1$

$2x - 3y = 5$

2 $\frac{1}{5}x + y = 1$

$x - y = 5$

3 $\frac{1}{3}x + \frac{1}{4}y = 3$

$3x - \frac{1}{2}y = 5$

4 $\frac{1}{2}x + \frac{1}{5}y = 1$

$\frac{1}{3}x - \frac{1}{5}y = 4$

5 $\frac{2x - 3y}{4} = \frac{15}{2}$

$\frac{3x - 2y}{5} = \frac{15}{2}$

6 $\frac{x + 1}{3} + y = 8$

$x - \frac{y + 1}{3} = -4$

7 $\frac{x - 1}{6} + y = 6$

$\frac{y - 1}{4} + x = 8$

8 $\frac{x + 2y}{3} = 4$

$\frac{2x + y}{4} = \frac{5}{2}$

15.8 Problem solving using simultaneous equations

Learning intentions

When a problem involves two variables, simultaneous equations may be used.

Example

At a multiplex the total cost for 1 adult and 3 children was £15.50.
The cost for 2 adults and 4 children was £24.
Find the cost for

(**a**) an adult   (**b**) a child   (**c**) 3 adults and 5 children

Let the cost, in £s, for an adult be a and the cost, in £s, for a child be c.

Then $a + 3c = 15.5$
and $2a + 4c = 24$

Now solve these simultaneously.

$a + 3c = 15.5$ ①
$2a + 4c = 24$ ②

$2 \times$ ① $2a + 6c = 31$
② $2a + 4c = 24$
Subtract $2c = 7$
$c = 3.5$

Substitute for c in equation ①
$a + 3c = 15.5$
$a + 3 \times 3.5 = 15.5$
$a + 10.5 = 15.5$
$a = 5$

Check using equation ②
L.H.S. $= 2a + 4c$
$= 2 \times 5 + 4 \times 3.5$
$= 10 + 14$
$= 24 =$ R.H.S.

 Total cost £15.50

 Total cost £24

(**a**) Adult cost is **£5**
(**b**) Child cost is **£3.50**
(**c**) Cost for 3 adults and 5 children $= 3 \times 5 + 5 \times 3.50 =$ **£32.50**

Exercise 15.8

1 At a multiplex the total cost for
3 adults and 2 children was £50.
The cost for 1 adult and 3 children was £26.
Find the cost for (**a**) an adult,
(**b**) a child (**c**) 2 adults and 4 children.

 Total cost £50

 Total cost £26

2 At a leisure centre, the total charged for 2 adults and 3 children was £31.
The cost for 3 adults and 1 child was £29. Find the cost for
(**a**) an adult, (**b**) a child (**c**) 3 adults and 3 children.

3 The total of Zaira's age and her father's age is 112. Her father is 36 years older
than Zaira. Form two simultaneous equations and use them to find Zaira's age.

4 In *Bargain Discs*, Raghnaid bought 2 CDs and 3 DVDs for a total cost of
£32.50. Bob bought 3 CDs and 2 DVDs for a total of £30.
Find the cost of 2 CDs and 2 DVDs.

5 The diagram shows an old wall held in position by a wooden prop.
The value of x is 68° larger than y. Form two simultaneous equations
and hence find the values of x and y.

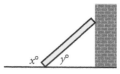

6 A transporter carries cars and motorcycles. It can carry a total of ten vehicles. Each car weighs 1·5 tonnes. Each motorcycle weighs 500 kilograms. On one journey the total weight carried was 11 tonnes. How many cars and how many motorcycles were on the transporter?

7 In *Cuppa Cofaidh*, the cost of 3 teas and 2 coffees is £6.60. The cost of 2 teas and 1 coffee is £3.90. Find the cost of 4 teas and 5 coffees.

8 The breadth of a school football pitch is 20 metres shorter than the length. If the perimeter of the pitch is 160 metres, find the length of the pitch.

9 In the *Intermediate maths challenge*, 5 marks are awarded for each correct answer, but 2 marks deducted for each wrong answer. Justine scored a total of 65 marks. If she answered a total of 20 questions, how many did she answer correctly and how many were answered incorrectly?

10 A group of two hundred and ten supporters of Bathgate Thistle travel to their local cup final filling 5 small and 10 large minibuses. One hundred and ninety-two fans of Linlithgow Rose fill 6 small and 8 large minibuses to travel. How many fans could travel in 8 large and 2 small minibuses?

11 The formula used to calculate velocity is $v = u + at$, where v is final velocity, u is initial velocity, t is time and a is acceleration.
When $t = 1$, $v = 15$ and when $t = 6$, $v = 65$.
(**a**) Find the value of u and of a.
(**b**) Using these values for u and a, calculate v when $t = 15$

15.9 Solving simultaneous equations by substitution

Learning intentions

Substitution is another useful method for solving simultaneous equations.

Example

Solve these simultaneous equations algebraically using substitution.

(**a**) $y = 2x - 1$
    $3y - 2x = 5$

(**b**) $x - 8y = 20$
    $5x - 7y = 1$

(**a**)
$$y = 2x - 1 \quad ①$$
$$3y - 2x = 5 \quad ②$$

From equation ① $y = 2x - 1$
Substitute in equation ②
$$3y - 2x = 5$$
$$3(2x - 1) - 2x = 5$$
$$6x - 3 - 2x = 5$$
$$4x = 8$$
$$x = 2$$

Substitute for x in equation ①
$$y = 2x - 1$$
$$y = 4 - 1$$
$$y = 3$$

Check using equation ②
$$\text{L.H.S.} = 3y - 2x$$
$$= 9 - 4$$
$$= 5 = \text{R.H.S.}$$
$$x = 2 \text{ and } y = 3$$

(**a**)
$$x - 8y = 20 \quad ①$$
$$5x - 7y = 1 \quad ②$$

Rearrange equation ① $x = 8y + 20 \quad ③$
Substitute in equation ②
$$5x - 7y = 1$$
$$5(8y + 20) - 7y = 1$$
$$40y + 100 - 7y = 1$$
$$33y = -99$$
$$y = -3$$

Substitute for x in equation ③
$$x = 8y + 20$$
$$x = -24 + 20$$
$$x = -4$$

Check using equation ②
$$\text{L.H.S.} = 5x - 7y$$
$$= (-20) - (-21)$$
$$= 1 = \text{R.H.S.}$$
$$x = -4 \text{ and } y = -3$$

Exercise 15.9

Solve each pair of simultaneous equations algebraically using substitution.

1 $a = b$
$2a - b = 5$

2 $c = 2a$
$6a - c = 8$

3 $e = 2f$
$3e - 10f - 12 = 0$

4 $p = 3q$
$2p - 3q = 12$

5 $x = y + 3$
$3x + 2y = 4$

6 $x = 2y - 1$
$3x - 2y = 5$

7 $2x - y = 2$
$5x - 4y = -1$

8 $y - 2x = 3$
$5y - 2x + 1 = 0$

9 Solve each pair of simultaneous equations algebraically using the most appropriate method.

(**a**) $3x - 5y = 14$
$6x - 5y = 13$

(**b**) $p = 2q - 4$
$2q + 3p = 12$

(**c**) $14x + 3y = -13$
$21x + 7y = -7$

(**d**) $c = 1 - 3a$
$3a - 4c = 16$

Coursework task

Display boxes

A manufacturer supplies display boxes which are used to protect exhibits at trade shows etc.

The boxes have no base, but the walls are made of good quality wood to enhance their appearance and the tops are made from a high quality of laminated glass.

All the wood used is the same thickness and material.

The cost of the boxes depends only on the amount of wood and the amount of glass used.

The following six boxes (which are shown below with cost and dimensions) were sent to a museum for an exhibition.

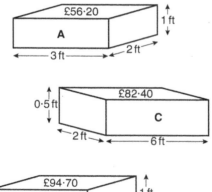

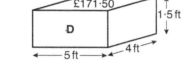

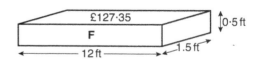

1 For each box calculate the area of wood and the area of glass required.

2 (**a**) If £g is the cost per square foot of the glass and £w is the cost per square foot of the wood, show that for Box A

$$6g + 10w = 56.20$$

 (**b**) Find a similar expression, in terms of g and w, for each of the other boxes.

3 The curator was anxious to save money and queried the bill.
She maintained that one of the boxes had been wrongly priced.

 (**a**) Find which of the boxes is incorrectly priced.

 (**b**) Find the correct price for this box.

Review exercise 15: Am I a successful learner?

1 Solve each pair of simultaneous equations algebraically using elimination.

(**a**) $3a + 2b = 7$
    $5a - 2b = 1$

(**b**) $4x + 5y = 17$
    $4x + 2y = 14$

(**c**) $7a + 3b = 26$
    $5a - 2b = 60$

(**d**) $9p - 10q = 15$
    $4p - 5q\ = 5$

(**e**) $x + y - 8 = 0$
    $x = y + 2$

(**f**) $5x + 3y - 10 = 0$
    $6x - y = -11$

(**g**) $\frac{1}{2}x - \frac{1}{3}y = \frac{1}{2}$
    $\frac{1}{8}x - \frac{1}{9}y = 0$

(**h**) $\dfrac{3x - 2y}{4} = 1$

    $\dfrac{2x + 3y}{3} = \frac{1}{6}$

2 Solve each pair of simultaneous equations algebraically using substitution.

(**a**) $x = 1 + y$
    $x + 5y = 7$

(**b**) $c = d + 4$
    $c + 3d = 16$

(**c**) $x = 2y + 2$
    $3x - 5y - 4 = 0$

(**d**) $p = 8q - 20$
    $5p - 7q = -1$

3 Solve each pair of simultaneous equations algebraically using the most appropriate method.

(**a**) $2x + 3y = 7$
    $4x + 5y = 13$

(**b**) $x = 7y + 9$
    $x + 12y + 10 = 0$

(**c**) $7x + 2y = 11$
    $6x - 5y + 4 = 0$

(**d**) $p = 1 - 3q$
    $7q + p + 3 = 0$

(**e**) $x = 4y - 5$
    $3x + y = 11$

(**f**) $3a + 22 = 2b$
    $b + 2a + 3 = 0$

(**g**) $4x - 3y = 5$
    $2x + 5y = 9$

(**h**) $p = 6q$
    $2q + p - 16 = 0$

4 Robert weighs 25 kilogrammes more than James. Their total weight is
155 kilogrammes. Form two equations to model this problem and solve
them simultaneously to find Robert's weight.

5 At the Film Centre the total charge for 3 adults and 2 children was £58.
If the cost for 2 adults and 3 children was £52, find the cost for
(**a**) an adult, (**b**) a child (**c**) 2 adults and 4 children.

6 *Uisge-beathe* sell water in two sizes of bottles. The total volume of 3 large and
4 small bottles is 3·42 litres. The total volume of 2 large and 5 small is 3·05 litres.

 (**a**) What is the volume of each size of bottle?

 (**b**) What is the total volume of 5 large and 2 small bottles?

7 *Woodsheds* make garden huts in two different sizes. Each week they make
a total of 60 huts. The small hut has a floor area of 10 square metres. The
large hut has a floor area of 15 square metres. The total area of flooring
used each week is 700 square metres. How many huts of each size do
they make each week?

Summary 15: What I learned in this chapter.

Elimination

Simultaneous equations may be solved by eliminating one of the variables.

- multiply each equation if necessary
- add or subtract equations as appropriate

$$2x + 3y = 6 \qquad ①$$
$$5x + 2y = -7 \qquad ②$$

$2 \times ①$ $\qquad 4x + 6y = 12$
$3 \times ②$ $\qquad 15x + 6y = -21$

Subtract $\quad 11x \quad = -33$ $\boxed{y \text{ is eliminated}}$
$$x \quad = -3$$

Substitute for x in equation ①
$$2x + 3y = 6$$
$$-6 + 3y = 6$$
$$3y = 12$$
$$y = 4$$

Check using equation ②
$$\text{L.H.S.} = 5x + 2y$$
$$= (-15) + 8$$
$$= -7 = \text{R.H.S.}$$

$x = -3$ and $y = 4$

- Equations may need to be rearranged before elimination takes place.

$$4x = 3y + 10 \qquad ①$$
$$4y = 20 - 3x \qquad ②$$

Rearrange $\quad 4x - 3y = 10 \qquad ③$
$$3x + 4y = 20 \qquad ④$$

then solve as above

- Writing equations without fractions may ease the question.

$$\tfrac{1}{2}x + \tfrac{1}{3}y = \tfrac{1}{2} \qquad ①$$
$$\tfrac{1}{3}x - \tfrac{2}{3}y = -5 \qquad ②$$

$6 \times ①$ $\qquad 3x + 2y = 3 \qquad ③$
$3 \times ②$ $\qquad x - 2y = -15 \qquad ④$

then solve as above

Substitution

Substituting for one of the variables may be a more appropriate method.

$$y = 2x - 1 \qquad ①$$
$$3y - 2x = 5 \qquad ②$$

From equation ① $y = 2x - 1$

Substitute for y in equation ②
$$3y - 2x = 5$$
$$3(2x - 1) - 2x = 5$$
$$6x - 3 - 2x = 5$$
$$4x = 8$$
$$x = 2$$

Substitute for x in equation ①
$$y = 2x - 1$$
$$y = 4 - 1$$
$$y = 3$$

Check using equation ②
$$\text{L.H.S.} = 3y - 2x$$
$$= 9 - 4$$
$$= 5 = \text{R.H.S.}$$

$x = 2$ and $y = 3$

16 Straight line

16.1 Gradient

Look at the ski tows shown. Starting with the least steep, it is possible to list them in order.
Clearly, section B is steepest, section C is the next steepest and section A is the least steep.
How is steepness measured?

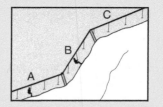

The measure of steepness is called the **gradient**.

$$\text{Gradient} = \frac{\text{vertical distance}}{\text{horizontal distance}}$$

Example

Find the gradient of each slope.

(a)

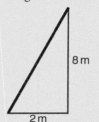

8 m

2 m

$\text{Gradient} = \dfrac{\text{vertical distance}}{\text{horizontal distance}}$

$= \dfrac{8\,\text{m}}{2\,\text{m}}$

$= 4$

(b)

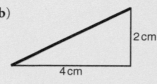

2 cm

4 cm

$\text{Gradient} = \dfrac{\text{vertical}}{\text{horizontal}}$

$= \dfrac{2\,\text{m}}{4\,\text{m}}$

$= \dfrac{1}{2}$

(c)

2 m

60 cm

$\text{Gradient} = \dfrac{\text{vertical}}{\text{horizontal}}$

$= \dfrac{2\,\text{m}}{60\,\text{cm}}$

$= \dfrac{200\,\text{cm}}{60\,\text{cm}}$

$= \dfrac{10}{3}$

Units must match

Exercise 16.1

1 Find the gradient of each slope.

(a)

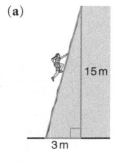

15 m

3 m

(b)

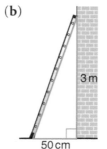

3 m

50 cm

(c)

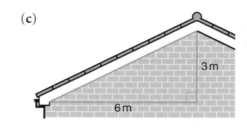

3 m

6 m

(d)

40 cm

2 m

(e)

30 cm

4·5 m

2 Calculate the gradient for sections (**a**) to (**e**) marked on this roller coaster.

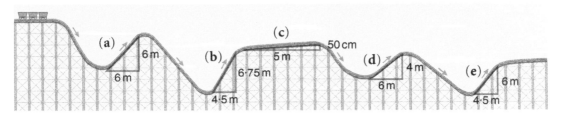

3 For safety reasons the gradient of a children's slide must be no more than 1·9. Which of these slides do not meet the safety regulations?

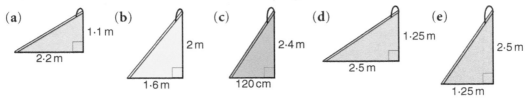

4 Calculate the vertical height for each given gradient.

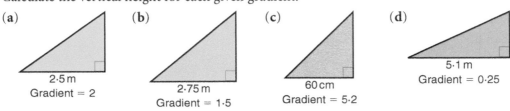

5 Calculate the missing side in each right angled triangle and hence find the gradient of each slope.

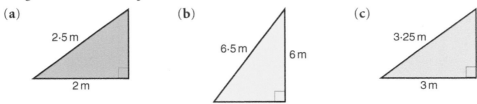

6 The Cairngorm railway starts at 610 metres above sea level. The top station is 1097 metres above sea level. If the length of the railway is 2 kilometres, calculate the average gradient of the railway.

16.2 Negative gradients

From left to right:
- lines sloping **up** have a **positive** gradient
- lines sloping **down** have a **negative** gradient.

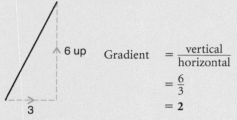

$$\text{Gradient} = \frac{\text{vertical}}{\text{horizontal}}$$
$$= \frac{6}{3}$$
$$= 2$$

6 down

$$\text{Gradient} = \frac{\text{vertical}}{\text{horizontal}}$$
$$= \frac{-6}{3}$$
$$= -2$$

−6 since vertical distance is down

Example

Find the gradient of each slope.

(a)
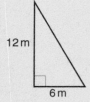

12 m, 6 m

$$\text{Gradient} = \frac{\text{vertical}}{\text{horizontal}}$$
$$= \frac{-12\,\text{m}}{6\,\text{m}}$$
$$= -2$$

(b)
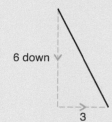

$$\text{Gradient} = \frac{\text{vertical}}{\text{horizontal}}$$
$$= \frac{-2}{8}$$
$$= -\frac{1}{4}$$

Count vertical and horizontal distances

Exercise 16.2

1 Find the gradient of each slope.

(a) 3 m, 0·5 m (b) 2 m, 0·25 m (c) 9 m, 27 m
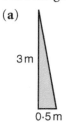 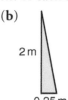 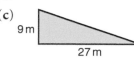

(d) 60 cm, 12 m (e) 50 cm, 2·5 m

2 Calculate the gradient of each slope.

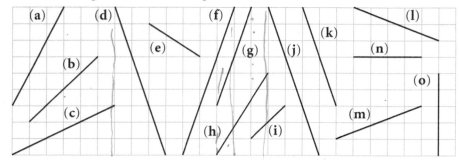

The gradient of a **horizontal** line is **0**.

Gradient $= \dfrac{\text{vertical}}{\text{horizontal}}$

$= \dfrac{0}{\text{horizontal}}$

$= 0$

No vertical distance

The gradient of a **vertical** line is **undefined**.

Gradient $= \dfrac{\text{vertical}}{\text{horizontal}}$

$= \dfrac{\text{vertical}}{0}$

$=$ undefined

No horizontal distance

3 The Leaning Tower of Pisa is 60 metres tall. The top of the tower overhangs the bottom by 75 centimetres.

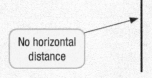
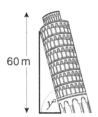

60 m

(**a**) Calculate the gradient of its slope.

(**b**) Use trigonometry to find angle y, the angle of incline to the horizontal.

(**c**) The base of the tower has sunk into the ground by a total of 3·75 metres on one side, but by only 1·86 metres on the other side as shown on the diagram. The width of the tower is 19·6 metres. Calculate the length marked x.

(**d**) Hence calculate the gradient of the slope in this triangle.

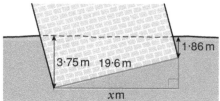

1·86 m

3·75 m   19·6 m

x m

16.3 Gradients on Cartesian diagrams

Learning intentions

Example

Find the gradient of the line joining A$(1, 2)$ and B$(9, 4)$

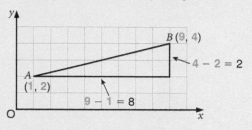

$B(9, 4)$

$4 - 2 = 2$

A $(1, 2)$

$9 - 1 = 8$

Plot the points.
Find vertical and horizontal distances.
Calculate the gradient.

Gradient $= \dfrac{\text{vertical}}{\text{horizontal}}$

$= \dfrac{2}{8}$

$= \dfrac{1}{4}$

In general, if A is the point (x_1, y_1) and B is the point (x_2, y_2)

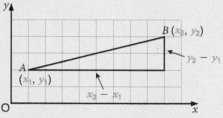

$B(x_2, y_2)$

$y_2 - y_1$

A (x_1, y_1)

$x_2 - x_1$

Gradient $= \dfrac{\text{vertical}}{\text{horizontal}}$

$= \dfrac{y_2 - y_1}{x_2 - x_1}$

This is called the **gradient formula**, where the gradient is denoted by m.

$$m_{AB} = \dfrac{y_2 - y_1}{x_2 - x_1}$$

Example

Calculate the gradient of the line joining each pair of points.

(a) A(2, 3) and B(8, 5) (b) C(0, 9) and D(4, 1) (c) E(−3, −2) and F(4, 5)

(a)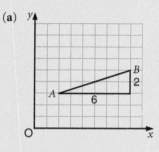

$$m_{AB} = \frac{\text{vertical}}{\text{horizontal}} \quad \text{or} \quad m_{AB} = \frac{y_2 - y_1}{x_2 - x_1}$$

$$= \frac{2}{6} \qquad\qquad = \frac{5 - 3}{8 - 2}$$

$$= \frac{1}{3} \qquad\qquad = \frac{2}{6}$$

$$\qquad\qquad\qquad = \frac{1}{3}$$

(b)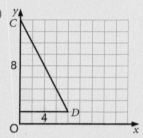

$$m_{CD} = \frac{\text{vertical}}{\text{horizontal}} \quad \text{or} \quad m_{CD} = \frac{y_2 - y_1}{x_2 - x_1}$$

$$= \frac{-8}{4} \qquad\qquad = \frac{1 - 9}{4 - 0}$$

$$= -2 \qquad\qquad = \frac{-8}{4}$$

$$\qquad\qquad\qquad = -2$$

(c)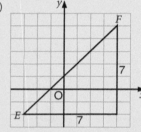

$$m_{EF} = \frac{\text{vertical}}{\text{horizontal}} \quad \text{or} \quad m_{EF} = \frac{y_2 - y_1}{x_2 - x_1}$$

$$= \frac{7}{7} \qquad\qquad = \frac{5 - (-2)}{4 - (-3)}$$

$$= 1 \qquad\qquad = \frac{7}{7}$$

$$\qquad\qquad\qquad = 1$$

Exercise 16.3

1 Find the gradient of each line.

(a) 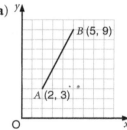 (b) 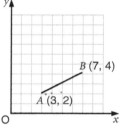 (c) 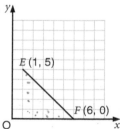 (d)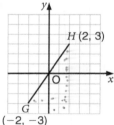

2 Calculate the gradient of the line joining each pair of points.

(a) A(1, 2) and B(6, 12) (b) C(−2, 4) and D(6, 8)
(c) E(−2, −3) and F(5, 4) (d) G(1, 9) and H(5, −3)
(e) I(2, 5) and J(6, 5) (f) K(6, 9) and L(6, 2)
(g) M(3, 4) and N(−2, −6) (h) P(−2, −3) and Q(−4, −9)

3 (a) Plot each pair of points.
  (i) A(2, 3) and B(6, 11)   (ii) C(−2, −4) and D(1, 2)
  (iii) E(3, −2) and F(5, 2)

(b) Calculate the gradient of the line joining each pair of points.

(c) Describe geometrically anything you notice about all of the lines.

4 (a) Plot each pair of points.
  (i) A(1, 10) and B(3, 2)   (ii) C(−3, 9) and D(1, −7)
  (iii) E(−2, −1) and F(0, −9)

(b) Calculate the gradient of the line joining each pair of points.

(c) Describe geometrically anything you notice about all of the lines.

5 For each set of points
  (i) plot the points on a Cartesian diagram
  (ii) calculate the gradients m_{AB}, m_{BC} and m_{AC}
  (iii) find a formula for y in terms of x
  (iv) what do you notice?

(a)

	A	B	C
x	0	1	3
y	0	2	6

(b)

	A	B	C
x	0	1	3
y	0	1	3

(c)

	A	B	C
x	0	2	6
y	0	1	3

(d)

	A	B	C
x	−3	−2	0
y	6	4	0

16.4 Straight line graphs through the origin

Learning intentions

The gradient between any two points on a straight line is always the same.

When the points in this table are plotted, a straight line can be drawn through all the points.

x	−2	0	2	4
y	−4	0	4	8

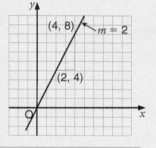

The equation $y = 2x$ represents the relationship between the co-ordinates of all points on the straight line.
The gradient between any two points on the line is 2 and the line passes through the origin.
In the equation $y = 2x$, the **coefficient** of x is 2.

In general, if a line has gradient m and passes through the origin then the equation of the line is
$$y = mx$$

The equation represents the relationship between the coordinates of all points on the straight line.

Example 1

Write the gradient of the line with equation

(a) $y = 5x$ (b) $y = -\frac{1}{2}x$ (c) $2y = 4x$

(a) $y = 5x$ (b) $y = -\frac{1}{2}x$ (c) $2y = 4x$ | Make y the subject. |
    $m = 5$ $m = -\frac{1}{2}$ $y = 2x$
                                                           $m = 2$

Example 2

Find the equation of the line through O and A.

(a) O(0, 0) and A(4, 12)

(b) O(0, 0) and A(8, −2)

(a)
$$m_{OA} = \frac{y_2 - y_1}{x_2 - x_1}$$
$$= \frac{12 - 0}{4 - 0}$$
$$= 3$$
Hence **y = 3x**

(b)
$$m_{OA} = \frac{y_2 - y_1}{x_2 - x_1}$$
$$= \frac{-2 - 0}{8 - 0}$$
$$= -\frac{1}{4}$$
Hence $\mathbf{y = -\frac{1}{4}x}$

Example 3

Do the points P(5, 10) and Q(6, 14) lie on the line $y = 2x$?

Substitute (5, 10) for x and y in the equation.

LHS: $y = 10$
RHS: $2x = 2 \times 5 = 10$

Hence point P **lies** on the line since $y = 2x$.

Substitute (6, 14) for x and y in the equation.

LHS: $y = 14$
RHS: $2x = 2 \times 6 = 12$

Hence point Q **does not lie** on the line since $y \neq 2x$.

Exercise 16.4

1 Write the gradient of the line with equations

(a) $y = 4x$ (b) $y = -2x$ (c) $y = \frac{3}{4}x$

(d) $2y = 6x$ (e) $3y = 5x$

2 Find the equation of the line through O and A.

(a) 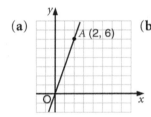 (b) 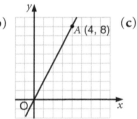 (c) 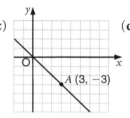 (d)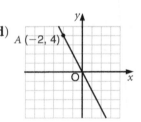

3 In each case plot the point A and find the equation of the line through O and A.

(a) A(5, 15)   (b) A(−2, −6)

(c) A(−4, −2)   (d) A(6, −2)

4 Which of the points A(8, 24) and B(−5, −20) lies on the line $y = 4x$?

5 The points A(2, a), B(b, 12), C(−1, c) and D(d, −6) lie on the line $y = 3x$. Find the value of a, b, c and d.

6 The points A(6, a), B(b, 8), C(−8, c) and D(d, 3) lie on the line $y = \frac{1}{2}x$. Find the value of a, b, c and d.

16.5 Further straight line graphs

Learning intentions

To sketch the graph of $y = 2x + 1$, some values for x can be chosen and the corresponding values for y calculated, as shown in the table.

x	0	1	3
y	1	3	7

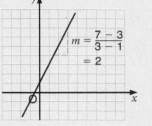

$$m = \frac{7 - 3}{3 - 1}$$
$$= 2$$

These values can then be plotted and joined to give a straight line.
The gradient calculated between any two points on the line is 2.

On the same diagram sketch the graph of $y = 2x + 4$
The gradient of this line is also 2.

x	0	1	3
y	4	6	10

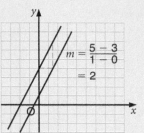

$$m = \frac{5 - 3}{1 - 0}$$
$$= 2$$

Lines which have the same gradient are parallel.

Exercise 16.5

1 Examine each set of graphs.
For each set of graphs what is **(i)** similar   **(ii)** different?

(a)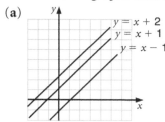
$y = x + 2$
$y = x + 1$
$y = x - 1$

(b)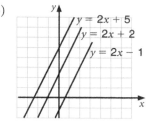
$y = 2x + 5$
$y = 2x + 2$
$y = 2x - 1$

(c)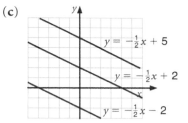
$y = -\frac{1}{2}x + 5$
$y = -\frac{1}{2}x + 2$
$y = -\frac{1}{2}x - 2$

2 Sketch each set of graphs on the same diagram.
For each set of graphs what is **(i)** similar   **(ii)** different?

(a) $y = 2x + 1$ (b) $y = 3x + 2$ (c) $y = -2x + 4$
$\ y = 2x$ $\ y = 3x$ $\ y = -2x$
$\ y = 2x - 2$ $\ y = 3x - 1$ $\ y = -2x - 2$

3 Sketch each set of graphs on the same diagram.
For each set of graphs what is **(i)** similar   **(ii)** different?

(a) $y = 2x + 1$ (b) $y = 2x - 1$ (c) $y = 2x - 1$
$\ y = x + 1$ $\ y = x - 1$ $\ y = x - 1$
$\ y = 3x + 1$ $\ y = 3x - 1$ $\ y = 3x - 1$

4 Without drawing the graphs represented by the following equations make a conjecture about the gradient and where the graph crosses the y-axis for each of the following.
(a) $y = 5x + 4$ (b) $y = -3x - 1$ (c) $y = \frac{1}{2}x + 10$

16.6   Equations of a straight line

Learning intentions

It is possible to identify both the gradient and the **y-intercept** of a graph from its equation.

The graph of $y = 2x + 1$ has gradient 2 and cuts the y-axis at $(0, 1)$

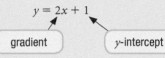

gradient   y-intercept

> The **y-intercept** is where the graph crosses the y-axis

$m = 2$

In general, if the equation of the graph is of the form $y = mx + c$, then the gradient is m and the y-intercept is $(0, c)$

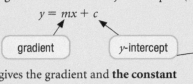

gradient   y-intercept

The **coefficient of x** gives the gradient and **the constant** gives the y-intercept.

> The **constant** in an equation does not include a variable

Example

State the gradient and y-intercept of the graph represented by each equation and hence sketch the graph.

(a) $y = 2x - 3$ **(b)** $y = -3x + 6$ **(c)** $2y = 4x + 6$

(a) $y = x - 3$
Gradient = 2, y-intercept is $(0, -3)$

- plot the y-intercept
- use gradient to find other points
- draw the line

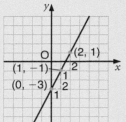

Gradient $= 2 = \dfrac{2}{1} : \dfrac{2 \text{ up}}{1 \text{ along}}$

(b) $y = -3x + 6$
Gradient = -3, y-intercept is $(0, 6)$

- plot the y-intercept
- use gradient to find other points
- draw the line

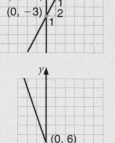

Gradient $= -3 = \dfrac{-3}{1} : \dfrac{3 \text{ down}}{1 \text{ along}}$

(c) $2y = x + 6$
$y = \frac{1}{2}x + 3$
Gradient $= \frac{1}{2}$, y-intercept is $(0, 3)$

- plot the y-intercept
- use gradient to find other points
- draw the line

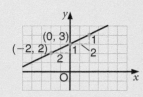

Gradient $= \frac{1}{2} : \dfrac{1 \text{ up}}{2 \text{ along}}$

or $\dfrac{\frac{1}{2} \text{ up}}{1 \text{ along}}$

Exercise 16.6

1 State the gradient and y-intercept of the graph represented by each equation and sketch its graph.

(**a**) $y = 3x + 2$ (**b**) $y = -2x + 6$ (**c**) $y = -x + 6$ (**d**) $y = \frac{1}{2}x - 4$ (**e**) $y = -\frac{1}{3}x + 6$

2 Sketch each straight line.

(**a**) $y = 2x - 1$ (**b**) $y = \frac{1}{3}x + 3$ (**c**) $y = x + 2$ (**d**) $y = -\frac{1}{2}x + 4$ (**e**) $y = -x - 5$

16.7 Equations from graphs

Learning intentions

It is possible to find an equation from its graph.
For a straight line with gradient, m, and y-intercept, c, the equation is $y = mx + c$

Example

Find the equation of each graph.

(**a**)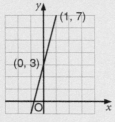

(**b**)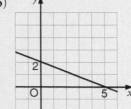

(**a**) Graph is a straight line hence
   equation is $y = mx + c$
   y-intercept is $(0, 3)$ so $c = 3$

   $m = \dfrac{7 - 3}{1 - 0}$

   $ = 4$

   So $y = 4x + 3$

(**b**) Graph is a straight line hence
   equation is $y = mx + c$
   y-intercept is $(0, 2)$ so $c = 2$

   $m = \dfrac{0 - 2}{5 - 0}$

   $ = \dfrac{-2}{5}$

   So $y = -\dfrac{2}{5}x + 8$

Exercise 16.7

1 Find the equation of each graph.

(**a**) 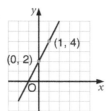   (**b**) 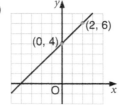   (**c**) 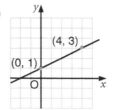   (**d**)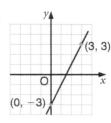

(**e**) 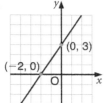   (**f**) 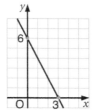   (**g**) 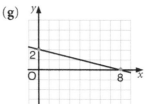   (**h**)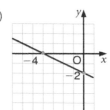

2 Write the equations of each line with the given gradient and y-intercept.

	(a)	(b)	(c)	(d)	(e)	(f)
Gradient	2	4	-3	$\frac{1}{2}$	$\frac{3}{4}$	$-\frac{2}{3}$
y-intercept	$(0, 3)$	$(0, -2)$	$(0, 5)$	$(0, 4)$	$(0, -5)$	$(0, \frac{1}{2})$

3 Find the equation of the line between each pair of points

	(a)	(b)	(c)	(d)	(e)	(f)
Point A	$(0, 5)$	$(0, -3)$	$(0, -2)$	$(0, 5)$	$(0, 4)$	$(0, -5)$
Point B	$(4, 9)$	$(-3, 0)$	$(4, 8)$	$(6, 7)$	$(3, -4)$	$(4, -10)$

4 (a) Plot the points A$(-2, 2)$, B$(0, 5)$ and C$(3, 3)$ and join them to form a triangle.
  (b) Calculate the lengths of the sides of the triangle.
  (c) Prove that the triangle is right angled at B.
  (d) Find the equations of the sides AB and CB.
  (e) Comment on the gradients of each of these lines.

5 (a) Plot the points A$(-3, -1)$, B$(0, 3)$ and C$(8, -3)$ and join them to form a triangle.
  (b) Calculate the lengths of the sides of the triangle.
  (c) Prove that the triangle is right angled at B.
  (d) Find the equations of the sides AB and CB.
  (e) Comment on the gradients of each of these lines.

6 For each set of points
  (i) plot them on a Cartesian diagram
  (ii) join the points
  (iii) state what can be said about all points on each line.

(a)	$(2, 4)$	$(3, 4)$	$(5, 4)$	$(9, 4)$
(b)	$(1, 6)$	$(2, 6)$	$(3, 6)$	$(10, 6)$
(c)	$(-1, 3)$	$(0, 3)$	$(5, 3)$	$(6, 3)$
(d)	$(-4, -2)$	$(-1, -2)$	$(5, -2)$	$(10, -2)$

7 For each set of points
  (i) plot them on a Cartesian diagram
  (ii) join the points
  (iii) state what can be said about all points on each line.

(a)	$(2, 1)$	$(2, 4)$	$(2, 6)$	$(2, 9)$
(b)	$(1, 0)$	$(1, 8)$	$(1, 5)$	$(1, 8)$
(c)	$(-1, -1)$	$(-1, 1)$	$(-1, 4)$	$(-1, 6)$
(d)	$(-4, -4)$	$(-4, -1)$	$(-4, 1)$	$(-4, 6)$

Equations of **horizontal** lines are of the form $y = a$ Equations of **vertical** lines are of the form $x = a$

Example

Write the equation of each line.

(a)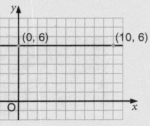

(b)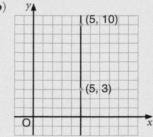

(a) $y = 6$ (b) $x = 5$

16.8 Variables other than y and x

Learning intentions

Many situations use variables other than x and y.

Example

Find the equation of each graph.

(a)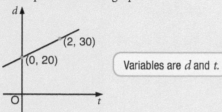

Variables are d and t.

(b)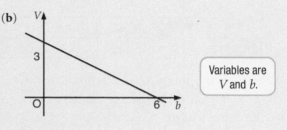

Variables are V and b.

(a) Graph is a straight line hence equation
is of the form $y = mx + c$
For variables d and t,
$$d = mt + c$$
$$m = \frac{30 - 20}{2 - 0}$$
$$m = 5$$
$$c = 20$$

So $d = 5t + 20$

(b) Graph is a straight line hence equation
is of the form $y = mx + c$
For variables V and b,
$$V = mb + c$$
$$m = \frac{0 - 3}{6 - 0}$$
$$m = -\frac{1}{2}$$
$$c = 3$$

So $V = -\frac{1}{2}b + 3$

Exercise 16.8

1 Find the equation of each graph.

(a)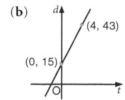

(b)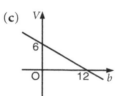

(c)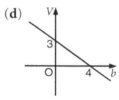

(d)

(e)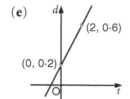

(f)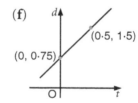

(g)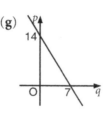

(h)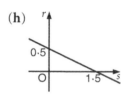

2 Chris has collected the following data from an experiment on the
extension of a spring.

Weight (W)	0 kg	2 kg	4 kg	6 kg	8 kg
Extension (E)	25 mm	45 mm	65 mm	85 mm	105 mm

(a) Plot the data on a graph.
(b) Join the points.
(c) Find the equation of the line.

3 The following data shows temperatures in degrees Fahrenheit and their equivalents in degrees Celsius.

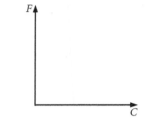

Celsuis (C)	0	20	50	80	100
Fahrenheit (F)	32	68	122	176	212

(a) Plot the data on a graph and find the equation of the line through the points.

(b) Use your equation to find the following Celsius temperatures in degrees Fahrenheit.
 (i) 25°   (ii) 65°   (iii) 76°   (iv) −20°

4 The depth of water in a cylinder is 15 centimetres. When the tap is turned on, the depth of water increases at a rate of 2 centimetres every second.

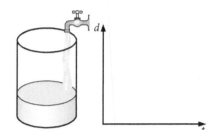

(a) Make a table and draw a graph to represent this situation.

(b) Find the equation of your graph.

(c) If the tap is closed after 12 seconds, what depth of water will be in the cylinder?

5 The cost of postage from an internet seller is calculated according to the weight of each package.
The table shows the cost for certain packages.

Weight (W)	0 g	50 g	100 g	300 g	500 g
Cost (C)	20p	30p	40p	80p	120p

(a) Draw a graph to represent this data.

(b) Find the equation of your graph.

(c) Find the cost of a package weighing 200 grams.

(d) What is the weight of a package which costs £1 for postage?

6 The depth of water in a tank when full is 150 centimetres. When the tap is turned on, the depth of water decreases at a rate of 10 centimetres every minute.

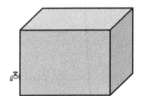

(a) Draw a graph to represent this situation.

(b) Find the equation of your graph.

(c) If the tap is closed after 7·5 minutes, what depth of water will be in the tank?

7 A coastguard rescue vessel travels due east from its base towards a yacht in danger at a constant speed of 60 kilometres per hour. The yacht is 80 kilometres from the coastguard base.

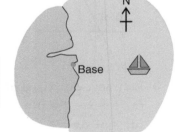

(a) Copy and complete this table showing the distance from the yacht.

Time (t)	0 min	10 min	20 min	30 min	40 min
Distance from yacht (d)	80 km				

(b) Draw a graph to represent this data.

(c) Find the equation of your graph.

(d) Use your equation to find the distance from the yacht after 45 minutes.

(e) How long will it take for the rescue boat to reach the yacht?

16.9 Rearranging the equation to give $y = mx + c$

Learning intentions

Equations of straight line graphs may not always be in the form $y = mx + c$.
Rearranging of the equation may make it easier to graph the equation.

Example

Rearrange each equation and hence sketch its graph.

(a) $2y - 6x = 8$

(b) $2x + 4y - 8 = 0$

(a) $2y - 6x = 8$
$$2y = 6x + 8$$
$$y = 3x + 4$$
Hence $m = 3$ and $c = 4$
- plot the y-intercept
- use gradient to find other points
- draw the line

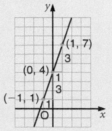

(b) $2x + 4y - 8 = 0$
$$4y = -2x + 8$$
$$y = -\tfrac{1}{2}x + 2$$
Hence $m = -\tfrac{1}{2}$ and $c = 2$
- plot the y-intercept
- use gradient to find other points
- draw the line

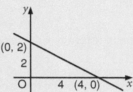

Exercise 16.9

1 Rearrange each equation and hence find the gradient and y-intercept for each line.

(a) $2y - 4x = 2$ (b) $3y + 6x = 9$

(c) $4y - 2x = 6$ (d) $4y + 6x = -8$

(e) $4x + 2y + 6 = 0$ (f) $y + 3x - 4 = 0$

2 Match each equation to its graph.

A $x + 2y = 20$ **B** $3y + x + 6 = 0$ **C** $2y - 9x = 2$ **D** $x - 2y + 4 = 0$

(i) 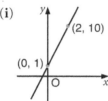   (ii) 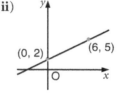   (iii) 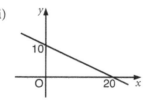   (iv)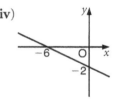

3 Rearrange each equation and hence sketch its graph.

(a) $y + x - 2 = 0$ (b) $y + 2x = 5$ (c) $2y - 6x = 2$

(d) $3y + 6x = 12$ (e) $x + 2y - 4 = 0$ (f) $y + 4x - 5 = 0$

(g) $3y + x = 7$ (h) $2x + 4y - 10 = 0$ (i) $3y + 2x = 6$

(j) $\tfrac{1}{2}x + \tfrac{1}{3}y = \tfrac{1}{2}$ (k) $\dfrac{2x - y}{3} = \dfrac{1}{3}$ (l) $\dfrac{3x - y}{5} = 1$

16.10   Graphs of the form $ax + by = c$

Learning intentions

Equations representing straight lines may be written in the form $y = mx + c$.
It may be more efficient to sketch a straight line graph using the x-intercept and y-intercept.

Example

Sketch the graph of each equation

(a) $2y + 3x = 6$
$\qquad\qquad\qquad\qquad\qquad\qquad\qquad\qquad$ **(b)** $3y - 4x = 12$

(a) $2y + 3x = 6$
$\quad$ Graph cuts the y-axis when $x = 0$
$\quad$ Substitute 0 for x $\qquad 2y + 0 = 6$
$\qquad\qquad\qquad\qquad\qquad\quad y = 3 \qquad$ Cuts at $(0, 3)$ $\qquad$ Plot these
$\quad$ Graph cuts the x-axis when $y = 0$ $\qquad\qquad\qquad\qquad\qquad$ points and
$\quad$ Substitute 0 for y $\qquad 0 + 3x = 6$ $\qquad\qquad\qquad\qquad\qquad$ join to form a
$\qquad\qquad\qquad\qquad\qquad\quad x = 2 \qquad$ Cuts at $(2, 0)$ $\qquad$ straight line

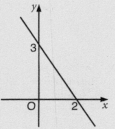

(b) $3y - 4x = 12$
$\quad$ Graph cuts the y-axis when $x = 0$
$\quad$ Substitute 0 for x $\qquad 3y - 0 = 12$
$\qquad\qquad\qquad\qquad\qquad\quad y = 4 \qquad$ Cuts at $(0, 4)$ $\qquad$ Plot these
$\quad$ Graph cuts the x-axis when $y = 0$ $\qquad\qquad\qquad\qquad\qquad$ points and
$\quad$ Substitute 0 for y $\qquad 0 - 4x = 12$ $\qquad\qquad\qquad\qquad\qquad$ join to form a
$\qquad\qquad\qquad\qquad\qquad\quad x = -3 \quad$ Cuts at $(-3, 0)$ $\qquad$ straight line

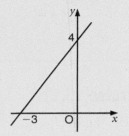

Exercise 16.10

1 Find the x and y-intercepts and hence match each equation to its graph.

$\quad$ **A** $x + 2y = 4$ $\qquad$ **B** $3y + x = -6$ $\qquad$ **C** $4y - 2x = 4$ $\qquad$ **D** $4x - 2y = -2$

(i)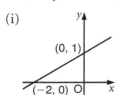
$\quad$ (ii)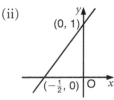
$\quad$ (iii)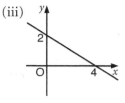
$\quad$ (iv)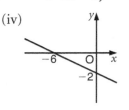

2 Find the x and y-intercepts and hence sketch the graph of each equation.

$\quad$ **(a)** $y - x + 3 = 0$ $\qquad\qquad$ **(b)** $3y - 2x = 6$

$\quad$ **(c)** $2y - 3x = 12$ $\qquad\qquad$ **(d)** $3y + 6x = 6$

$\quad$ **(e)** $3x + 4y = 6$ $\qquad\qquad$ **(f)** $3y - 4x = 8$

$\quad$ **(g)** $\frac{1}{2}y + 3x = 6$ $\qquad\qquad$ **(h)** $2x - \frac{1}{2}y = 3$

$\quad$ **(i)** $\frac{1}{2}y + \frac{1}{3}x = 2$

16.11 Solving simultaneous equations graphically

Learning intentions

$2x + 3y = 6$ represents the straight line containing all points whose co-ordinates have this relationship.
$4x + 2y = 8$ represents the straight line containing all points whose co-ordinates have this relationship.
The point of intersection of the lines represents the values which satisfy both equations simultaneously.
$P(1\frac{1}{2}, 1)$ is the solution to the simultaneous equations.

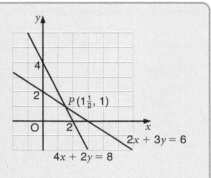

Example

Solve the following pair of simultaneous equations graphically.
$$2x - y = -1$$
$$2x + y = 5$$

Sketch the graphs of each equation.
Graphs cross at $P(1, 3)$
Solution is $x = 1, y = 3$.

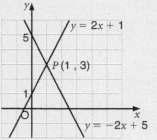

Exercise 16.11

1 Use the graphs to find the solution to each pair of simultaneous equations.

(a) 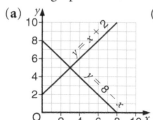 (b) 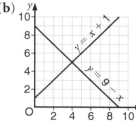 (c) 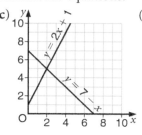 (d)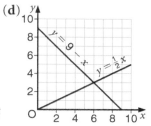

2 For each pair of equations, draw graphs to find the point of intersection.

(a) $y = -x + 4$
    $y = x + 2$

(b) $y = -x + 6$
    $y = x$

(c) $y = 3x + 9$
    $y = 3 - 3x$

(d) $y = 2x - 8$
    $y = -2x + 2$

3 For each pair of equations, draw graphs to solve them simultaneously.

(a) $2x + y = 5$
    $x + y = 3$

(b) $2x + y = 1$
    $x + 2y = -1$

(c) $5x + y = 4$
    $x - 2y = 3$

(d) $3x + 2y = 0$
    $2x + 3y = -5$

4 Solve these simultaneous equations graphically.

(a) $x + y = 0$
    $4x + 3y = 3$

(b) $2y + 3x = 5$
    $y + x = 2$

(c) $2y + 5x = 16$
    $y = x + 1$

(d) $3x + 4y = -7$
    $2x + y = -3$

16.12   Intersection using algebra

Learning intentions

Simultaneous equations may be solved algebraically. This method may be used to find where two lines intersect.

Example

Find algebraically the point of intersection of the lines with the equations
$y = x + 2$ and $y = 2x - 3$

Solve the equations simultaneously.

$$y = x + 2 \qquad ①$$
$$y = 2x - 3 \qquad ②$$

Substitute $x + 2$ for y in equation ②

$$x + 2 = 2x - 3$$
$$2 + 3 = 2x - x$$
$$x = 5$$

Replace in equation ①

$$y = 5 + 2$$
$$y = 7$$

Point of intersection is $(5, 7)$

Remember that simultaneous equations may be solved using elimination or substitution.

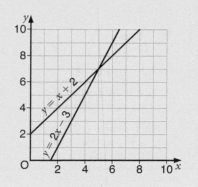

Exercise 16.12

1 (i) State the point of intersection of each pair of lines.
     (ii) Prove algebraically the point of intersection.

(**a**) $y = x$
        $y = 2x - 5$

(**b**) $y = 2x$
        $y = 6x - 8$

(**c**) $y = 3x$
        $y = \frac{3}{2}x - 6$

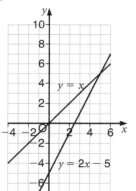
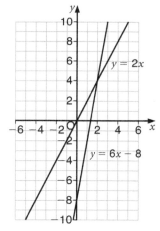
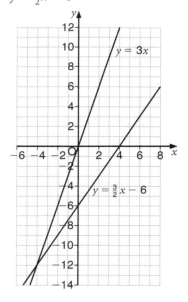

2 For each pair of equations
   (i) sketch the graphs
   (ii) use the sketch to find the point of intersection
   (iii) solve each pair of equations algebraically to check the graphical solution.

(**a**) $y = 4 - 2x$
         $-2x - 3y = -4$

(**b**) $5x + 4y = -13$
         $6x - 4y = 2$

(**c**) $2y + 3x = -1$
         $y - 3x = 4$

(**d**) $-3x + 4y = 7$
         $3x + y = -2$

(**e**) $y = x + 3$
         $3y + 2x = 4$

(**f**) $y = 2x - 1$
         $3y = 2x + 5$

(**g**) $y = 2x - 2$
         $5x = 4y - 1$

(**h**) $y = 2x + 3$
       $5y - 2x + 1 = 0$

16.13 Solving problems

Learning intentions

Example

Two companies offer dinghies for hire. *Sail Ahoy* charges £10 per hour plus a standing charge of £20. At *Depth Charges* the cost is £5 per hour plus a standing charge of £50. Which company represents the best value?

Let *C* be the total cost and *h* the number of hours.

Sail Ahoy	*Depth Charges*
$C = 10h + 20$	$C = 5h + 50$

Sketch the graph of each equation.

The graphs cross when $h = 6$ and $C = 80$.
Both companies charge the same at this point. £80 for 6 hours

Sail Ahoy is the cheaper for hires of less than 6 hours.
Depth Charges is the cheaper for hires of more than 6 hours.

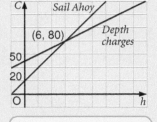

The equation may be solved using algebraic methods

Exercise 16.13

1 Two companies offer the same model of car for hire. *Higher Cars* charges £5 per hour plus a standing charge of £30. At *Mental Rentals* the cost is £8 per hour plus a standing charge of £15.

  (**a**) Write two equations to represent this information.

  (**b**) On the same diagram, draw graphs representing the equations.

  (**c**) Which company represents the best value for money? Explain fully.

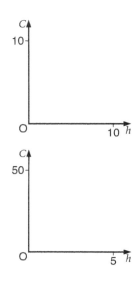

2 Bob wants to hire a Karaoke machine for a party. *Club Karaoke* charges £8 per hour. *Laser Karaoke* has a standing charge of £12 plus £4 per hour.

  (**a**) Write two equations to represent this information.

  (**b**) On the same diagram, draw graphs representing the equations.

  (**c**) After how many hours is the charge the same for both companies?

  (**d**) What is this charge?

3 *City cabs* charge a standing fee of £1 plus £3.50 per mile. *Town Taxis* charge a standing fee of £3 plus £2.50 per mile. Explain when it would be most economical to use *City cabs* and when *Town Taxis* should be used.

4 *Crocodile* internet company charge postage of £5 plus 20p per CD ordered. *Aligator* charge postage of £4 plus 30p per CD ordered. Which company offers best value for money? Explain fully.

5 *Sinking Feeling Plumbers* have a call out charge of £50. In addition they charge £20 per hour. *Shower of Cowboys* has a call out charge of £60 plus £15 per hour. Which firm offers the best value?

6 The flight path of a jet may be described by the equation $y = 2x - 4$. The flight path of another jet may be described by the equation $y = 8 - 2x$. Find the coordinates of the point where the paths cross.

7 *The Bank of Scotia* credit card charges £10 plus 20% on all purchases. *The Alba Bank* credit card charges £30 plus 10% on all purchases. Which bank should you choose?

16.14　Equations from graphs: further techniques

Learning intentions

It is possible to find the equation of a straight line by
substituting points into the general equation $y = mx + c$

Example 1

Find the equation of the line.

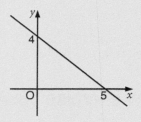

Straight line, hence $y = mx + c$
y-intercept is $(0, 4)$ hence
Substitute the point $(5, 0)$

$$y = mx + 4$$
$$0 = m \times 5 + 4$$
$$-4 = 5m$$
$$-\tfrac{4}{5} = m$$

So　　$$y = -\tfrac{4}{5}x + 4$$

Example 2

Find the equation of the line which passes through the points $(100, 250)$ and $(-90, -130)$.

Straight line, hence $y = mx + c$

$$y = mx + c$$

Substitute the point $(100, 250)$　　$250 = 100m + c$　①
Substitute the point $(-90, -130)$　$-130 = -90m + c$　②

Solve as simultaneous equations.

$$380 = 190m$$
$$2 = m$$
$$250 = 100 \times 2 + c$$
$$c = 50$$

The equation is $y = 2x + 50$

Example 3

Pedil Bikes offers mountain bikes and road bikes for hire. The cost of hiring 3 mountain bikes and 2 road bikes is £24. The cost of hiring 2 mountain bikes and 4 road bikes is £32. Find the cost of hiring each kind of bike.

Let m be the cost of hiring a mountain bike and r the cost of
hiring a road bike.

$3m + 2r = 24$
$2m + 4r = 32$
Each equation may be shown as a graph.

The graphs intersect when $m = 4$ and $r = 6$.
The cost of hiring a mountain bike is **£4** and a road bike **£6**.

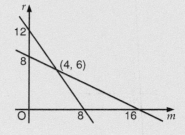

Exercise 16.14

1 Find the equation of each graph.

(a)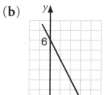

(b)

(c)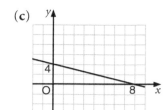

(d)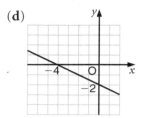

2 Find the equation of the line joining each pair of points

(**a**) $(100, 350), (300, 600)$ (**b**) $(150, 250), (250, 500)$ (**c**) $(156, 498), (312, 576)$

(**d**) $(0·5, 4·5), (3·5, 16·5)$ (**e**) $(123, -235), (-37, 85)$ (**f**) $(-0·25, 7·5), (0·75, 3·6)$

(**g**) $(-34, -456), (-34, -276)$ (**h**) $(0·25, 0·6), (0·42, 0·6)$

3 *Chain Reaction* offers mountain bikes and road bikes for hire. The cost of hiring 3 mountain bikes and 2 road bikes is £46. The cost of hiring 2 mountain bikes and 3 road bikes is £44.

(**a**) Write two equations to represent this information.

(**b**) On the same diagram draw graphs representing the equations.

(**c**) Find the cost of hiring each kind of bike.

Review exercise 16: Am I a successful learner?

1 Find the gradient of each line.

(**a**) 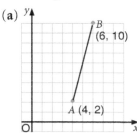   (**b**)    (**c**) 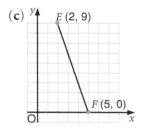   (**d**)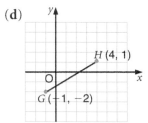

2 Calculate the gradient of the line between each pair of points.

(**a**) $A(5, 8)$ and $B(12, 22)$ (**b**) $C(-2, -3)$ and $D(6, -8)$

3 Find the equation of the line through O and A.

(**a**) 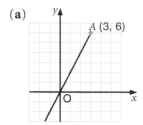   (**b**) 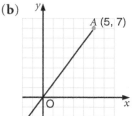   (**c**) 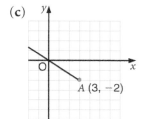   (**d**)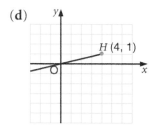

4 State the gradient and y-intercept for the graph represented by each of the following equations and hence sketch the graphs.

(**a**) $y = 4x + 1$ (**b**) $y = -3x + 4$ (**c**) $y = \frac{1}{2}x - 4$

(**d**) $2y = -x + 5$ (**e**) $-2y = 3x + 4$

5 Find the equation of each graph

(**a**) 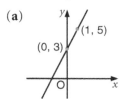   (**b**) 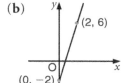   (**c**) 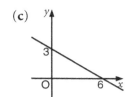   (**d**)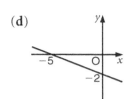

6 Which of the the points P(4, 11) and Q(−5, −7) lie on the line $y = 2x + 3$?

7 Find the equation of each graph.

(a) 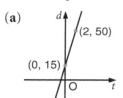 **(b)** 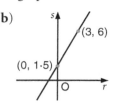 **(c)** 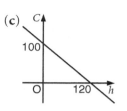 **(d)**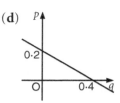

8 The depth of water in a tank is 20 centimetres. When the tap is turned on the depth of water increases at a rate of 5 centimetres every second.

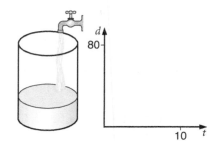

(a) Draw a graph to represent this situation.

(b) Find the equation of the graph.

(c) If the tap is closed after 10 seconds, what depth of water will be in the cylinder?

9 A boat travels due north from buoy B at a constant speed of 20 kilometres per hour. The buoy is 5 kilometres due north of Port P.

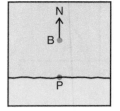

(a) Copy and complete this table showing the distance from Port P.

Time (*t*)	0 h	1 h	2 h	3 h	4 h
Distance (*d*)	5 km				

(b) Draw a graph to represent this data.

(c) Find the equation of the graph.

(d) Find the distance from P after $5\frac{1}{2}$ hours.

(e) How long will it take for the boat to be 100 kilometres from Port P?

10 Rearrange and hence sketch the graph of each equation.
 (a) $y - 2x - 2 = 0$ (b) $y + 3x = 6$ (c) $2y + x - 6 = 0$

11 Without rearranging equations, sketch the graph of each equation.
 (a) $y - x = 4$ (b) $3y + 2x = 6$ (c) $3y + 4x = 12$

12 Use the graphs to find the solution to each pair of simultaneous equations.

(a) 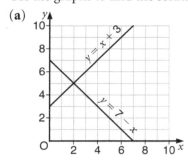   **(b)**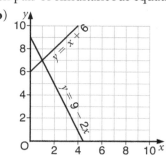

13 *Sparky Electrical* has a call out charge of £40. In addition they charge £20 per hour. *Wired* has a call out charge of £50 plus £18 per hour. Which firm offers best value?

14 For each pair of equations
  (i) draw graphs to represent the equations and find the point of intersection.
  (ii) solve the equations algebraically to check your answer.
  (a) $y = -x + 8$ (b) $3x + 2y = 12$
      $y = x - 2$ $2x - 4y = 0$

15 At the Film Centre the total charge for 3 adults and 2 children was £44. The cost for 2 adults and 3 children was £41.
  (a) Write two equations to represent this information.
  (b) On the same diagram, draw graphs representing the equations.
  (c) Find the cost of entry for adults and children.

16 Find the equation of the line joining each pair of points.
  (a) $(-26, 87), (14, 47)$ (b) $(21, 42), (53, 86)$

17 Find the equation of each line.

(a) 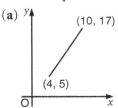 (b) 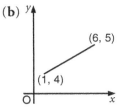 (c) 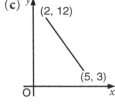 (d)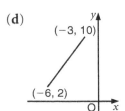

Summary 16: What I learned in this chapter.

Gradient

From left to right:
- lines sloping **up** have a **positive** gradient
- lines sloping **down** have a **negative** gradient.
- The gradient of a **horizontal** line is **0**.
- The gradient of a **vertical** line is **undefined**.
- **Parallel** lines have the **same gradient**

$$\text{Gradient} = \frac{\text{vertical distance}}{\text{horizontal distance}} = \frac{y_2 - y_1}{x_2 - x_1}$$

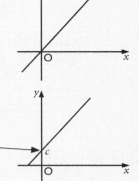

Equations of a line

$y = mx$ represents a line with gradient m which passes through the origin $(0, 0)$
$y = mx + c$ represents a line with gradient m and y-intercept $(0, c)$

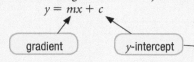

The **coefficient of x** gives the gradient and **the constant** gives the y-intercept.

Sketching straight line graphs

Equations of straight line graphs may not always be in the form $y = mx + c$.
Rearranging the equation may make it easier to graph the equation.
$2y - 6x = 8$
$\quad\quad 2y = 6x + 8$
$\quad\quad\; y = 3x + 4$
Hence gradient $= 3$, y-intercept is $(0, 4)$

- plot the y-intercept
- use gradient to find other points
- draw the line

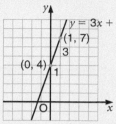

$\text{Gradient} = \dfrac{3}{1} : \dfrac{3 \text{ up}}{1 \text{ along}}$

At times it may be more efficient to sketch the graph using the x and y-intercepts.
$2y + 3x = 6$
Graph cuts the y-axis when $x = 0$
$\quad\quad\quad\quad 2y + 0 = 6$
$\quad\quad\quad\quad\quad\; y = 3 \quad$ Cuts at $(0, 3)$
Graph cuts x-axis when $y = 0$
$\quad\quad\quad\quad 0 + 3x = 6$
$\quad\quad\quad\quad\quad\; x = 2 \quad$ Cuts at $(2, 0)$

Plot these points and join
to form a straight line

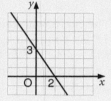

Simultaneous equations

The point of intersection of the graphs is where both equations are satisfied simultaneously.
$P(1, 3)$ is the solution to the simultaneous equations.

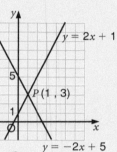

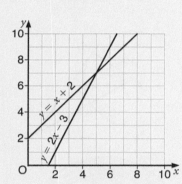

The point of intersection can be found
by solving simultaneous equations algebraically.

$\quad\quad\quad y = x + 2 \;\text{①}$
$\quad\quad\quad y = 2x - 3\;\text{②}$

Substitute $x + 2$ for y in equation ② $\quad x + 2 = 2x - 3$
$\quad\quad\quad\quad\quad\quad\quad\quad\quad\quad\quad\quad x = 5$
Replace in equation ① $\quad\quad\quad\quad\quad y = 5 + 2$
$\quad\quad\quad\quad\quad\quad\quad\quad\quad\quad\quad\quad y = 7$

Point of intersection is $(5, 7)$

Further techniques

It is possible to find the equation of a straight line by substituting points into the general equation $y = mx + c$

Straight line hence $y = mx + c$

y-intercept is $(0, 4)$ $\quad\quad\quad\quad\quad\quad y = mx + 4$
Substitute the point $(5, 0)$ $\quad\quad\quad\quad 0 = m \times 5 + 4$
$\quad\quad\quad\quad\quad\quad\quad\quad\quad\quad\quad -4 = 5m$
$\quad\quad\quad\quad\quad\quad\quad\quad\quad\quad -\frac{4}{5} = m$
$\quad\quad\quad\quad\quad\quad\quad\quad\quad\quad\quad\; y = -\frac{4}{5}x + 4$

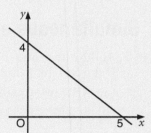

When two points on a graph are known: $(100, 250)$ and $(-90, -130)$, solving simultaneous
equations algebraically may be used to find the equation of the line.

Straight line hence $y = mx + c$

Substitute each point into the general equation $\quad\quad\quad\quad 250 = 100m + c$
$\quad\quad\quad\quad\quad\quad\quad\quad\quad\quad\quad\quad\quad\quad\quad\quad -130 = -90m + c$
Solve as simultaneous equations. $\quad\quad\quad\quad\quad\quad\quad\quad 380 = 190m$
$\quad\quad\quad\quad\quad\quad\quad\quad\quad\quad\quad\quad\quad\quad\quad\quad\quad\; 2 = m$
$\quad\quad\quad\quad\quad\quad\quad\quad\quad\quad\quad\quad\quad\quad\quad 250 = 100 \times 2 + c$
$\quad\quad\quad\quad\quad\quad\quad\quad\quad\quad\quad\quad\quad\quad\quad\quad\; c = 50$

The equation is $y = 2x + 50$

Review 4

Exercise 4A

Circle geometry

1 Find the depth of water in the tunnel of diameter 10 metres.

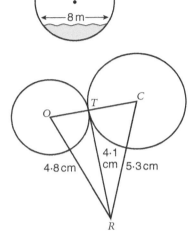

2 The circles with centres O and C touch at T.
TR is a common tangent.
$RO = 4\cdot8$ cm, $RT = 4\cdot1$ cm and $RC = 5\cdot3$ cm
Calculate the distance between the centres of
the circles.

3 PQ is a tangent to the circle.
Calculate the length of RQ.

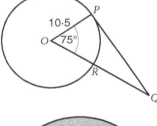

4 A semi circular arch is supported
by wooden beams. Calculate the
length of the horizontal beam if
the sloping beams are both
7·3 metres long.

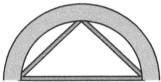

Simultaneous equations

5 At the film centre the total charge for 2 adults and one child was £16.
If the cost for 3 adults and 4 children was £34

(**a**) write two equations to represent this information

(**b**) find the cost of entry for   (**i**) an adult   (**ii**) a child.

6 Solve simultaneously:

(**a**) $2y + 3x = 8$ (**b**) $y = 3x$ (**c**) $5x + 3y = 12$
    $5y + 2x = -2$ $2x + 5y = 34$ $2x - 7y - 13 = 0$

7 Rolf is a gardener in the park. He plants geraniums and daisies and has 630
plants in total. Geraniums cost 9 pence each and daisies cost 5 pence each.
If the plants cost £39.50 altogether, how many geraniums did he have?

8 A conference centre has a large hall which is five times bigger than the small hall. The two halls hold 168 altogether. How many people will the large hall hold?

Straight line

9 Find the equation of each line.

(**a**)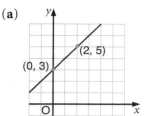

(**b**)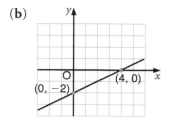

(**c**)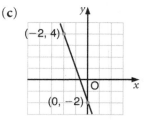

10 Find the gradient and the y-intercept for the following equations and sketch the line.

(**a**) $y = 2x + 4$

(**b**) $y = x - 3$

(**c**) $y = -3x - 1$

(**d**) $5y + 10x - 25 = 0$

11 Find the equation of the graph.

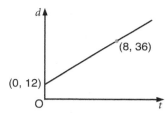

Exercise 4B (cumulative)

1 Expand and simplify:

(**a**) $(x - 3)(x + 7)$

(**b**) $(x - 4)(x + 4)$

(**c**) $(2x - 1)(3x - 5)$

(**d**) $(4x + 3)(2x - 3y + 5)$

2 In the triangle, DB = 15 centimetres, AC = 24 centimetres and DE = 16 centimetres. Find the length of AD.

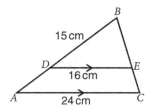

3 A house was valued at £134 000 in 2004 and £168 420 in 2007. What was the percentage increase in value?

4 Calculate the length of a and b.

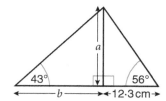

5 Evaluate the formula $E = \frac{mv^2}{2}$, when $m = 4 \cdot 5$ and $v = 7$

6 Solve:

(a) $3x - 2y = 20$
$4x + 5y = -27$

(b) $y = 2x + 1$
$5x + 3y = 25$

7 Rearrange the following formulae to make x the subject:

(a) $P = 2(x - a) - b$

(b) $A = \frac{d}{s}(x - t)$

(c) $v = \sqrt{\frac{3xt}{m}}$

8 A circular children's play park, with radius 16 metres, is to be surrounded by a fence in the shape of a triangle. The edges of the triangle are tangents to the circle and the distance from the centre of the park to the corner of the fence is 34 metres.
Calculate

(a) the total length of fence used.

(b) the area contained inside the fence.

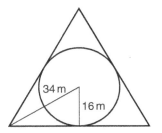

9 A child's ticket to Barton Towers theme park costs 40% of the adult ticket price. Calculate the adult ticket price if a child's ticket costs £7.50.

10 Abbie bought a car for £7995. In the first year the value depreciated by 15%, in the second year by 22% and in the third year by 20%. How much was the car worth after 3 years?

11 The number of absences at a school are recorded over three weeks in January.

18	24	20	31	27
20	23	34	30	12
14	17	36	32	20

(a) Construct a stem and leaf diagram and hence find the median and the quartiles.

(b) Calculate the semi-interquartile range.

(c) Draw a box plot to represent the data.

12 (a) Find the equation of the line which :

(i) passes through $(0, 8)$ with gradient 2

(ii) passes through $(0, -2)$ and $(5, -17)$.

(b) Find algebraically the point of intersection of these two lines.

13 Solve:

(a) $6 - 3(w + 2) = 30$

(b) $4(3w - 2) < 6(w + 1)$

(c) $(x + 2)(2x - 5) = 2(x - 1)(x + 3)$

(d) $(2a - 5)^2 = 4(a - 1)^2$

14 (a) Calculate the length of AB.

(b) Hence find the area of triangle ABC.

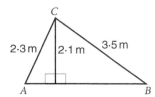

15 Roberta has dug a vegetable patch in her garden. She measures the length, breadth and diagonal. Is the garden rectangular?

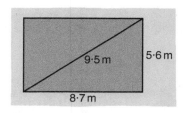

16 If £1 is worth $1.72, change $500 into pounds sterling.

17 Adam rolls two dice and adds the score.
  (**a**) What is the probability that his score is   (**i**) even   (**ii**) nine?
  (**b**) If he throws the dice 120 times, how often would he expect a score of 4?

18 (**a**) Mr Brown makes wooden toy boxes.
          Calculate the volume of this toy box.
  (**b**) Mr Brown also produces a model of this toy box,
          with all the dimensions halved.
          Find the volume of the smaller toy box.

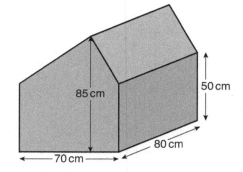

19 A map has a scale 1 : 40 000
  (**a**) What distance on the ground is represented by 3·5 centimetres on the map?
  (**b**) What distance on the map does an actual distance of 2·4 kilometres represent?

20 The angle of elevation of the cliff top from two boats is shown in the diagram.
  If the cliff top is 21 metres high calculate x, the distance between the boats.

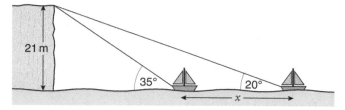

21 Form an equation and solve it to find the value of x.

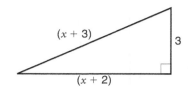

17 Factorising

17.1 Factors

Learning intentions

The factors of 18: $18 = 1 \times 18$
$18 = 2 \times 9$
$18 = 3 \times 6$

Use factor pairs

The factors of 18 are 1, 2, 3, 6, 9, 18

Algebraic expressions also have factors.

The factors of $6y$:
$6y = 1 \times 6y$
$6y = 2 \times 3y$
$6y = 3 \times 2y$
$6y = 6 \times y$

The factors of $6y$ are
1, 2, 3, 6, y, $2y$, $3y$, $6y$

The factors of $4a^2$:
$4a^2 = 1 \times 4a^2$
$4a^2 = 2 \times 2a^2$
$4a^2 = 4 \times a^2$
$4a^2 = a \times 4a$
$4a^2 = 2a \times 2a$
The factors of $4a^2$ are
1, 2, 4, a, $2a$, $4a$, a^2, $2a^2$, $4a^2$

Example 1

Find the highest common factors of 16 and 20.

The factors of 16 are 1, 16, 2, 8, 4
The factors of 20 are 1, 20, 2, 10, 4, 5
The highest common factor is **4**.

The common factors
are 1, 2 and 4.

Example 2

Find the largest common factor of $4x$ and $6x$.

The factors of $4x$ are 1, $4x$, 2, $2x$, 4, x,
The factors of $6x$ are 1, $6x$, 2, $3x$, 3, $2x$, 6, x.
The largest common factor is **$2x$**

The common factors
are 1, 2, x and $2x$.

Exercise 17.1

1 Write the factors of each number. Hence find the highest common factor of :

  (**a**) 30 and 27   (**b**) 16 and 40   (**c**) 24 and 18   (**d**) 40 and 50

2 Write the factors of each term. Hence find the largest common factor of:

  (**a**) $8x$ and $6x$ (**b**) $10x$ and $15x$ (**c**) $7x$ and $5x$ (**d**) $12a$ and $15a$

3 Find the largest common factor of:

  (**a**) 6 and $18x$ (**b**) 4 and $12t$ (**c**) 10 and $4y$ (**d**) 9 and $15x$

  (**e**) $5x$ and $15x$ (**f**) $12y$ and $18y$ (**g**) $6x$ and $9x$ (**h**) $14p$ and $21p$

4 Find the largest common factor of:

  (**a**) x^2 and x^4 (**b**) $4x$ and $6x^2$ (**c**) $5pq$ and $10pr$ (**d**) $3ab$ and $2a^2$

  (**e**) b^3 and $2b^2$ (**f**) abc and abd (**g**) $3xz$ and $6x^2$ (**h**) $12pq$ and $15p^2$

17.2   Common factors

Learning intentions

Expand $4(2x + 5) = 8x + 20$ 4 and $(2x + 5)$ are two factors of $8x + 20$

The reverse process of expanding brackets is called **factorising**.

Example

Factorise: (a) $3x - 15$ (b) $16xy + 15x$ (c) $\pi r^2 + \pi d + 2\pi$ (d) $6x^3 - 2x^2$

(a) $3x - 15 = 3(x - 5)$ 3 is the common factor.   (b) $16xy + 15x = x(16y + 15)$ x is the common factor.

(c) $\pi r^2 + \pi d + 2\pi = \pi(r^2 + d + 2)$ (d) $6x^3 - 2x^2 = 2x^2(3x - 1)$

Exercise 17. 2

1 Factorise:

(a) $3x + 18$ (b) $2x + 10$ (c) $2x - 6 + 8y$

(d) $3x - 21 - 27z$ (e) $4y + 6$ (f) $-35 + 49t + 28x$

(g) $-15x + 48$ (h) $64 - 16z$ (i) $45y - 75 + 150t$

2 Find the missing dimensions of each rectangle.

(a) $\uparrow$ 2 Area = $16x + 18$

(b) $\uparrow$ 3 Area = $18x - 6$

(c) Area = $24x - 16$ $\longleftarrow$ 8 $\longrightarrow$

(d) Area = $40 - 25x$ $\longleftarrow$ 5 $\longrightarrow$

3 Factorise:

(a) $2ab + \pi a$ (b) $2x^2 + 3x + 5xa$ (c) $7t - at$

(d) $2tp^2 + 11p^2q$ (e) $5x + x^2 - 2xp$ (f) $x^5 - x^2$

(g) $10v^2 - \pi v^5$ (h) $x + x^4 - x^5$ (i) $abc + 3at$

4 Factorise:

(a) $4\pi x - 2\pi b$ (b) $10x^2 - 5x$ (c) $12av^2 - 3v$

(d) $6zx + 2z^2$ (e) $5x + 10xt$ (f) $2ab - 4ac - 12a^2$

(g) $4ab + 8ab^2$ (h) $3xy + 3x$ (i) $y^2 + y^3$

(j) $\pi v^5 - \pi v^2$ (k) $5x^3 + x^4$ (l) $\pi x^3 + 2\pi x^2$

(m) $5pq^2r^2 - 25pq^2r^3$ (n) $4atr + 4a^2tr$ (o) $6ax^2 - 3ax + 5x$

5 Factorise:

(a) $6a + 10b + 12c$ (b) $\pi ax + \pi ab + \pi ay$ (c) $12ax^2 + 5x - 10bx$

(d) $x^3 + x^4 + x^5$ (e) $x^2y + xy^2 + xy^3$ (f) $2px^2 + 12px + 18$

(g) $6x^2 + 10x - 4$ (h) $9y^2 - 12x - 3$ (i) $5\pi x + 15\pi x^2 + 20$

(j) $2p^2 - 20p + 6$ (k) $3q^2 - 3q + 15$ (l) $10r^2 - 20r + 100$

6 Factorise:
(**a**) $2xyz + xyt$
(**b**) $10abc + 3ab$
(**c**) $x^2yz + xya$
(**d**) $x^2yz + xy^2z$
(**e**) $2a^2st + 4ast$
(**f**) $5pq^2r + 6apq$

7 Copy and complete.
(**a**) $14 \times 8 + 14 \times 22$
  $= 14(8 + 22)$
  $= 14 \times 30$
  $=$

(**b**) $24 \times 43 + 24 \times 17$
  $= 24(\quad)$

(**c**) $18 \times 26 - 18 \times 16$
  $=$

17.3 Difference of two squares

Learning intentions

Expand (**a**) $(x + 6)(x - 6)$

(**a**) $(x + 6)(x - 6) = x^2 - 6x + 6x - 36$
  $= x^2 - 36$

(**b**) $(x + y)(x - y)$

(**b**) $(x + y)(x - y) = x^2 - xy + xy - y^2$
  $= x^2 - y^2$

Geometrically this shaded area may be calculated in two ways.

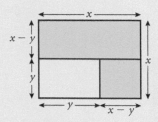

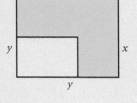

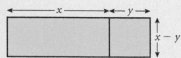

Shaded area $=$ area of large square $-$ area of small square
  $= x^2 - y^2$

Shaded area $= (x + y)(x - y)$

So $x^2 - y^2 = (x + y)(x - y)$

An algebraic expression of the type $x^2 - y^2$ is called a **difference of two squares**.

Example 1
Factorise:
(**a**) $y^2 - 25$

(**b**) $x^2 - b^2$

(**a**) $y^2 - 25$
  $= (y + 5)(y - 5)$

(**b**) $x^2 - b^2$
  $= (x + b)(x - b)$

Example 2
Factorise:
(**a**) $4a^2 - 25x^2$

(**b**) $a^2b^2 - x^2y^2$

(**c**) $18x^2 - 200y^2$

Common factor of 2

(**a**) $4a^2 - 25x^2$
  $= (2a)^2 - (5x)^2$
  $= (2a + 5x)(2a - 5x)$

(**b**) $a^2b^2 - x^2y^2$
  $= (ab)^2 - (xy)^2$
  $= (ab + xy)(ab - xy)$

(**c**) $18x^2 - 200y^2$
  $= 2(9x^2 - 100y^2)$
  $= 2[(3x)^2 - (10y)^2]$
  $= 2(3x + 10y)(3x - 10y)$

Exercise 17.3

1 Express each shaded area as a difference of two squares:

(a)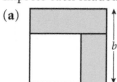

(b)

(c)

(d)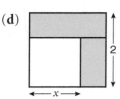

2 Factorise:

(a) $x^2 - 16$

(b) $y^2 - 25$

(c) $t^2 - 4$

(d) $f^2 - 64$

(e) $g^2 - 400$

(f) $b^2 - 900$

(g) $t^2 - 169$

(h) $x^2 - 225$

(i) $x^2 - b^2$

(j) $x^2 - t^2$

(k) $x^2 - a^2$

(l) $z^2 - \pi^2$

3 Factorise:

(a) $4x^2 - b^2$

(b) $z^2 - 81y^2$

(c) $x^2 - 49a^2$

(d) $64t^2 - x^2$

(e) $100x^2 - 121b^2$

(f) $100z^2 - 49p^2$

(g) $36x^2 - 169a^2$

(h) $25x^2 - 81t^2$

4 Factorise fully by first taking out a common factor:

(a) $5y^2 - 5a^2$

(b) $11z^2 - 11t^2$

(c) $\pi r^2 - \pi x^2$

(d) $45x^2 - 20t^2$

(e) $300x^2 - 243b^2$

(f) $48z^2 - 27p^2$

(g) $75x^2 - 12a^2$

(h) $32y^2 - 8x^2$

(i) $tx^2 - ty^2$

(j) $2sr^2 - 2sq^2$

(k) $8ct^2 - 2cr^2$

(l) $aby^2 - abr^2$

5 Factorise fully:

(a) $(ab)^2 - (st)^2$

(b) $t^2y^2 - d^2s^2$

(c) $f^2g^2 - 4p^2q^2$

(d) $9a^2b^2 - 4x^2y^2$

(e) $49a^2b^2 - 81x^2y^2$

(f) $36a^2b^2 - 100x^2y^2$

(g) $x^4 - 9y^2$

(h) $16x^4 - 25r^2$

6 Factorise fully:

(a) $x^2 - b^2$

(b) $36z^2 - 81p^2$

(c) $a^2 - \pi^2$

(d) $9a^2 - 25x^2$

(e) $a^4 - 16y^2$

(f) $t^2 - 400$

(g) $49x^2 - 100a^2$

(h) $\pi y^2 - \pi z^2$

(i) $63x^2 - 28t^2$

(j) $81x^4 - 25y^2$

(k) $45x^2 - 20t^2$

(l) $48z^2 - 27t^2$

7 Factorise:

(a) $(x - 3)^2 - 9$

(b) $(x - 5)^2 - 16$

(c) $(x - 4)^2 - 25$

8 Copy and complete:

(a) $(t - 1)^2 - (t - 3)^2$

$= ((t - 1) - (t - 3))((t - 1) + (t - 3))$

$= 2(2t - 4)$

$= 4(t - 2)$

(b) $(r + 2)^2 - (r - 5)^2$

(c) $(x + 1)^2 - (x - 2)^2$

17.4 Trinomials

Learning intentions

An expression with three terms is called a **trinomial**.

Expand
$(x + 5)(x + 2)$
$= x^2 + 2x + 5x + 10$
$= x^2 + 7x + 10$

5 + 2   5 × 2

Expand
$(x + 6)(x + 4)$
$= x^2 + 4x + 6x + 24$
$= x^2 + 10x + 24$

6 + 4   6 × 4

This process may be reversed

$x^2 + 7x + 10$ may be factorised to give
$(x + 5)(x + 2)$

$x^2 + 10x + 24$ may be factorised to give
$(x + 6)(x + 4)$

Example

Factorise

(a) $x^2 + 7x + 12$

Look for two numbers that multiply to give 12 and add to give 7.

(a) $x^2 + 7x + 12$
  $= x^2 + 3x + 4x + 12$
  $= x(x + 3) + 4(x + 3)$ Factorise
  $= (x + 4)(x + 3)$ Common factor

Check by multiplying out.

(b) $x^2 + 10x + 25$

Look for two numbers that multiply to give 25 and add to give 10.

(b) $x^2 + 10x + 25$
  $= x^2 + 5x + 5x + 25$
  $= x(x + 5) + 5(x + 5)$ Factorise
  $= (x + 5)(x + 5)$ Common factor
  $= (x + 5)^2$

Check by multiplying out.

Exercise 17.4

1 Expand:
  (a) $(x + 7)(x + 2)$
  (b) $(p + 4)(p + 1)$
  (c) $(t + 2)(t + 3)$
  (d) $(x + 4)(x + 10)$
  (e) $(y + 3)(y + 15)$
  (f) $(x + 3)(x + 3)$

2 Find two numbers that multiply to give 24 and add to give:
  (a) 14   **(b)** 11   **(c)** 10   **(d)** 25

3 Find two numbers that add to give 12 and multiply to give:
  (a) 20   **(b)** 35   **(c)** 27   **(d)** 32

4 Copy and complete to factorise:
  (a) $x^2 + 8x + 12$
    $= x^2 + 6x + 2x + 12$
    $= x(x + 6) + 2(\quad)$
    $= (x + 2)(\quad)$

  (b) $x^2 + 15x + 50$
    $= x^2 + 5x + 10x + 50$
    $= x(\quad) + 10(\quad)$
    $= (\quad)(x + 5)$

  (c) $x^2 + 10x + 21$
    $= x^2 + 7x + 3x + 21$
    $= x(\quad) + 3(\quad)$
    $= (x + 3)(\quad)$

  (d) $x^2 + 7x + 10$
    $= x^2 + 5x + \quad + 10$
    $= x(\quad) + (\quad)$
    $= (x + 2)(\quad)$

  (e) $x^2 + 3x + 2$
    $= x^2 + 2x + x + 2$
    $= x(x + 2) + (\quad)$
    $= (x + 1)(\quad)$

  (f) $x^2 + 15x + 56$
    $= x^2 + 7x + 8x + 56$
    $= x(\quad) + 8(\quad)$
    $= (\quad)(x + 7)$

5 Find an expression for the missing dimension in each rectangle:

(**a**) Area = $x^2 + 3x + 2$ ⟵ $x + 2$ ⟶

(**b**) Area = $x^2 + 8x + 15$ ⟵ $x + 5$ ⟶

(**c**) Area = $x^2 + 8x + 16$ $x + 4$

6 Factorise fully by first taking out the common factor.

(**a**) $2x^2 + 6x + 4$ (**b**) $3x^2 + 30x + 63$ (**c**) $4x^2 + 20x + 24$
(**d**) $4x^2 + 32x + 64$ (**e**) $3x^2 + 18x + 24$ (**f**) $2x^2 + 12x + 10$
(**g**) $5x^2 + 55x + 140$ (**h**) $7x^2 + 42x + 63$ (**i**) $3x^2 + 27x + 42$
(**j**) $3x^2 + 27x + 24$ (**k**) $5x^2 + 40x + 75$ (**l**) $2x^2 + 20x + 48$

17.5 Negative terms

Learning intentions

$(x - 3)(x - 7)$
$= x^2 - 7x - 3x + 21$
$= x^2 - 10x + 21$

$-3 + (-7)$ -3×-7

$(x - 2)(x - 5)$
$= x^2 - 5x - 2x + 10$
$= x^2 - 7x + 10$

$-5 + (-2)$ -5×-2

Reversing the process

$x^2 - 10x + 21$
$= (x - 3)(x - 7)$

$x^2 - 7x + 10$
$= (x - 5)(x - 2)$

Example

Factorise:
(**a**) $x^2 - 5x + 4$

(**b**) $x^2 - 10x + 16$

(**a**) $x^2 - 5x + 4$
$= x^2 - 4x - 1x + 4$
$= x(x - 4) - (x - 4)$
$= (x - 1)(x - 4)$

Look for two numbers which multiply to give 4 and add to give (-5).

Factorise

Common factor

So $x^2 - 5x + 4$
$= (x - 4)(x - 1)$
Check by multiplying out.

(**b**) $x^2 - 10x + 16$
$= x^2 - 8x - 2x + 16$
$= x(x - 8) - 2(x - 8)$
$= (x - 2)(x - 8)$

Look for two numbers which multiply to give 16 and add to give (-10).

Factorise

Common factor

So $x^2 - 10x + 16$
$= (x - 2)(x - 8)$
Check by multiplying out.

Exercise 17.5

1 Expand and simplify:

(**a**) $(x - 4)(x - 3)$ (**b**) $(x - 7)(x - 2)$ (**c**) $(x - 1)(x - 6)$
(**d**) $(x - 2)(x - 2)$ (**e**) $(x - 5)(x - 9)$ (**f**) $(x - 12)(x - 4)$

2 Copy and complete:
(**a**) $x^2 - 5x + 6$
$= x^2 - 3x - 2x + 6$
$= x(\quad) - 2(\quad)$
$= (x - 2)(\quad)$
(**d**) $x^2 - 10x + 16$
$= x^2 - 8x - 2x + 16$
$= x(\quad) - (\quad)$
$= (x - 2)(\quad)$

(**b**) $x^2 - 10x + 24$
$= x^2 - 6x - 4x + 24$
$= x(\quad) - 4(\quad)$
$= (\quad)(x - 6)$
(**e**) $x^2 - 14x + 49$
$x^2 - 7x - \quad + 49$
$x(\quad) - (\quad)$
$= (x - 7)(\quad)$
$=$

(**c**) $x^2 - 2x + 1$
$= x^2 - x - x + 1$
$= x(\quad) - (\quad)$
$= (x - 1)(\quad)$
(**f**) $x^2 - 15x + 44$
$x^2 - 4x - \quad + 44$
$= (\quad) - (\quad)$
$= (\quad)(x - 4)$

3 Factorise:

(a) $x^2 - 11x + 30$ (b) $x^2 - 6x + 8$ (c) $x^2 - 11x + 10$

(d) $x^2 - 8x + 15$ (e) $x^2 - 12x + 20$ (f) $x^2 - 10x + 25$

(g) $x^2 - 11x + 24$ (h) $x^2 - 10x + 9$ (i) $x^2 - 15x + 44$

(j) $x^2 - 15x + 50$ (k) $x^2 - 7x + 12$ (l) $x^2 - 14x + 49$

4 Factorise fully by first taking out the common factor:

(a) $2x^2 - 20x + 32$ (b) $3x^2 - 12x + 9$ (c) $2x^2 - 12x + 18$

(d) $10x^2 - 100x + 90$ (e) $6x^2 - 54x + 120$ (f) $4x^2 - 48x + 144$

(g) $x^3 - 8x^2 + 12x$ (h) $x^3 - 6x^2 + 8x$

17.6 Negative constants

Learning intentions

Example

Factorise: (a) $x^2 + 2x - 8$ (b) $x^2 - 4x - 12$

(a) $x^2 + 2x - 8$
$= x^2 + 4x - 2x - 8$
$= x(x + 4) - 2(x + 4)$
$= (x - 2)(x + 4)$

> Look for two numbers which multiply to give (-8) and add to give 2.

So $x^2 + 2x - 8$
$= (x - 4)(x + 2)$
Check by multiplying out.

(b) $x^2 - 4x - 12$
$= x^2 + 2x - 6x - 12$
$= x(x + 2) - 6(x + 2)$
$= (x - 6)(x + 2)$

> Look for two numbers which multiply to give (-12) and add to give (-4).

So $x^2 - 4x - 12$
$= (x - 6)(x + 2)$
Check by multiplying out.

Exercise 17.6

1 Expand:

(a) $(x - 3)(x + 2)$ (b) $(x + 3)(x - 2)$ (c) $(x + 4)(x - 7)$

(d) $(x - 4)(x + 7)$ (e) $(x + 7)(x - 5)$ (f) $(x - 9)(x + 3)$

(g) $(x - 12)(x + 4)$ (h) $(x + 6)(x - 1)$

2 Copy and complete:

(a) $x^2 - 5x - 24$
$= x^2 - 8x + 3x - 24$
$= x(\quad) + 3(\quad)$
$= (x + 3)(\quad)$

(b) $x^2 + 11x - 12$
$= x^2 + 12x - x - 12$
$= x(x + 12) - (\quad)$
$= (\quad)(x + 12)$

(c) $x^2 - 5x - 14$
$= x^2 - 7x + 2x - 14$
$= x(\quad) + 2(\quad)$
$= (x + 2)(\quad)$

3 Factorise:

(a) $x^2 + x - 6$ (b) $x^2 + 4x - 60$ (c) $x^2 + x - 20$ (d) $x^2 + 2x - 63$

(e) $x^2 - 3x - 40$ (f) $x^2 - 11x - 12$ (g) $x^2 - 2x - 24$ (h) $x^2 + 6x - 27$

(i) $x^2 - 2x - 3$ (j) $x^2 + 3x - 40$ (k) $x^2 + 8x - 20$ (l) $x^2 - 5x - 36$

4 Factorise fully by first taking out the common factor:

(a) $2x^2 + 2x - 12$ (b) $3x^2 - 12x - 63$ (c) $5x^2 + 15x - 20$

(d) $4x^2 + 20x - 24$ (e) $2x^2 - 6x - 20$ (f) $x^3 - 2x^2 - 8x$

(g) $7x^3 - 28x^2 - 84x$ (h) $6x^2 - 30x - 84$

17.7 Further trinomials

Learning intentions

Expand
$$(2x + 3)(x + 5)$$
$$= 2x^2 + 10x + 3x + 15$$
$$= 2x^2 + 13x + 5$$

> Notice that the product of the outer coefficients equals the product of the inner coefficients.

$$(2x - 3)(x - 7)$$
$$= 2x^2 - 14x - 3x + 21$$
$$= 2x^2 - 17x + 21$$

Example

Factorise:

(a) $2x^2 - 5x - 12$

(b) $3x^2 + 13x - 10$

(a) $2x^2 - 5x - 12$
$$= 2x^2 - 8x + 3x - 12$$
$$= 2x(x - 4) + 3(x - 4)$$
$$= (2x + 3)(x - 4)$$
So $2x^2 - 5x - 12$
$$= (2x + 3)(x - 4)$$
Check by multiplying out.

> Look for two numbers which add to give -5 and multiply to give -24, the product of the outer terms.

(b) $3x^2 + 13x - 10$
$$= 3x^2 - 2x + 15x - 10$$
$$= x(3x - 2) + 5(3x - 2)$$
$$= (x + 5)(3x - 2)$$
So $3x^2 + 13x - 10$
$$= (x + 5)(3x - 2)$$
Check by multiplying out.

> Look for two numbers which add to give 13 and multiply to give -30, the product of the outer terms.

Exercise 17.7

1 Multiply out:

(a) $(2x - 3)(x + 5)$ **(b)** $(x - 1)(3x - 7)$ **(c)** $(5x + 4)(x - 2)$

(d) $(x + 3)(2x + 7)$ **(e)** $(2x - 9)(3x + 4)$ **(f)** $(4x + 7)(2x - 3)$

(g) $(3x - 5)(4x - 1)$ **(h)** $(10x + 3)(2x - 1)$ **(i)** $(7x + 4)(8x - 3)$

2 Copy and complete:

(a) $2x^2 + 11x + 5$
$2x^2 + 10x + x + 5$
$= 2x(\quad) + (\quad)$
$= (2x + 1)(\quad)$

(b) $5x^2 + 8x + 3$
$5x^2 + 3x + 5x + 3$
$= x(5x + 3) + (\quad)$
$= (\quad)(5x + 3)$

(c) $3x^2 + 5x + 2$
$3x^2 + 3x + 2x + 2$
$= 3x(\quad) + 2(\quad)$
$= (3x + 2)(\quad)$

(d) $2x^2 + 5x + 3$
$2x^2 + 2x + 3x + 3$
$= 2x(x + 1) + 3(\quad)$
$= (2x + 3)(\quad)$

(e) $5x^2 + 7x + 2$
$= 5x^2 + 5x + x + 2$
$= 5x(\quad) + 2(\quad)$
$= (\quad)(x + 1)$

(f) $3x^2 + 10x + 3$
$= 3x^2 + 9x + x + 3$
$= 3x(x + \quad) + (\quad)$
$= (\quad)(x + 3)$

3 Factorise:

(a) $2x^2 + 7x + 5$ **(b)** $3x^2 + 22x + 7$ **(c)** $7x^2 + 8x + 1$

(d) $11x^2 + 34x + 3$ **(e)** $2x^2 + 7x + 3$ **(f)** $5x^2 + 11x + 2$

(g) $2x^2 + 17x + 21$ **(h)** $2x^2 + 11x + 5$

4 Factorise:

(a) $2x^2 + 3x - 2$ **(b)** $3x^2 + 8x - 3$ **(c)** $2x^2 - 9x - 5$

(d) $3x^2 - 2x - 5$ **(e)** $2x^2 - 3x - 2$ **(f)** $5x^2 - 24x - 5$

(g) $2x^2 - x - 1$ **(h)** $3x^2 + 5x - 2$ **(i)** $5x^2 + 2x - 7$

(j) $7x^2 + 13x - 2$ **(k)** $3x^2 - 7x - 6$ **(l)** $3x^2 - 16x + 5$

(m) $3x^2 - 5x - 2$ **(n)** $5x^2 - 4x - 1$ **(o)** $2x^2 - 7x - 15$

(p) $3x^2 + 5x - 2$ **(q)** $7x^2 + 34x - 5$ **(q)** $3x^2 + 4x - 15$

17.8 Further examples

Exercise 17.8

1 Factorise:

(a) $4x^2 - 8x + 3$ (b) $4x^2 + 5x + 1$ (c) $8x^2 + 30x + 7$

(d) $12x^2 + 20x + 3$ (e) $4x^2 - 3x - 1$ (f) $2x^2 - 15x - 8$

2 Factorise:

(a) $2x^2 + 11x + 15$ (b) $6x^2 - x - 2$ (c) $2x^2 - 8x + 6$

(d) $4x^2 + 8x - 5$ (e) $12x^2 - 5x - 3$ (f) $3x^2 - 17x + 10$

(g) $16x^2 + 58x + 7$ (h) $5x^2 + 11x - 12$ (i) $12x^2 - 4x - 1$

(j) $3x^2 + 8x - 16$ (k) $20x^2 + 12x + 1$ (l) $2x^2 - 11x + 12$

(m) $6x^2 + 17x - 3$ (n) $2x^2 - 19x + 9$ (o) $3x^2 + 14x + 15$

3 Factorise fully by first taking out the common factor:

(a) $4x^2 + 26x + 12$ (b) $15x^2 - 21x - 18$ (c) $21x^2 - 35x - 14$

(d) $28x^2 - 46x + 6$ (e) $12x^2 + 4x - 8$ (f) $16x^2 - 4x - 6$

4 Factorise:

(a) $10x^2 + 19x + 6$ (b) $6x^2 - 13x + 6$ (c) $9x^2 - 24x + 16$

(d) $8x^2 + 6x - 9$ (e) $12x^2 - 2x - 4$ (f) $25x^2 - 20x + 4$

5 Factorise:

(a) $10x^2 + 7x - 12$ (b) $4x^2 - 16x + 15$ (c) $9x^2 + 24x + 16$

(d) $8x^2 - 14x - 15$ (e) $4x^2 + 12x + 9$ (f) $6x^2 + 11x - 10$

6 Given the area, find an expression for the breadth of each rectangle.

(a)   Area = $3x^2 - x - 14$ $\longleftarrow x + 2 \longrightarrow$

(b)   Area = $6x^2 - 7x - 5$ $\longleftarrow 2x + 1 \longrightarrow$

(c)   Area = $4x^2 - 16x + 15$ $\longleftarrow 2x - 5 \longrightarrow$

(d)   Area = $8x^2 - 6x + 1$ $\longleftarrow 2x - 1 \longrightarrow$

17.9 Further factorisation

Learning intentions

When factorising an expression look for:
- a common factor
- a difference of two squares
- factorisation of trinomials

Example 1

Factorise:

(a) $12x^2 - 75$ (b) $12x^2 - 2x - 30$

(a) $12x^2 - 75$
$$= 3(4x^2 - 25)$$
$$= 3(2x + 5)(2x - 5)$$

(b) $12x^2 - 2x - 30$
$$= 2(6x^2 - x - 15)$$
$$= 2(6x^2 - 10x + 9x - 15)$$
$$= 2(2x(3x - 5) + 3(3x - 5))$$
$$= 2(2x + 3)(3x - 5)$$

Example 2

Factorise:

(a) $15 - x - 2x^2$

(b) $2a^2 + ab - 6b^2$

(c) $x^4 + 5x^3 - 14x^2$

(d) $x^4 + 5x^2 + 6$

(a) $15 - x - 2x^2$
$= 15 - 6x + 5x - 2x^2$
$= 3(5 - 2x) + x(5 - 2x)$
$= (3 + x)(5 - 2x)$

(b) $2a^2 + ab - 6b^2$
$= 2a^2 + 4ab - 3ab - 6b^2$
$= 2a(a + 2b) - 3b(a + 2b)$
$= (2a - 3b)(a + 2b)$

> Look for two expressions which multiply to give $-12a^2b^2$ and add to give ab.

(c) $x^4 + 5x^3 - 14x^2$
$= x^2(x^2 + 5x - 14)$
$= x^2(x^2 - 2x + 7x - 14)$
$= x^2(x(x - 2) + 7(x - 2))$
$= x^2(x + 7)(x - 2)$

(d) $x^4 + 5x^2 + 6$
$= (x^2)^2 + 5(x^2) + 6$
$= x^4 + 3x^2 + 2x^2 + 6$
$= x^2(x^2 + 3) + 2(x^2 + 3)$
$= (x^2 + 2)(x^2 + 3)$

Exercise 17.9

1 Factorise:

(a) $3x^2 + 7x + 2$
(b) $9 - 4x^2$
(c) $8a^2 + 10a - 3$
(d) $2y^2 + 3y - 5$
(e) $3x^2 + 3x - 6$
(f) $6x^2 + 13x + 6$
(g) $x^2 + 2x - 35$
(h) $x^2 - 10x + 21$
(i) $2x^2 + 3x - 27$
(j) $6x^2 + 17x - 3$
(k) $4y^2 - 12y - 27$
(l) $5b^2 + 21b + 18$

2 Factorise:

(a) $15x^2 - 2x - 8$
(b) $2x^2 - 25x + 12$
(c) $9x^2 - 100$
(d) $3x^2 - 12$
(e) $3x^2 - 18x + 27$
(f) $12 - 108x^2$
(g) $4x^2 - 10x - 6$
(h) $12x^2 + 20x - 25$
(i) $5x^2 + 11x + 2$
(j) $15x^2 - 2x - 8$
(k) $7x^2 + 23x - 20$
(l) $3x^2 - 2x - 16$

3 Factorise:

(a) $12 - x - x^2$
(b) $15 + 2x - x^2$
(c) $6 - x - x^2$
(d) $12 - 7x + x^2$
(e) $2 + x - x^2$
(f) $2 - x - 3x^2$
(g) $5 + 3x - 2x^2$
(h) $2 - 7x + 6x^2$
(i) $12 - 2x - 4x^2$
(j) $3 + 8x - 3x^2$
(k) $1 + 3x - 18x^2$
(l) $1 - x - 12x^2$

4 Factorise fully:

(a) $x^4 + 11x^2 + 30$
(b) $y^4 + 2y^2 - 15$
(c) $s^4 - 1$
(d) $a^3 - a$
(e) $1 - (x - y)^2$
(f) $b^4 - b^6$

5 Expand and factorise:

(a) $3(2x^2 + 7) - 23x$
(b) $4x(x + 4) + 15$
(c) $(x + 1)^2 - 9$
(d) $(x - 3)(x + 5) + 16$
(e) $(3x - 1)(x + 2) - (7x + 3)$
(f) $(x + 4)(x + 5) - (x + 2)(x - 1)$
(g) $(3x + 1)(x - 1) - (x - 1)^2$
(h) $(x + 3)(x - 2) + (x + 1)^2$

6 Factorise:

(a) $c^2 + 2bc + b^2$
(b) $a^2 + 3ab + 2b^2$
(c) $t^2 - ts - 2s^2$
(d) $p^2 + pt - 6t^2$
(e) $5t^2 - 9pt - 2p^2$
(f) $3t^2 + 5qt + 2q^2$
(g) $2q^2 + 5sq + 3s^2$
(h) $2x^2 + 11xy + 5y^2$
(i) $2p^2 + 5pq - 3q^2$
(j) $9x^2 + 6xy - 8y^2$
(k) $6a^2 + 13ab + 2b^2$
(l) $6r^2 - 5rt - 4t^2$

17.10 Identities

Learning intentions

Example 1
Prove that $z(z + 4) + 4 = (z + 2)^2$

$$\begin{aligned} \text{LHS} &= z(z + 4) + 4 \\ &= z^2 + 4z + 4 \\ &= (z + 2)(z + 2) \\ &= (z + 2)^2 = \text{RHS} \end{aligned}$$

> LHS stands for left hand side;
> RHS for right hand side

Example 2
Prove that the shaded area is $\pi(R - r)(R + r)$.

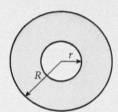

Area of large circle $= \pi R^2$
Area of small circle $= \pi r^2$
Shaded area $= \pi R^2 - \pi r^2$
$\qquad = \pi(R^2 - r^2)$
$\qquad = \pi(R - r)(R + r)$

Exercise 17.10

1 Prove that:
  (a) $(x + 3)(x - 1) + 4 = (x + 1)^2$
  (b) $(x - 3)^2 + 12x = (x + 3)^2$
  (c) $(a - b)^2 = (b - a)^2$
  (d) $(3r - t)^2 = (t - 3r)^2$
  (e) $(a + b)^2 + (ab - 1)^2 = (1 + a^2)(1 + b^2)$
  (f) $(px + qy)^2 + (qx - py)^2 = (p^2 + q^2)(x^2 + y^2)$

2 Prove that the shaded area may
  be given by the expression $3x(x + 2)$.

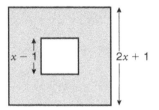

3 A circular hole is to be cut in a circular table.
  Tape is to be placed around the edge of the hole
  and around the perimeter of the table.
  Prove that the perimeter of the shaded area may
  be expressed as $6\pi(x - 1)$.

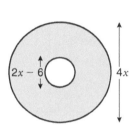

4 A wooden letter rack is made
  from 3 pieces of wood 1 centimetre thick
  with dimensions shown.
  Prove that the total area (A cm^2)
  of wood required can be given by
  the expression
  $A = (3x - 2)(x + 5)$

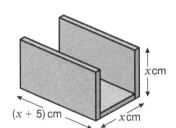

5 Given any three consecutive numbers, prove that the product of the first
  and last is always one less than the square of the middle number.

Review exercise 17: Am I a successful learner?

1 Factorise:
- (a) $x^2 + 6x + 9$
- (b) $x^2 + 4x + 4$
- (c) $x^2 - 2x - 24$
- (d) $x^2 - 36$
- (e) $x^2 + 3x - 18$
- (f) $x^2 + x - 6$
- (g) $x^2 + x - 7$
- (h) $x^2 + 14x - 72$
- (i) $x^2 - 2x - 3$
- (j) $x^2 - 100$
- (k) $x^2 - 5x - 24$
- (l) $x^2 + 18x + 45$

2 Factorise:
- (a) $3x^2 + 14x + 15$
- (b) $x^2 - 3x + 2$
- (c) $2a^2 - 5a - 3$
- (d) $2y^2 + 3y - 5$
- (e) $2x^2 - 7x + 3$
- (f) $2x^2 + 7x + 3$
- (g) $9 - 4x^2$
- (h) $5b^2 + 21b + 18$
- (i) $3x^2 - 11x + 6$
- (j) $6x^2 + 17x - 3$
- (k) $4y^2 - 12y - 27$
- (l) $9x^2 - 49$

3 Factorise fully:
- (a) $2x^2 - 12x + 18$
- (b) $3x^2 + 6x - 45$
- (c) $2x^2 - 8$
- (d) $2x^2 - 12x - 144$
- (e) $4x^2 + 24x - 28$
- (f) $3x^2 + 27x + 54$
- (g) $5x^2 - 45x + 90$
- (h) $18x^2 - 32$

4 Factorise:
- (a) $36 + 12x + x^2$
- (b) $x^2 - 4xy + 4y^2$
- (c) $4x^3 - 9x$
- (d) $3 + 8x - 3x^2$
- (e) $4x^2 - 5xy - 6y^2$
- (f) $1 + 3x - 18x^2$
- (g) $15 - 7x - 2x^2$
- (h) $2x^3 + 30x^2 + 112x$
- (i) $x^4 - 36$
- (j) $2x^2 - 5xy + 3y^2$
- (k) $x^4 + 2x^2 - 63$
- (l) $(x - 2)^2 - 16$

5 Expand and factorise:
- (a) $x(6x - 11) + 3$
- (b) $x(x + 1) - 3x$
- (c) $x(x + 1) + 6(x - 5)$

Summary 17: What I learned in this chapter.

When factorising an expression look for:
- a common factor
- a difference of two squares
- factorisation of trinomials

Common factor

$3x - 15 = 3(x - 5)$ $16xy + 15x = x(16y + 15)$ $\pi r^2 + \pi d + 2\pi = \pi(r^2 + d + 2)$ $x^3 - 2x^2 = x^2(x - 2)$

Difference of two squares

$y^2 - 25$
$= (y + 5)(y - 5)$

$4a^2 - 25x^2$
$= (2a)^2 - (5x)^2$
$= (2a + 5x)(2a - 5x)$

Factorisation of trinomials

(a) $x^2 + 7x + 12$
$= x^2 + 3x + 4x + 12$
$= x(x + 3) + 4(x + 3)$
$= (x + 4)(x + 3)$

(b) $x^2 + 2x - 8$
$= x^2 + 4x - 2x - 8$
$= x(x + 4) - 2(x + 4)$
$= (x - 2)(x + 4)$

(c) $12x^2 - 2x - 30$
$= 2(6x^2 - 1x - 15)$
$= 2(6x^2 - 10x + 9x - 15)$
$= 2(2x(3x - 5) + 3(3x - 5))$
$= 2(2x + 3)(3x - 5)$

18 Statistics 3

18.1 Types of data

Exercise 18.1

1 (a) Copy the table.

Categorical	Numerical	
	Discrete	Continuous

(b) Put each type of data in the correct column in the table.

Radiators in a household	Baby weights at birth	Favourite TV programmes
Town populations	Carbohydrate content of food	Race times
Makes of trainers	Armspans of 8 year olds	Number of words in essays
Birth rates	Engine sizes on cars	Number of peas in a pod
Water temperatures at sea	Airline passenger numbers	Holiday destinations
Examination pass rates	Shoe sizes	TV screen sizes
Microwave power outputs	Germination times	Class sizes
Child heights		

(c) Which types of data could go in more than one column?

(d) Find a new type of data for each of the three categories.

18.2 Cumulative frequency

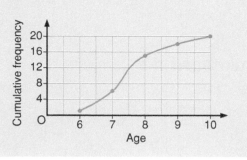

Example

The age of retirement for a group of fifty teachers was recorded.

(a) Make a cumulative frequency table and draw the cumulative frequency graph.

(b) How many had retired by age 55?

(c) How many retired between the ages of 56 and 59?

(d) Describe the retirement pattern for teachers.

51	56	58	58	59
60	58	59	60	60
60	60	52	54	59
58	59	60	60	60
59	59	58	53	55
60	60	60	59	59
59	59	58	58	57
52	57	59	59	60
60	60	60	60	60
59	58	57	59	60

(a)

Age	Tally	Frequency	Cumulative frequency
51	I	1	1
52	II	2	3
53	I	1	4
54	I	1	5
55	I	1	6
56	I	1	7
57	III	3	10
58	JHT III	8	18
59	JHT JHT IIII	14	32
60	JHT JHT JHT III	18	50

Total number in survey

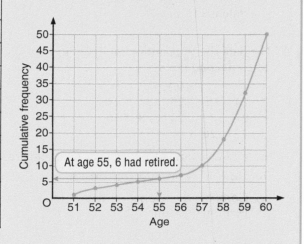

At age 55, 6 had retired.

(b) By age 55, **six** teachers had retired.

(c) Number who retired between the ages of 56 and 59 = 32 − 6 = **26**

(d) There is a very low retirement rate until the age of 57.
The rate rises sharply from age 58. The most common age of retirement is 60.

Exercise 18.2

1 (a) Draw a cumulative frequency table and graph for these retirement ages for lawyers.

50 52 61 54 54 56 60 54 55 55 56 58 58 54 53
52 56 59 54 55 57 60 58 52 58 59 60 58 52 55

(b) How many had retired by age 53?

(c) How many retired between the ages of 51 and 55?

(d) Describe the retirement pattern for this group of lawyers.

2 The figures show the age at which forty women gave birth to their first child.

26 25 23 34 33 30 17 17 28 29
22 19 18 29 30 38 41 32 26 24
23 28 27 27 34 33 38 28 29 31
22 32 32 19 21 20 20 27 27 29

(a) Draw a cumulative frequency table and graph.

(b) How many had given birth by age 28?

(c) What percentage gave birth between the ages of 21 and 31?

(d) Describe the child birth pattern in this data.

3 The data shows the ages at which a group of people married.

Women						Men					
28	29	38	45	23	22	30	31	29	46	35	30
24	19	28	22	26	29	29	22	34	38	32	36
27	23	28	21	21	29	30	25	27	22	27	28

(a) Draw a cumulative frequency table and graph for each set of data.

(b) How many people were surveyed in total?

(c) By the age of 25 how many (i) men and (ii) women were married?

(d) How many people married between the ages of 24 and 30?

(e) 'Men marry at a later age than women'. Do you agree with this statement?

4 The data shows germination times, in hours, for broad beans under different conditions.

Heat					No heat				
24	25	23	23	28	30	29	26	24	25
27	27	26	28	30	29	29	28	30	31
23	26	25	28	28	32	31	27	25	30

(a) Draw a cumulative frequency table and graph for each set of data.

(b) How many beans germinated in under 26 hours with no heat?

(c) Compare the two sets of data. Describe the effect of heat on germination times.

18.3 Mean, median, mode and range from a frequency table

Learning intentions

Remember

> Mean, median and mode are types of averages

For any set of data
- the range is the difference between the highest and lowest values
- the mean is found by adding all the data and dividing by the number of pieces of data
- the median is the middle value from an ordered list
- the mode is the value which occurs most frequently

These may be found from a frequency table.

Example

The frequency table shows the results of a survey on male waist sizes.

(a) Draw a cumulative frequency table.

(b) Find the range, mean, median and mode.

Waist size	Frequency
28	2
30	0
32	19
34	11
36	10
38	8

(a)

Waist size	Frequency	Total waist size (Waist × frequency)	Cumulative frequency
28	2	28 × 2 = 56	2
30	0	30 × 0 = 0	2
32	19	32 × 19 = 608	21
34	11	34 × 11 = 374	32
36	10	36 × 10 = 360	42
38	8	38 × 8 = 304	50
TOTAL	50	1738	

Total waist size of all fifty men

(b) Range = largest − smallest
        = 38 − 28 = **10**

Mean = $\dfrac{\text{total waist size}}{\text{number of pieces of data}} = \dfrac{1738}{50} = $ **34·8** to one decimal place

Median is the middle value.
For 50 pieces of data the middle values lies between the 25th and 26th values.
Both of these values are 34. Hence, median is **34**.

Mode is the most frequent value. Mode is **32**.

Exercise 18.3

1 The frequency table shows the results of a survey on family size.
Copy and complete the table to find the range, mean, median and mode of the data.

Number of children	Frequency	Total number of children	Cumulative frequency
0	11	0 × 11 = 0	11
1	14	1 × 14 = 14	25
2	22	2 × 22 = 44	
3	11		
4	4		
5	6		
6	2		
TOTAL			

2 In a survey of the power output of hairdriers, the frequency table shows the results.
Copy and complete the table to find the range, mean, median and mode of the power outputs.

Power output (kw)	Frequency	Total power output	Cumulative frequency
1	4		
1·25	6		
1·5	16		
1·75	2		
2	6		
2·25	1		

3 Class 5B conducted a survey on weekly spending money.
The frequency table shows the results of the survey.

(a) Copy the table and add a *Total spending* and a *Cumulative frequency* column to find the range, mean, median and mode of the data.

(b) Jim gets £18 each week and tells his parents that most people get more than him.
Do you agree with Jim?

Weekly spending (£)	Frequency
10	4
12	0
14	5
16	2
18	6
20	9
25	2
30	1
35	1

4 The table shows the results of a study on egg laying in a hen flock.
Copy the table and add a *Total number of eggs* and a *Cumulative frequency* column.

(a) Find the range, mean, median and modal number of eggs per nest.

(b) This breed of hen is sold as '3 per nest' stock.
Is this a fair description of the egg laying pattern?
How could you justify it?

Eggs per nest	Frequency
0	8
1	9
2	16
3	17
4	3
5	7

5 Boonbay chamber of commerce completed a survey of hotel prices in the area.

(a) Copy the frequency table and add a *Total cost* and a *Cumulative frequency* column to find the range, mean, median and mode of the data.

(b) In its advertising leaflet Boonbay claims hotel prices are cheaper than the national average of £82.
Do you agree with this? How might Boonbay justify the claim?

Room price (£)	Frequency
40	20
50	15
60	18
70	22
80	40
90	45
100	50
110	26
120	24

6 The data listed below shows the number of golf strokes taken at the tenth hole at the Tiger Lake course.

2	7	8	3	4	4	5	4	4	4
5	6	4	4	6	8	3	4	3	5
6	6	6	4	2	9	4	4	5	7

(a) Use a frequency table to find the range, mean, median and modal number of strokes at this hole.

(b) This is a par four hole, which means it should take four strokes to sink the ball.
From these statistics, do you think this should be a par four hole?

18.4 Interquartile range from a frequency table

Learning intentions

Remember

The median and quartiles indicate the distribution of the data by dividing it into four sections.

The range and interquartile range are measures of the spread of a set of data.

The interquartile range is the difference between the upper and lower quartiles.

These may be calculated from a cumulative frequency table.

The frequency table shows the results of a survey on annual incomes.

Maximum annual income	Frequency	Cumulative frequency
15 000	7	7
18 000	15	22
21 000	11	33
24 000	49	82
27 000	15	97
30 000	22	119
33 000	8	127
36 000	4	131

33rd value

66th value

99th value

The total number of pieces of data is 131. Hence the median is the 66th value.
Median is **£24 000**.

The lower half of the data set has items 1 to 65. Hence the lower quartile is the 33rd value.
The 33rd value is £21 000
Lower quartile Q_1 is **£21 000**

The upper half of the data set has items 67 to 131. Hence upper quartile is the 99th value.
Upper quartile Q_3 is **£30 000**

Interquartile range is £30 000 − £21 000 = **£9 000**

Exercise 18.4

1 Add a cumulative frequency column to each table. Find the median,
   upper and lower quartiles, and semi-interquartile range.

(a)

Ticket prices	Frequency
12	22
15	17
18	5
24	12
30	21
45	9
50	12

(b)

Maximum bus passenger numbers	Frequency
28	4
45	11
50	8
52	21
55	7
60	6

2 For each data set, create a cumulative frequency table and calculate the semi-interquartile range.

(a) People per table booking

6	5	5	3	3	2	2	2
4	8	3	2	5	5	8	9
2	2	3	4	5	2	3	4
7	4	4	5	2	2	7	5
3	2	2	4	6	5	8	3

(b) Delayed flights per day

7	8	12	2	8	12	3	9
4	6	6	1	4	4	5	4
1	4	7	8	6	5	8	11

(c) Length of hospital stays (days)

4	6	2	2	12	3	5	1	4
1	4	7	4	4	5	2	2	2
3	3	8	5	7	4	2	2	6
4	5	9	2	4	6	7	6	7

(d) Applications per subject

20	25	20	35	35	35	40
20	20	45	30	20	25	35
45	25	40	35	35	40	35
20	25	20	35	40	45	50

18.5 Standard deviation

Learning intentions

The **standard deviation** of a set of data is a measure of the spread of the data. It is an indication of the distance or deviation of each piece of data from the mean.

If the standard deviation is a low figure, the data are relatively close to the mean. If the standard deviation is high, the data are relatively far from the mean.

Example

A group of eight friends weigh themselves. Calculate the mean and standard deviation of the group.

Weights (kg)
54 60 62 48
58 64 57 65

Mean $= \frac{468}{8} = 58 \cdot 5$

Call each piece of data x and the mean $\bar{x}$. So $\bar{x} = 58 \cdot 5$

Data x	Deviation $x - \bar{x}$	(Deviation)^2 $(x - \bar{x})^2$
54	−4·5	20·25
60	1·5	2·25
62	3·5	12·25
48	−10·5	110·25
58	−0·5	0·25
64	5·5	30·25
57	−1·5	2·25
65	6·5	42·25
		220·00

Squaring prevents positive and negative deviations from cancelling each other out

Total square deviation

Mean square deviation $= \frac{220}{8} = 27 \cdot 5$

Standard deviation $= \sqrt{\dfrac{\text{Total (deviation)}^2}{\text{Number of pieces of data}}} = \sqrt{\dfrac{220}{8}} = \sqrt{27 \cdot 5}$

$= \mathbf{5 \cdot 24}$ to 2 dp

Exercise 18.5

1 Ten large baking potatoes are weighed.

(**a**) Calculate the mean weight.

(**b**) Copy and complete the table to find the mean
square deviation and standard deviation.

Weights (g)

150	220	225	240	195
245	230	190	255	165

x	$x - \bar{x}$	$(x - \bar{x})^2$

2 For each set of data construct a table of deviation to find the mean
square deviation and standard deviation.

(**a**) Shoe sizes

3   8   6   6   5   9   10   10   4   4

(**b**) Test scores

23   24   18   16   30   30   21

(**c**) Birth weights (kg)

3·5   2·9   4·1   4·2   2·8   3·6   3·8   3·9

(**d**) Race times (mins)

42   47   53   54   46   39   51   42   42   54

18.6   Standard deviation from a sample

Learning intentions

It is more common to use a **sample** than all possible data
for statistical calculations.

From the sample, conclusions may be drawn about the
population.

> The set of all possible
> data is referred to as
> the **population.**

$$\text{Standard deviation of the population} = \sqrt{\frac{\text{Total square deviation}}{n}}$$

$$\text{Standard deviation of a sample} = \sqrt{\frac{\text{Total square deviation}}{n - 1}}$$

> n is the number of
> pieces of data.

In a sample, the calculated mean will be closer to each piece of data than the population mean. This would lead to
an underestimate of the size of the standard deviation. To compensate for this, the denominator is reduced by 1.
This gives a better measure of the spread of the data.

To express the standard deviation algebraically:

Term	Represents
s	standard deviation of a sample
n	number of pieces of data
x	piece of data
$\bar{x}$	mean
Σ	the sum of
$\Sigma(x - \bar{x})^2$	total square deviation

$$\bar{x} = \frac{\Sigma x}{n}$$

The sample standard deviation s is defined as $s = \sqrt{\dfrac{\Sigma(x - \bar{x})^2}{n - 1}}$

An alternative form, $s = \sqrt{\dfrac{\Sigma x^2 - \dfrac{(\Sigma x)^2}{n}}{n - 1}}$, often reduces rounding errors.

Example 1

A sample of ten courgettes from a sack are measured.

Using this sample, calculate the standard deviation in the length of the courgettes.

Lengths (cm)				
11	15	8	9	8
16	18	12	12	14

$$\bar{x} = \frac{\Sigma x}{n} = \frac{123}{10} = 12\cdot3$$

x	$x - \bar{x}$	$(x - \bar{x})^2$
11	$-1\cdot3$	$1\cdot69$
15	$2\cdot7$	$7\cdot29$
8	$-4\cdot3$	$18\cdot49$
9	$-3\cdot3$	$10\cdot89$
8	$-4\cdot3$	$18\cdot49$
16	$3\cdot7$	$13\cdot69$
18	$5\cdot7$	$32\cdot49$
12	$-0\cdot3$	$0\cdot09$
12	$-0\cdot3$	$0\cdot09$
14	$1\cdot7$	$2\cdot89$
$\Sigma x = 123$		$106\cdot1$

$$s = \sqrt{\frac{\Sigma(x - \bar{x})^2}{n - 1}}$$

Denominator is $n - 1$ since the calculation is based on a sample

$$= \sqrt{\frac{106\cdot1}{9}}$$

$n = 10$

$$= 3\cdot43 \text{ to 2 dp}$$

The standard deviation is **3·43** to two decimal places.

Example 2

The data show the systolic blood pressures for a sample of eight patients.

Calculate the mean and standard deviation.

Blood pressures (mm Hg)			
134	121	125	118
140	124	132	122

$$\bar{x} = \frac{1\,016}{8} = 127$$

x	x^2
134	17\,956
121	14\,641
125	15\,625
118	13\,924
140	19\,600
124	15\,376
132	17\,424
122	14\,884
$\Sigma x = 1\,016$	$\Sigma x^2 = 129\,430$

$$s = \sqrt{\frac{\Sigma x^2 - \frac{(\Sigma x)^2}{n}}{n - 1}} = \sqrt{\frac{129\,430 - \frac{(1\,016)^2}{8}}{7}}$$

$$= \sqrt{\frac{129\,430 - 129\,032}{7}}$$

$$= \sqrt{56\cdot85714}$$

$$= 7\cdot54$$

The mean is **127** and the standard deviation is **7·54** (to 2 d.p.)

Exercise 18.6

1 For each set of sample data calculate the mean and standard deviation.

(a) Shoe sizes

  3   4   4   5   6
  7   7   5   5   5

(b) Collar sizes

  14 14.5 15 15 15 16 17·5

(c) Tree heights in metres

  3   3.4   5   5.2   6   2.5

(d) Test scores

  8   7   8   9   10   5

(e) Leg lengths in inches

  28   32   31   31   33
  29   28   31   32   32

(f) Cycling speeds in kilometres per hour

  12   15   22   32   31   42
  25   26   39   27   23   29

2 The body mass index, is an indication of obesity. BMI data for a sample of nine students was recorded: 24, 23·1, 19·6, 22·1, 20·9, 22·3, 20·4, 21·5, 22
Calculate the mean and standard deviation.

3 The labels on tubes of ointment claim the contents as 75 millilitres. A quality check on a sample of ten tubes generates the results:

  76 ml, 72 ml, 71 ml, 70 ml, 76 ml, 71 ml, 72 ml, 74 ml, 73 ml, 71 ml

(a) Calculate the mean and standard deviation for this sample.

(b) Should the quality assessor be happy with the results?

4 For a unit assessment Mr Taylor samples test marks from each class.

5C$_1$					5B$_1$				5B$_2$			
25	25	21	18		19	23	29	27		21	12	16	18
27	23	20	25		18	20	22	24		17	17	19	20

(a) Calculate the mean and standard deviation for each class.

(b) Which class appears to be performing least well?

5 The data show the total cholesterol levels for a sample of ten patients.

Cholesterol levels (mmols/l)

  4·1   5·7   3·8   6·0   5·9
  6·2   4·9   3·5   6·3   5·9

(a) Calculate the mean and standard deviation.

(b) After six months of a diet and exercise regime the measurements are taken again.

  4·0   5·8   3·5   4·9   5·7
  6·3   4·6   3·4   5·8   5·4

  (i) Has the mean improved?
  (ii) Is there greater or less variation?

6 At *Slimmers Universe* the advertising slogan claims 'Every week, one kilogramme less'.
A sample of ten dieters are weighed at the beginning of the programme, and again eight weeks later.

Start weight in kilogrammes

  72   87   89   69   101
  88   92   73   73   81

End weight in kilogrammes

  64   81   80   64   90
  84   84   69   68   78

(a) Calculate the mean and standard deviation for each set of weights.

(b) Did this group achieve the weight loss implied by the slogan?

18.7 Further examples

Learning intentions

A calculator may be used for statistical calculations.
Each calculator has a STAT mode which calculates the mean and standard deviation of a data set.
Use the calculator instructions to investigate these functions on your calculator.

Exercise 18.7

1 Noreen keeps annual records of daily temperatures. The data shows a sample of daily maximum temperatures, in °C, during February 1998 and 2006.

	1998										2006								
2	4	4	3	5	3	4	3	0		3	7	6	8	6	7	9	6	8

(**a**) Calculate the mean and standard deviation for each set of temperatures.

(**b**) Find the median and calculate the semi-interquartile range for each set.

(**c**) On the same diagram, draw a box plot for each year.

(**d**) Do Noreen's figures suggest global warming may be a reality? Explain.

2 Dr Lebois is studying mortality records in an area which has been affected by civil unrest for ten years. He samples female ages at death before conflict began and now.

> Before conflict: 18, 43, 56, 69, 67, 70, 71, 72, 72
> Now: 11, 18, 21, 21, 38, 39, 47, 69, 75

(**a**) Draw a back-to-back stem and leaf diagram of this data.

(**b**) Calculate the mean and standard deviation for each data set.

(**c**) Dr Lebois claims that the unrest has reduced female life expectancy by 20 years. Does the data substantiate his claim?

3 Medical records in Eagleshaw Primary School record pupil weights, in kilograms, in Primary 7.
Mr Beale selected a random sample of twelve for 1956 and 2006.

> 1956: 25, 22, 27, 28, 25, 27, 23, 29, 25, 29, 31, 26
> 2006: 27, 31, 29, 32, 32, 28, 26, 25, 32, 34, 28, 29

(**a**) Calculate the mean and standard deviation of each year group.

(**b**) Do these figures indicate that childhood obesity might be an issue at Eagleshaw? Explain.

4 Mrs Hogg's class has undertaken an experiment on plant growth. The plant heights, in centimetres, are shown below.

> Group A: 12, 13.5, 13.8, 14.2, 14.5, 15, 15.2, 16, 17, 18
> Group B: 14, 14.5, 14.8, 14.9, 15, 15.2, 15.6, 15.7, 15.8, 15.9
> Group C: 11, 12.5, 15.4, 15.8, 16, 16.3, 17, 17.5, 18.4, 19.5

(**a**) Calculate the mean and standard deviation for each group.

(**b**) Find the median and quartiles for each group, and draw comparative box plots.

(**c**) The class has to choose a plant group to find:
(**i**) the most consistent size (**ii**) the largest plants.
Which group would you recommend for each desired outcome?

Review exercise 18: Am I a successful learner?

1 Copy and complete the table.

Data	Type		
	Categorical	Numerical, discrete	Numerical, continuous
Computers in a school		✓	
Makes of car			
Test scores			
Flight destination			
Arm spans			

2 The ages at which forty people passed the driving test is shown below.

17 27 23 24 32 17 18 28 43 19
18 43 56 32 26 27 19 18 19 20
19 35 36 19 18 17 28 32 38 45
45 18 17 46 61 32 33 19 17 21

(a) Draw a cumulative frequency table and graph of this data.

(b) By age 50 what percentage of the group had passed the test?

(c) How many passed the test between the ages of 25 and 35?

3 For a sponsored swim of 50 laps of a pool, the time taken, in minutes, by each participant was recorded.

66, 65, 67, 59, 59, 67, 69, 49, 70, 70,
65, 64, 61, 73, 72, 65, 60, 64, 79, 70,
66, 67, 72, 67, 59, 67, 70, 71, 70, 67,
73, 72, 72, 64, 69, 71, 66, 68, 69, 66,
59, 59, 68, 65, 67, 61, 64, 59, 63, 72

(a) Draw a cumulative frequency table of this data.

(b) Use the table to find the range, mean, median and mode of these times.

(c) Find the upper and lower quartiles, and calculate the interquartile range.

4 In two branches of Drimark stores, the managers have recorded a sample of dress sizes sold during a half hour period.

Branch A   Branch B
10 12 12 14 14 14 14 16   12 12 12 12 14 16 16 18

(a) Calculate the mean and standard deviation for each branch.

(b) Is there evidence of a difference in dress sizes between the two branches?

Summary 18: What I learned in this chapter.

Types of data

Data may be either categorical or numerical.

Categorical	Numerical	
	Discrete	Continuous
Data collected in categories – colours, nationalities, types	Data restricted to a number of specific values – shoe size, goals scored, fish caught	Data unrestricted within a range – height, weight, length
Describe	Count	Measure

Cumulative frequency tables

A **cumulative frequency table** shows the running total of the frequency of events as they accumulate.
A **cumulative frequency graph** displays this information.

Age	Frequency	Cumulative frequency
6	3	3
7	9	12
8	4	16

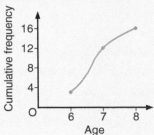

For any set of data:
- the range is the difference between the highest and lowest values
- the mean is found by adding all the data and dividing by the number of pieces of data
- the median is the middle value from an ordered list
- the mode is the value which occurs most frequently

> Mean, median and mode are types of average.

These may be calculated from a cumulative frequency table.

Waist size	Frequency	Total waist size (Waist × frequency)	Cumulative frequency
28	2	28 × 2 = 56	2
30	0	30 × 0 = 0	2
32	19	32 × 19 = 608	21
34	11	34 × 11 = 374	32
36	10	36 × 10 = 360	42
38	8	38 × 8 = 304	50
TOTAL	50	1738 Total waist size of all fifty men	

Range = largest − smallest
  = 38 − 28 = **10**

Mean = $\dfrac{\text{total waist size}}{\text{number of pieces of data}} = \dfrac{1738}{50} = $ **34·8** to one decimal place

Median is the middle value.
For 50 pieces of data, the middle values lies between the 25th and 26th values.
Both of these values are 34. Hence, median is **34.**

Mode is the most frequent value. Mode is **32.**

Interquartile range from a frequency table

Maximum annual income	Frequency	Cumulative frequency
15 000	7	7
18 000	15	22
21 000	11	33
24 000	49	82
27 000	15	95
30 000	22	119
33 000	8	127
36 000	4	130

The total number of pieces of data is 131. Hence the median is the 66th value.
Median is **£24 000**.

The lower half of the data set has items 1 to 65. Hence the lower quartile is the 33rd value.
The 33rd value is £21 000
Lower quartile is **£21 000**

The upper half of the data set has items 67 to 131. Hence upper quartile is the 99th value.
Upper quartile is **£30 000**

The interquartile range is £30 000 − £21 000 = **£9 000**

Standard deviation

The standard deviation of a data set is a measure of the spread of data.

To express the standard deviation algebraically:

Term	Represents
s	standard deviation
n	number of pieces of data
x	piece of data
$\overline{x}$	mean
Σ	the sum of
$\Sigma(x - \overline{x})^2$	total square deviation

Standard deviation $s = \sqrt{\dfrac{\Sigma(x - \overline{x})^2}{n - 1}}$

or $\qquad s = \sqrt{\dfrac{\Sigma x^2 - \dfrac{(\Sigma x)^2}{n}}{n - 1}}$　　　This form reduces rounding errors.

19 Earning and spending

19.1 Personal income

Most people in employment pay income tax under the **PAYE** system.

> PAYE stands for *Pay As You Earn*

The employer deducts income tax, national insurance and superannuation from the **gross** income.

The employee receives the **net** income once deductions are removed.

> National insurance contributions are complicated to calculate.

Gross income
− Deductions
Net income

> Superannuation is the private pension contribution.

Income tax is calculated as a percentage of **taxable income**, after tax free allowances have been deducted.

An income may be quoted as an annual figure, a monthly or weekly wage, or as an hourly rate.

Overtime is usually paid at a higher rate. This may be time and a half, double time or treble time.

The government sets a minimum wage for adults and young people. An employer cannot legally pay less than this amount.

Example 1

Use the tables to calculate the net income after tax on
(**a**) a salary of £22500 for a man aged 35
(**b**) an income of £62500 for a woman aged 76.

Income tax personal allowances (£)	
Age up to 64	£5225
Age 65 to 74	£7550
Age 75 and over	£7690

Tax rates	
£0 − £2230	10%
£2231 − £34600	22%
over £34600	40%

(**a**) Taxable income   £22500 − £5225   =   £17275

     Tax   10% of £2230   =   £   223
                  22% of £15045   =   £ 3309·90
                                     £ 3532·90

     Net income   £22500 − £3532·90 =   **£18967·10**

(**b**) Taxable income   £62500 − £7690   =   £54810

     Tax   10% of £2230   =   £   223
                  22% of £32370   =   £ 7121·40
                  40% of £20210   =   £ 8084
                                 £15428·40

> £34600 − £2230 = £32370
> £54810 − £34600 = £20210

     Net income   £62500 − £15428·18 =   **£47071·60**

Example 2

Susan, aged 40, earns £8·50 an hour for a 35 hour working week.
She earns time and a half for 3 hours extra each week and double time for 12 hours she worked over Christmas.
Calculate her annual net income.

Weekly income   35 × £8·50 = £297·50
                      3 × £12·75 = £ 38·25
                                 £335·75

> Time and a half rate = 1·5 × £8·50 = £12·75

Annual income   52 × £335·75 = £17459
                    12 × £17   = £ 204
                                £17663

> Double time = 2 × £8·50 = £17

Taxable income   £17663 − £5225   = £12438
Tax   10% of £2230   = £ 223
               22% of £10208   = £ 2245·76
                             £2468·76

Discussion points

What are the advantages and disadvantages of a minimum wage?
How do private pension schemes work?
For what are national insurance contributions used?

Annual net income   £17663 − £2468·76 =   **£15194·24**

Exercise 19.1

1 For each monthly wage summary (in £) calculate the missing value.

(a) Gross income   13870
Income tax   879
National insurance   674
Net income   ☐

(b) Gross income   57630
Income tax   9985
National insurance   2800
Superannuation   ☐
Net income   41750

(c) Gross income   23255
Income tax   ☐
National insurance   104
Net income   19452

(d) Gross income   87565
Income tax   23850
National insurance   ☐
Superannuation   7250
Net income   53543

2 Use the tax allowances and tax rates from the teaching panel to calculate the net income after tax for each gross income.

(a) £16250, person aged 23

(b) £47260, person aged 53

(c) £12780, person aged 82

(d) £82650, person aged 61

3 A hotel claims it pays employees more than the minimum wage. If the minimum wage is £6·20, is this claim true for the employees below?

(a) Anna is paid £530 for 90 hours work.

(b) Tom is paid £590 for 80 hours plus 10 hours at time and a half.

4 Calculate the annual net income after tax for each young employee.

(a) Omar earns £9·20 per hour. He works 24 hours per week.

(b) Sally earns £8·40 per hour for 18 hours per week. She also works 6 hours' overtime at time and a half each week.

(c) Myra earns £84 per hour, working a 32 hour week.

(d) Derek works at weekends only. The basic hourly rate is £15. He works 10 hours at double time.

5 As a salesman, Phil, aged 52, earns £350 per week plus 15% commission on all sales. Calculate his income after tax in a week when his sales are

(a) £760

(b) £1235

(c) £1800.

19.2 Fuel bills

Learning intentions

Gas and electricity are supplied by a number of companies charging different prices.

Fuel bills are based on the amount of fuel consumed

Your electricity charges					Total (£)
Period 10/02/06 to 28/02/06					
Description	**Start**	**End**	**Units**	**Price(kWh@p)**	
Domestic				242@8·310	£20·11
Meter: P879029648	69874	70116	242		
Standing charge				19days@11·270	£2·14
Period 01/03/06 to 01/05/06					
Description	**Start**	**End**	**Units**	**Price(kWh@p)**	
Domestic				681@9·075	£61·80
Meter: P879029648	70116	70797	681		
Standing charge				62days@11·270	£6·99
Total electricity					**£91·04**

Discounts	Total (£)
Gas & electricity discount	−£3·33
Total discounts	**−£3·33**

Your total charges		Total (£)
Total charges excl VAT	£87·71	£91·04
VAT at 5·00% on £91·04		£4·39
Your total charges are		**£92·61**

> Price may change during period of the bill.

> $$\begin{array}{r} 70116 \\ \text{Units} = \underline{-69874} \\ 242 \end{array}$$
> $$\begin{array}{r} \text{Units} = 70797 \\ \underline{-70116} \\ 681 \end{array}$$

> Discount may be for prompt payment.

> VAT is 5%

Your gas charges					Total (£)
Period 10/02/06 to 28/02/06 (Calorific value: 40·1 Volume correction: 1·022640)					
Description	**Start**	**End**	**Units**	**Price(kWh@p)**	
Domestic standard				2063@1·760	£36·31
Meter: 06075912	9952	10016	64		
Standing charge				19days@9·990	£1·90
Period 01/03/06 to 01/05/06 (Calorific value: 40·1 Volume correction: 1·022640)					
Description	**Start**	**End**	**Units**	**Price(kWh@p)**	
Domestic standard				4836@2·051	£99·19
Meter: 06075912	16	166	150		
Standing charge				62days@9·990	£6·19
Total gas					**£143·59**
VAT at 5·00% on £143·59					£7·18
Your total charges are					**£150·77**

> Calculation of kWh from gas units is complex.

Discussion points

Different companies claim to offer cheaper prices for fuel. Investigate this by checking the information on fuel company websites.

(CI) (EC)

Exercise 19.2

For each bill calculate the missing values at (**a**), (**b**), (**c**), (**d**), (**e**), (**f**), (**g**) and (**h**).

1

Your electricity charges					Total (£)
Period 10/11/05 to 09/02/06					
Description	**Start**	**End**	**Units**	**Price(kWh@p)**	
Domestic				(**a**)@8·310	(**b**)
Meter: P879029648	68621	69874	(**a**)		
Standing charge				92days@11·270	£10·37
Total electricity					(**c**)
VAT at 5·00% on (**c**)					(**d**)
Your total charges are					(**e**)

2

Your gas charges					Total (£)
Period 10/11/05 to 09/02/06 (Calorific value: 40·3 Volume correction: 1·022640)					
Description	**Start**	**End**	**Units**	**Price(kWh@p)**	
Domestic Standard				9606@1·760	(**b**)
Meter: 06075912	9654	9952	(**a**)		
Standing charge				92days@9·990	£9·19
Total gas					(**c**)

3

Your electricity charges					Total (£)
Period 10/02/06 to 28/02/06					
Description	**Start**	**End**	**Units**	**Price(kWh@p)**	
Domestic				1324@8·310	(**b**)
Meter: P879029648	78253	(**a**)	1324		
Standing charge				19days@11·270	£2·14
Period 01/03/06 to 01/05/06					
Description	**Start**	**End**	**Units**	**Price(kWh@p)**	
Domestic				9420@9·075	(**d**)
Meter: P879029648	(**a**)	(**c**)	9420		
Standing charge				62days@11·270	£6·99
Total electricity					(**e**)

Discounts	Total (£)
Gas & electricity discount	−£5·02
Total Discounts	−£5·02

Your total charges	Total (£)
Total charges excl VAT	(**f**)
VAT at 5·00% on (**f**)	(**g**)
Your total charges are	(**h**)

4

Your electricity charges					Total (£)

Period 10/02/06 to 28/02/06

Description	Start	End	Units	Price(kWh@p)	
Domestic				998@8·310	**(b)**
Meter: P879029648	93861	**(a)**	998		
Standing charge				19days@11·270	£2·14

Period 01/03/06 to 01/05/06

Description	Start	End	Units	Price(kWh@p)	
Domestic				**(c)**@9·075	**(d)**
Meter: P879029648	70116	70797	**(c)**		
Standing charge				62days@11·270	**(e)**
Total electricity					**(f)**

There has been a price change for ScottishPower customers. As a result, we have estimated how much energy you have used up to this price change, based on your previous bills, where available.

Discounts	Total (£)
Gas & electricity discount	−£3·33
Total Discounts	−£3·33

Your total charges	Total (£)
Total charges excl VAT	**(g)**
VAT at 5·00% on **(g)**	**(h)**
Your total charges are	**(i)**

5

Your gas charges					Total (£)

Period 10/02/06 to 28/02/06 (Calorific value: 40·1 Volume correction: 1·022640)

Description	Start	End	Units	Price(kWh@p)	
Domestic Standard				2063@1·760	**(a)**
Meter: 06075912	9952	10016	64		
Standing charge				19days@9·89	**(b)**

Period 01/03/06 to 01/05/06 (Calorific value: 40·1 Volume correction: 1·022640)

Description	Start	End	Units	Price(kWh@p)	
Domestic Standard				4836@2·051	**(c)**
Meter: 06075912	16E	166A	150		
Standing charge				62days@9·89	**(d)**
Total gas					**(e)**
VAT at 5·00% on **(e)**					**(f)**
Your total charges are					**(g)**

6

YOUR GAS USAGE ESTIMATED			
Meter: G4A00767580201	Reading last time	Reading this time	Units
Gas Unrestricted kWh	7546	8476[E]	930
Correction factor 1·02264		Calorific value 39·6738	
Total metric units used		951·05 cu mtrs	
Units converted to kilowatt hours		10481·05 kWh	

YOUR GAS BILL

Your Tariff is General Saver

Standard energy		
10481·05 kWh at 2·520p each		**(a)**
Standing charge at 11·400p for 93 day[s]		**(b)**
Less prompt payment discount applied	−£9·56	
Total charges before VAT		**(c)**
VAT at 5·00% on charges of (**c**)		**(d)**

TOTAL CHARGES THIS BILL INCLUDING VAT	**(e)**
TOTAL FROM PREVIOUS BILL	**£286.72**
Payment received 28 February 2007	−£286.72
LESS YOUR PAYMENTS, THANK YOU	**−£286.72**
PLEASE PAY	**(f)**

19.3 Insurance

Learning intentions

Insurance is a means of compensation in the event of an accident, loss, theft or damage to property or people. The insurance **premium** is the cost of insurance. This is usually an annual charge, or a one off payment, but it may be paid in monthly instalments.

Example 1

M & F Insurance charge £6 a month to insure the life of a 35 year old, non-smoking male for £50 000. Smokers are charged 11% more.

(**a**) Over 20 years, how much will a non-smoker pay for the insurance cover?

(**b**) How much extra will a smoker pay over a period of 35 years?

(**c**) *Sesco Insurance* charge £5·80 for the same level of cover. In percentage terms, how much cheaper is this?

(**a**) For one year premium $= 12 \times £6$ $= £72$
Over 20 years premium $= 20 \times £72$ $= £1440$

(**b**) Over 35 years premium $= 35 \times £72$ $= £2520$
Extra cost for a smoker $= 0·11 \times £2520$ $= £277·20$

(**c**) Difference in cost $= £6·00 - £5·80$ $= 0·20$
Percentage difference $= \frac{0·20}{6·00} \times 100$ $= 3·33\%$

Discussion points

Who or what is protected by these forms of insurance: car, house, travel, pet, life, appliance, income? What other forms of insurance are there? Are there types of insurance which may not be worth the cost?   CI EC RC

Example 2

Sara has two quotations for car insurance. *Laird's* have offered £756 with a 30% discount for a two year **no claim bonus**. *Sudbury* has offered £684 with a 25% discount for carrying a £200 **excess**. Which quote should Sara accept and why?

Laird's final premium $= £756 - 30\% = £529·20$
Sudbury's final premium $= £684 - 25\% = £513$

Sara is safer to accept *Laird's* quote. It is only £16·20 more expensive but she will not have to pay the first £200 of any claim

A **no claim bonus** is a percentage reduction if no insurance claims are made

An **excess** must be paid by the motorist. The insurance company pays the remainder of the claim.

Exercise 19.3

1 The table shows the monthly premiums charged for life insurance cover for £75000.

Monthly premium (£) for £75 000

Age next birthday

	22	23	24	25	26	27	28	29	30	31	32
Male, non-smoker	55	56	57	57·50	58	59	59·50	60	61	61·50	62
Male, smoker	61	62	63	64	64·50	65	66	67	67·50	68	69
Female, non-smoker	51	52	53	54	54·50	55	56	57	57·50	58	59
Female, smoker	58	59	60	61	61·50	62	63	64	65	65·50	66

(a) Find the annual premium for a
   (i) 23 year old female, non-smoker
   (ii) 31 year old male, smoker
   (iii) 30 year old female, non-smoker

(b) Over 10 years, how much more will a 29 year old male pay than a female, if they are both non-smokers?

(c) An insurance company claims it is at least 10% cheaper than any other company. If this is true, what is its maximum possible annual premium for a 30 year old female smoker?

2 Greta has had a life insurance policy since her second birthday.
The original premium was 5p per week.
At 21 she increased the premium to £1 per month. At 50 she increased it again to an annual premium of £72. Greta is now 87 years old.

(a) How much has she paid in her lifetime?

(b) If the policy eventually pays out £15 000, what is the percentage gain over the premiums paid?

3 The table shows the monthly premium for £100 000 of temporary life cover for a female aged 45, from six different companies.

M & F	£13·20
General Life	£13·65
Sesco	£14·40
Norfolk Union	£15·09
Hull	£15·50
Smith & Jones	£17·95

(a) How much more expensive per year is *Norfolk Union* than *General Life*?

(b) As a percentage, how much more expensive is *Smith & Jones* than *Sesco*?

(c) For a smoker, the premiums are generally 20% higher. How much more is this for a woman who has a policy with *General Life* for 15 years?

4 Elaine pays an annual premium of £430 for pet insurance for her dog. During the year she claimed for two vets' bills of £285 and £525, and £150 for a referral to an animal behaviourist.
How much has she saved by taking out insurance?

5 Claire has been quoted £1052 per annum to insure her pet cats. She can save 5% by applying on line.
How much of a saving is this?

6 Sarah's car insurance premium is £865 per year minus a 20% no claim bonus.
She also has a £350 excess on this policy.
After an accident, Sarah has a repair bill of £485. Should she pay the bill herself or claim it on her insurance policy and lose the no claim bonus?

7 From the table find the annual travel insurance premium for
(**a**) a couple requiring European cover
(**b**) a family travelling to the USA
(**c**) an individual travelling to Australia.

Annual travel insurance premiums

Annual multi-trip rates	European	Worldwide excluding USA, Canada and the Caribbean Islands	Worldwide including USA, Canada and the Caribbean Islands
Individual	£56·42	£64·61	£84·93
Couple/single parent family	£89·14	£102·08	£134·20
Family	£97·55	£111·88	£147·33

8 (**a**) Use the table below to find the cost of travel insurance for
(**i**) an 8 day holiday for a family travelling to France
(**ii**) a 17 day trip for an adult travelling to New Zealand
(**iii**) a 31 day holiday for a couple travelling to Canada.

Single trip travel insurance premiums

Single trip rates	European			Worldwide excluding USA, Canada and the Caribbean Islands			Worldwide including USA, Canada and the Caribbean Islands		
	Adult	Family	Couple/single parent family	Adult	Family	Couple/single parent family	Adult	Family	Couple/single parent family
Up to 5 days	£16·72	£31·76	£27·58	£35·20	£68·74	£58·09	£50·29	£98·58	£82·98
6 to 10 days	£21·08	£40·48	£34·78	£37·51	£73·36	£61·90	£53·62	£105·23	£88·47
11 to 17 days	£23·41	£45·14	£38·62	£41·45	£81·23	£68·39	£59·29	£116·57	£97·82
18 to 24 days	£26·66	£51·65	£43·99	£47·08	£92·49	£77·68	£67·39	£132·78	£111·20
25 to 31 days	£29·15	£56·64	£48·11	£52·18	£102·70	£86·10	£74·74	£147·48	£123·33

(**b**) Can you think of a reason why insurance to the USA is more expensive than to other parts of the world?

9 Ian's home and contents insurance costs £1250 per annum. He pays this in monthly instalments but this costs 8% more. How much is each monthly instalment?

10 Lara paid £154 for wedding insurance.

Wedding insurance

	Tier 1	Tier 2	Tier 3	Tier 4
Price	£59·00	£99·00	£154·00	£189·00
Cancellation Cover	£5,000	£8,000	£12,500	£17,500
Wedding Attire	£2,500	£3,500	£4,000	£5,000
Photographs/Video	£2,000	£2,250	£2,500	£3,000
Wedding Rings	£2,500	£2,500	£3,500	£3,500
Wedding Presents	£2,500	£3,000	£4,000	£5,000
Wedding Deposits	£2,000	£2,000	£3,500	£5,000
Transport and Flowers	£2,250	£2,500	£2,750	£3,000
Cake	£2,500	£2,750	£3,000	£3,250
Legal Expenses	£10,000	£10,000	£10,000	£10,000
Public Liability	£2,500,000	£2,500,000	£2,500,000	£2,500,000
Stress Counselling	Yes	Yes	Yes	Yes
Marquees*	Unavailable	£20,000	£20,000	£20,000

(**a**) From the table how much cover does she have for
    (**i**) clothes   (**ii**) presents   (**iii**) the cake?

(**b**) What is the percentage difference in cancellation cover between tier 1 and tier 4?

19.4 Spending

Learning intentions

Paying for goods and services may be done with cash, cheque, credit, debit or store card.

Method of payment	Effect
Cash	Immediate payment
Cheque or debit card	Removed from bank account within a few days
Credit or store card	Added to credit card account, to be repaid on a monthly basis. Interest charges and fees added if the **balance** is not paid in full.

Discussion point

What are the advantages and disadvantages associated with using credit and debit cards? CI EC

Balance means the amount owed or in credit

Example

For this credit card statement calculate:

(**a**) the next month's balance if there are no further purchases but only the minimum £12 is paid

(**b**) by how much the debt has actually reduced.

Balance from previous statement	£386·20
24 APR BP Underwood S/St	46·32
26 APR F R Miller	19·30
29 APR HL Express	11·18
NEW BALANCE	535·00

Monthly interest rate 1·27%
Minimum payment £12

(**a**) New balance   £535 − £12 = £523
    Interest   1·27% of £523 = £ 6·64
                        £529·64
    Next month's total will be **£530·99**

(**b**) £12 paid, £6·64 charged in interest. Reduction in debt is **£5·36**

Exercise 19.4

 1 Calculate how much is in each bank account after each debit card purchase. Interest on overdrafts is charged at 11%.

> An overdraft is money owed to the bank.

   (**a**) Opening amount   £380   (**b**) Opening amount   £45
        Debit card purchase   £98   Debit card purchase   £53

   (**c**) Opening amount   £2345   (**d**) Opening amount   £456
        Debit card purchase   £3500   Debit card purchase   £134

2 For each credit card account, calculate
   (**i**) next month's balance   (**ii**) the reduction in debt, if any.

   (**a**) Current balance   £358   (**b**) Current balance   £45
        Repayment   £60   Repayment   £12
        Interest   1·527%   Interest   1·602%

   (**c**) Current balance   £875   (**d**) Current balance   £2350
        Repayment   £800   Repayment   £1000
        New spending   £235   New spending   £755
        Interest   1·523%   Interest   1·530%

> Interest is not charged on new spending.

3 A credit card company has a monthly minimum repayment of £11 and a monthly interest rate of 1·571%.
If Sarah has a debt of £63 and repays the minimum amount each month, calculate

   (**a**) how many months it will take to clear the debt
   (**b**) how much more than £63 she will have paid.

19.5 Investing and saving

Learning intentions

Money may be invested in many ways: banks and building societies, stocks and shares, premium bonds, property, or other ways.
Issues to consider include:
- interest gained
- risk associated with investment
- length of time of investment
- ease of access to the funds.

Discussion point

What are the risks of investing in stocks and shares?

EC RC

Exercise 19.5

1 Work in pairs or small groups.
Copy the table below and complete it to indicate your estimate of the benefits and risks associated with each form of investment.

Type of investment	Risk – high, medium or low	Potential gain – high, medium or low
Bank account	low	
Shares in a high street store		
Premium bonds		
Lottery tickets		
Building society account		
Property		
Money in a sock under the bed		
Gold or jewellery		
Shares in a new internet company		
Pension fund		

2 Discuss the results of the paired or group working.

19.6 Borrowing

Learning intentions

There are several ways to borrow money. The amount you can borrow may depend on your **credit score**. This is a measure of your ability to repay the money.

Method of borrowing	Description
Credit card	Minimum amount must be repaid each month. High interest charges.
Overdraft	A bank account with a negative balance. High interest charges plus other charges if not agreed in advance.
Personal loan	From a bank, finance company, store or supermarket. Lower interest rate. Repaid over a fixed number of years.
Doorstep lender	Finance company. Extremely high interest rates – up to 170%!
Mortgage	Loan to purchase a house. Repaid over 20 or 25 years. Amount of loan depends on income of borrower.
Student loan	The amount a student may borrow depends on parental income. This is repaid after graduation. Some students also qualify for a bursary which does not require to be repaid.

Discussion point

What factors would influence a credit score?

The considerations in borrowing money are
- the interest rate (APR)
- the length of time to repay
- the ability to make the repayments.

Example

Michael needs £4500 for roof repairs. He is considering two options.

A Use his credit card at 1·607% per month and repay £250 each month.
B Take a personal loan at 6·9% per annum and repay over two years.

(a) Under option B what will his monthly payment be?
(b) Under option A how much interest will he have paid after 4 months?
(c) Which option would you recommend and why?

(a) Interest   6·9% of £4500 × 2 = £621
     Total to repay   £4500 + £621 = £5121
     Monthly repayment   £5121 ÷ £24 = **£213·38**

> Interest is 1·607% of £4500 = £72·32

(b) Month 1   £4500   + £72·32 − £250 = £4322·32
     Month 2   £4322·32 + £69·46 − £250 = £4141·78
     Month 3   £4141·78 + £66·56 − £250 = £3958·34
     Month 4   £3958·34 + £63·61 − £250 = £3771·95
                £271·95   Interest after 4 months is **£271·95**

(c) Option B. The total amount he will repay is much less for a personal loan than for a credit card debt.

Exercise 19.6

1 Calculate the monthly repayment for each personal loan.

(a) Amount borrowed   £1200
    Interest rate   7·2% p.a.
    Length of time   1 year

(b) Amount borrowed   £3600
    Interest rate   6·5% p.a.
    Length of time   2 years

(c) Amount borrowed   £5600
    Interest rate   4·95% p.a.
    Length of time   4 years

(d) Amount borrowed   £130 800
    Interest rate   4·8% p.a.
    Length of time   25 years

2 Susan's monthly repayment on a fixed rate mortgage is £825.

(a) How much will she repay over 20 years?

(b) She borrowed £172 000 to buy her house. How much interest has she paid?

(c) If her house is now worth £435 000, how much better off is she now?

3 The table shows the monthly repayments for a loan of £1500 over 1 and 2 years.

(a) What is the monthly repayment for a two year loan?

(b) What total amount is repaid over one year?

	1 year	2 years
Monthly repayment	129·64	67·01
Total interest	55·69	108·30

19.7 Personal budgeting

Learning intentions

For young people, living independently is more expensive than living at home. It is important to budget carefully and avoid unnecessary debt.

Discussion point

Is all debt a bad thing? When is debt a sensible option?

EC RC

Exercise 19.7

1 (a) Using the table of estimated costs, decide which of the people below could afford to move into a shared flat.

Sarah has a net monthly income of £1250

Derek earns £6·10 net per hour. He works 35 hours per week.

Deborah earns £330 per week. She has a monthly loan repayment of £35.

Michael has an annual salary of £22 700. He also has a student loan to repay at £85 per month.

(b) Clothes and entertainment are not mentioned in the list of estimated costs.

Does this change the decision about who can afford to move away from home?

Estimated monthly costs (£)	
Rent	420
Gas, electricity, water	40
Council tax	35
TV licence	11
Food	40
Laundry	15
Insurance	20
Broadband	15
Transport	60

Review exercise 19: Am I a successful learner?

1 If tax free personal allowances amount to £6200, calculate the income tax payable on an income of

(a) £14 250   (b) £29 256.

Tax rates	
0–2230	10%
2231–34 600	22%

2 Steven earns £8·20 per hour. Calculate his weekly gross income if he works a 36 hour week plus 5 hours of overtime at double time.

3 From the information given below, calculate the total electricity bill.

Meter readings	
Start	End
69864	70305

Unit price (p)   8·31

Standing charge (p)   57 days@9·99

VAT   5%

4 Paul's annual car insurance premium is currently £993 minus a 30% no claim bonus. A rival company quotes him a premium of £585.

(**a**) Is the new quote cheaper than his existing premium?

(**b**) What other considerations should he take into account?

5 Omar owes £75 on his credit card. Each month he makes the minimum repayment of £12. The monthly interest rate is 1·571%.

(**a**) How long will it take Omar to pay off the debt?

(**b**) How much interest will he have paid in total?

6 Calculate the monthly repayment figure for each personal loan.

(**a**) Amount borrowed   £2500
Interest rate   7·5% pa
Length of time   2 years

(**b**) Amount borrowed £7000
Interest rate   4·8% pa
Length of time   3 years

7 Michael has £500 to invest. He is considering buying 500 lottery tickets or buying 500 premium bonds. What would you advise him to do and why?

Summary 19: What I learned in this chapter.

Personal income

Gross income
− Deductions
Net income

Deductions include income tax, national insurance and superannuation.

Income tax is calculated as a percentage of taxable income after tax free allowances have been deducted.

Fuel bills

Present meter reading
− Previous meter reading
Units used

Gas and electricity bills are calculated from the number of units used.

VAT is charged at a lower rate on utility bills.

Insurance

There are many forms of insurance: life, house and contents, car, travel, pet, wedding.
The cost of insurance is called the premium. It is usually an annual charge but may be paid in instalments.

Spending

Paying for goods and services may be done by cash, cheque, credit, debit or store card.

Method of payment	Effect
Cash	Immediate payment
Cheque or debit card	Removed from bank account within a few days
Credit or store card	Added to credit card account, to be repaid on a monthly basis. Interest charges and fees added if the **balance** is not paid in full.

Borrowing

There are several ways to borrow money.

Method of borrowing	Description
Credit card	Minimum amount must be repaid each month. High interest charges.
Overdraft	A bank account with a negative balance. High interest charges plus other charges if not agreed in advance.
Personal loan	From a bank, finance company, store or supermarket. Lower interest rate. Repaid over a fixed number of years.
Doorstep lender	Finance company. Extremely high interest rates – up to 170%!
Mortgage	Loan to purchase a house. Repaid over 20 or 25 years. Amount of loan depends on income of borrower.
Student loan	The amount a student may borrow depends on parental income. This is repaid after graduation. Some students also qualify for a bursary which does not require to be repaid.

Investing and saving

Money may be invested in many ways: banks and building societies, stocks and shares, premium bonds, property,
Issues to consider include:

- interest gained
- risk associated with investment
- length of time of investment
- ease of access to the funds.

Personal budgeting

Living independently is more expensive than living at home. It is important to budget carefully and avoid unnecessary debt.

Review 5

Exercise 5A

Factorising

1 Factorise fully

(a) $6y + 8$

(b) $14a - 35a^2$

(c) $b^2 - 36$

(d) $x^2 + 6x + 5$

(e) $9z^2 - 1$

(f) $36xy^2 - 18x^2y + 27x^2y^2$

(g) $6w^2 - 24v^2$

(h) $b^2 - 8b - 9$

(i) $6s^2 + 4s - 10$

(j) $3y^3 - 27y$

(k) $8y^2 - 20y + 8$

(l) $12g^5h^3 - 8g^3 + 20g^3h$

(m) $21 + 13x + 2x^2$

(n) $16x^4y^3 - 4x^2y$

(o) $3a^2 - 7ab - 6b^2$

2 The area of the rectangle can be represented by $(3x^2 - 2x - 1)$ cm².
Find possible expressions for the length and breadth of the rectangle.

> Area $= 3x^2 - 2x - 1$ cm

3 The shaded area is given by $\pi R^2 - \pi r^2$.

Factorise $\pi R^2 - \pi r^2$ fully.

Hence calculate the shaded area when
R = 75 mm and r = 25 mm.

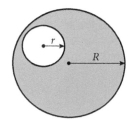

Statistics 3

4 In a 10 kilometre road race the times, in minutes, for the runners to finish the race are shown.

```
37  63  44  58  90  85  77  38  42  87  58  67  49  51
55  43  75  66  63  69  45  44  89  72  36  84  44  53
```

(a) Draw a cumulative frequency table and graph.

(b) Find the median and quartiles.

(c) Describe the pattern for the finishing times of the runners.

5 In an experiment the growth of a sample of plants was measured, in millimetres, and recorded.

```
61·4   38·8   36·8   40·2   53·9   45·0   42·1   59·6
```

(a) Calculate the mean and standard deviation of the sample.

(b) In a separate experiment eight plants were given a new plant food and their growth recorded. For these plants the mean was 51·3 millimetres and standard deviation 10·1 millimetres.
Comment on the effectiveness of the plant food.

Earning and spending

6 Bernie earns a basic £320 per week plus $12\frac{1}{2}$% commission on sales.
Calculate his gross income in a week when his sales total is £856.

7 Find (a), (b), (c), (d) and (e) in the gas bill below.

Gas price (p)	2025 @ 1.72	= (a)
Standing charge (p)	81 days @ 9.81	= (b)
Subtotal		(c)
VAT at 5%		(d)
Total charges are		(e)

8 Use the table to find the cost of travel insurance for
   (a) a 3 day trip to Rome for one adult
   (b) a 15 day holiday to Canada for 2 adults.

Single trip travel insurance premiums

Single trip rates	European			Worldwide excluding USA, Canada and the Caribbean Islands			Worldwide including USA, Canada and the Caribbean Islands		
	Adult	Family	Couple/single parent family	Adult	Family	Couple/single parent family	Adult	Family	Couple/single parent family
Up to 5 days	£16·72	£31·76	£27·58	£35·20	£68·74	£58·09	£50·29	£98·58	£82·98
6 to 10 days	£21·08	£40·48	£34·78	£37·51	£73·36	£61·90	£53·62	£105·23	£88·47
11 to 17 days	£23·41	£45·14	£38·62	£41·45	£81·23	£68·39	£59·29	£116·57	£97·82

Exercise 5B (cumulative)

1 Evaluate each expression if $z = 5$, $w = -4$, $x = -2$ and $y = -3$:

   (a) $\dfrac{8z}{w}$ (b) $3x^2 - 2zy$ (c) $\dfrac{2y^2}{x}$

   (d) $\dfrac{3x^3}{2wy}$ (e) $\dfrac{4z^2 + 5x^2}{2y}$ (f) $\dfrac{(xw)^2 + 4(y - x)}{w + x}$

2 Solve each equation:

   (a) $3(2b - 1) = 2(2b + 3)$ (b) $4(2z - 5) + 4 = -12$

   (c) $-5(3 + 2w) = 3(w + 8)$ (d) $\dfrac{2m + 1}{3} = \dfrac{m - 3}{2} - \dfrac{m}{6}$

3 (a) Find an expression for the perimeter of the rectangle.
   (b) Find an expression for the area of the rectangle.
   (c) Given that the perimeter of the rectangle is 54 centimetres, find the area of the rectangle.

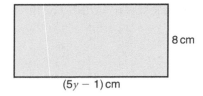

8 cm

$(5y - 1)$ cm

4 Find:

   (a) 25% of 64 m   (b) 40% of £120   (c) 5% of 820 g   (d) $66\frac{2}{3}$% of £19.23

5 A leather jacket is put on sale with a 20% discount. Boris buys the jacket in the sale for £116. How much did the jacket cost before the sale?

6 In June 1995 the population in Scotland was approximately $5·12 \times 10^6$. If the population fell at a steady rate of 1·75% per year for the next 3 years, calculate the population of Scotland in June 1998. Give your answer in scientific notation, to 3 significant figures.

7 For the school fête John makes a fruit punch by mixing orange juice, pineapple juice and lemonade in the ratio $3 : 1 : 5$. He sells the punch in 90 millilitre cups and estimates that he will sell 250 cups. How many litres of orange juice will he need to make the punch?

8 Jayne measured the circumference of her wall clock to be 62·8 centimetres. If the tip of the minute hand of the clock traces out 7·85 centimetres of the circumference, through what angle does the hand move?

9 Calculate the value of *x* in each diagram.

(**a**)

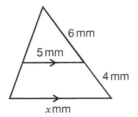

6 mm

5 mm

4 mm

x mm

(**b**)

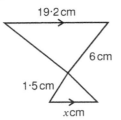

19·2 cm

6 cm

1·5 cm

x cm

(**c**)

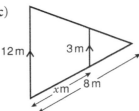

12 m 3 m

x m 8 m

10 Demi-Chem sells shampoo bottles which are similar.
If the larger bottle holds 540 millilitres of shampoo what volume of
shampoo does the smaller bottle hold?

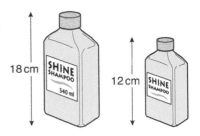

18 cm

12 cm

11 The diagram shows a cuboid with edges
15 centimetres, 8 centimetres and
6 centimetres.

(**a**) Use triangle *PTS* to calculate the
length of *PT*.

(**b**) Hence calculate the length of *PU*.

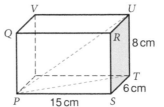

12 The points *W*(5, −3), *M*(4, 6) and *N*(−2, 4) are the vertices of a triangle.
Is the triangle right angled?

13 At a school fête, the time taken by pupils, in seconds, to solve a maths
puzzle was recorded. The times are recorded below

```
25   44   52   24   35   42   56   43   19   54
35   17   35   46   43   28   36   35   26   66
28   32   21   54   47   33   38   45   47   56
19   35   44   48   53   53   22   27   62   36
```

(**a**) Draw a stem and leaf diagram to represent this data.

(**b**) Find (**i**) the mode (**ii**) the median (**iii**) the quartiles.

14 Joanna measures the heights, in millimetres, of 20 plants in her
greenhouse. The results are displayed in the dot plot below.

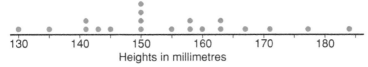

130 140 150 160 170 180
Heights in millimetres

(**a**) Write down the highest and lowest values.
(**b**) Find the quartiles.
(**c**) Find the interquartile range.
(**d**) Display the data in a box plot.

The box plot below shows the height of twenty
plants Joanna grew last year

(**e**) Comment on the heights of this year's
plants compared to those of last year.

125   139   152   163   189

15 Expand and simplify:
  (a) $8(4t + 4)$
  (b) $-6x(5 - 3x) + 5x^2$
  (c) $-7z(4z - 9) - 2z + 8z^2$
  (d) $(a + 5)(a - 2)$
  (e) $(h + 9)(3h - 6)$
  (f) $-3(2x - 3)(3x + 4)$
  (g) $(2p - 7)^2 - (p - 3)^2$
  (h) $3(y + 4)^2$
  (i) $14f^2 + 6(2f - 1)^2$
  (j) $(x - 3)(3x^2 + 5x + 4)$
  (k) $(2d - 3)(4d + 5)^2$
  (l) $-(4y + 2)(3y^2 - 5y - 1)$

16 Solve the equations:
  (a) $(y - 3)^2 + 24y = y^2$
  (b) $(x + 3)^2 - 9 = x^2$
  (c) $x^2 + 2x - 3 = (x - 5)^2$
  (d) $(2z - 1)^2 = 4z^2 + 9$
  (e) $(p + 8)^2 = (p - 1)^2$
  (f) $(3x + 1)^2 = (3x - 2)^2$

17 The sum of the first n natural numbers is given by the formula $S = \frac{1}{2}n(n - 1)$
  Calculate the sum of the first twenty natural numbers.

18 The formula $M = \frac{1}{2}wx(L - x)$ occurs in the theory of bending beams.
  Find M when $w = 200$, $L = 12$ and $x = 9$

19 Rearrange each of these formulae to make x the subject.
  (a) $y = \frac{1}{2}x + 5$
  (b) $p = \frac{ax}{2y}$
  (c) $T = \frac{1}{2}mn(x - n)$
  (d) $S = 3x^2 + 6p$
  (e) $K = \frac{2\sqrt{x}}{3L}$
  (f) $6wx^3y = \frac{2}{3}z$

20 Calculate the volume of each prism. Give your answers to 3 significant figures.
  (a)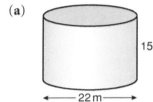
  (b)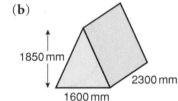
  (c)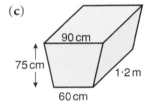

21 A cuboid has length $3x$ centimetres, width x centimetres and height $2x$ centimetres.
  Calculate the height if the volume of the cuboid is 1100 cubic centimetres.
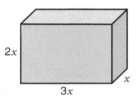

22 A block of candle wax, in the shape of a cube of side 0.4 metres is melted down and remoulded to make spherical candles. Each spherical candle has a diameter of 10 centimetres. How many candles can be formed? (Volume of sphere $= \frac{4}{3}\pi r^3$)

23 Find the maximum and minimum possible values for each measurement.
  (a) $5\cdot4 \pm 0\cdot1$ m
  (b) $20\cdot35 \pm 0\cdot002$ ml
  (c) 32 seconds

24 Calculate the value of x in each of these triangles.
  Give your answers correct to 2 significant figures.
  (a)
  (b)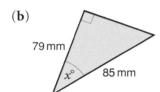
  (c)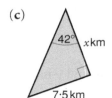

25 On an orienteering course Jim and Tom set off on a bearing of 037° and run for 1300 metres. They then change direction and travel due west until they are directly north from their starting point. Calculate how far they are from the starting point.

26 Ahmed fills a shopping bag with 8 apples, 6 oranges, 4 nectarines, 3 kiwi fruit, 9 pears and 6 plums.
  (**a**) State the probability that he chooses at random
      (**i**) a pear
      (**ii**) a kiwi fruit or an orange
      (**iii**) not an apple.
  (**b**) Ahmed eats an apple and a kiwi. What is the probability that the next fruit he chooses is a plum?

27 At the school prom the probabilities for each choice of meal are
      Chicken in white wine sauce   0·62
      Mushroom stroganoff   0·2
      Salmon mornay   0·18
  If 120 students attend, how many of each meal should the chef prepare?

28 Calculate the sizes of the marked angles in each diagram.
  (**a**)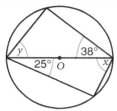

  (**b**)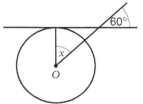

29 Find the length of *EB*.

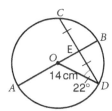

30 Solve each pair of simultaneous equations algebraically.
  (**a**) $2x + 3y = 7$
      $8x + 10y = 26$
  (**b**) $5p = 3q - 31$
      $6p - q + 19 = 0$
  (**c**) $\frac{1}{4}m + \frac{1}{10}n = \frac{1}{2}$
      $\frac{1}{6}m - \frac{1}{10}n = 2$

31 Aftab bought 3CDs and 4 DVDs for a total cost of £81. Carol bought 3DVDs and one CD for a total cost of £49.50. Find the cost of 2CDs and 2DVDs.

32 Find the gradient of the line joining each pair of points.
  (**a**) P(2, 4) and Q(9, 18)
  (**b**) W(−4, −5) and V(4, −10)

33 Write the gradient and *y*-intercept of each line and hence sketch the line.
  (**a**) $y = -2x + 9$
  (**b**) $3x + 2y = -16$
  (**c**) $\frac{7}{8}x - 5 - y = 0$

34 Find the equations of the following lines.

(a)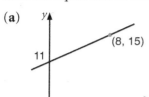

(b)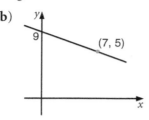

(c)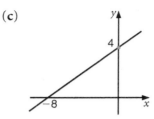

35 Factorise fully

(a) $z^2 + 5z - 6$

(b) $uv^2w + u^2vz$

(c) $x^3 - x^2$

(d) $9g^2 - 25h^2$

(e) $3 - 27c^2$

(f) $p^2 + 4p - 5$

(g) $4y^2 + 16y + 15$

(h) $f^3 + 5f^2 - 24f$

(i) $4b^3 - 64b$

(j) $2p^2 + 11p + 5$

(k) $1 - v^4$

(l) $x^2 + 2xy - 24y^2$

36 The cumulative frequency curve shows the weight, in grammes, of four hundred eggs which were sent as a sample to be packaged.
The eggs are sorted and packaged according to their size.

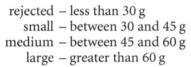

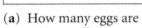

(a) How many eggs are
  (i) small
  (ii) large
  (iii) rejected?
(b) What is the probability that an egg chosen at random from this sample weighs
  (i) less than 40 g
  (ii) between 45 and 60 g
  (iii) greater than 60 g?
(c) Calculate the interquartile range.

37 A company which makes sweets advertises that each bag holds fifty sweets. As a quality control check they count the number of sweets in a sample of 6 bags.

    51   49   46   57   52   45

(a) Calculate the mean and standard deviation of the sample.

(b) The company introduces new efficiency measures to improve production. The mean are recalculated to be 49·1 and standard deviation 3·1 respectively.
Comment on the effectiveness of the efficiency measures.

Answers

Chapter 1

Exercise 1.1

1 (a) 48 kg   (b) £10·56   (c) £35   (d) 5·1 m
   (e) 17 km   (f) £3·40   (g) 306   (h) 29·1 mm
   (i) 616 kg   (j) 2   (k) £87·50 (l) 2·4
   (m) £360   (n) 13·8 m   (o) £4·20 (p) 1·6 ml
2 (a) £31·50   (b) £10·08   (c) £68·60
3 (a) 54   (b) 108   (c) 18
4 (a) (i) £1207·50   (b) (i) £45·50   (c) (i) £603·75
       (ii) £8107·50   (ii) £305·50   (ii) £4053·75
5 £30·45, £204·45
6 (a) £640   (b) £1920   (c) £192
7 £135
8 No, it contains 6·7% fat
9 £41 975
10 (a) 4   (b) 20 000   (c) 8·4

Exercise 1.2

1 (a) 31·0 m   (b) 27·2 km   (c) 4·0 g   (d) 32·4 kg
   (e) 264·6 kg   (f) 7·1 cm   (g) 19·2 ml   (h) 13·5 cm
   (i) 18·6 kg   (j) 450·5 g   (k) 33·9 ml   (l) 1076·4 km
2 £92·50
3 (a) £142·80   (b) £71·40   (c) £11·90   (d) £119
4 (a) £1360·80   (b) £113·40   (c) £245·70
5 £1585·02
6 (a) £20·83   (b) £11·73   (c) £1·49
7 (a) £13·50   (b) £613·50
8 (a) £24·38   (b) £51·84   (c) £451·54
9 (a) 316 220 000 cubic miles   (b) 13040 cubic miles
10 £101·25
11 Mega motors   £14 993·82
    Celebrity Cars £14 377·35
    Celebrity Cars is cheaper.
12 (a) £552   (b) £39·10
13 22 517

Exercise 1.3

1 (a) £83·08   (b) £236·60   (c) £34·16
2 (a) 31·16 l   (b) 10·8 km   (c) 9·315 tonnes
3 £5666·85
4 (a) £28 815 000 (b) £3289·38 per hour
5 1·456 m²
6 (a) £411·25   (b) £170·38   (c) £61·10
7 £162·63
8 £99 360
9 £20·65
10 £2·13
11 £3·37
12 £0·15

Exercise 1.11

1 (a) £365·40   (b) £153·02   (c) £2106·25   (d) £1719·14
2 £213 549·06
3 £6341·20
4 50·5
5 Not safe after 5 years, still 2·33 mg of pollutant.
6 £3558·25
7 £1709·70
8 4 years
9 4·65 years

Exercise 1.5

1 £5805·85
2 (a) Elliot   (b) Euan
3 32 years
4 (a) 49 600 km²   (b) 46 140·97 km²   (c) 40 903·63 km²

Exercise 1.6

1 (a) 42·6%   (b) 12·7%   (c) 60·1%   (d) 101·2%
2 (a) 40·9%   (b) 24·4%   (c) 30·2%   (d) 11·5%
3 (a) 15·8%   (b) £810·60

Exercise 1.7

1 (a) 30%   (b) 45%   (c) 40%
   (d) 24·19%   (e) 1·37%   (f) 3·04%
2 Maths 82%   Eng 77%   French 42%   Hist 75%   Phy 95%
3 (a) 22·8%   (b) 7·4%
4 74%
5 4·42%
6 13·6%
7 Yes, it's increased by 23·05%.
8 (a) £297·50   (b) £342·13   (c) 2·25%
9 She now earns 1% less than her original salary.
10 (a) 49·8%   (b) 18·8%   (c) 53·8%
    (d) 38·3%   (e) 47·6%
    (f) 47·6 > 46·2 S1 has more boys   (g) 12·3% increase

Exercise 1.8

1 (a) £585   (b) £127·20   (c) £112·50
2 £4000
3 £2250
4 (a) £360   (b) £238
5 (a) £21   (b) £113·79
6 80

Review exercise 1

1 (a) 4·8   (b) 15·5   (c) 108   (d) 53
   (e) 2·66   (f) £304·50   (g) £153   (h) 166·4 m
2 (a) £2240   (b) £166·25   (c) £460·25
3 (a) £8·31   (b) £43·87   (c) 8·91   (d) 40·7
4 (a) £470·40   (b) 195·4 m   (c) 328·02 kg
5 (a) 287 m   (b) £55·38   (c) £83·09
6 (a) £374·90   (b) £28·12
7 Haymarket, Heathcote Rd, Bridge St
8 51%
9 £229 083
10 No, he was 16 tickets short of target.
11 26%
12 89 888
13 £56
14 400 g
15 6 years
16 (a) 170 mg   (b) 4·26 hours

Chapter 2

Exercise 2.1

1 (a) −9   (b) 10   (c) −20   (d) −4
   (e) 3   (f) −13   (g) 21   (h) 10
   (i) 22   (j) −11   (k) 51   (l) 97
2 (a) 120   (b) −20   (c) 4   (d) 0
   (e) $-7\frac{1}{2}$ (f) −34   (g) −9   (h) 30
   (i) 0   (j) $-\frac{3}{10}$ (k) 0   (l) 2

Exercise 2.2

1 (a) $2b + 14c$ (b) $19x + 2y$ (c) $7q$
(d) $6y - 4$ (e) $-3w + 13z$ (f) 0
(g) $-4t + 3s$ (h) $-12v + 6w$ (i) $7 + 4t$
(j) $-3d - 7e + 2$ (k) $-2 - 2x - 5y$ (l) $10 + t$
2 (a) $-4t - 10s$ (b) $-11x - 3y$ (c) $6x + 8y - 18z$
(d) $7a - 9b - 4c$ (e) $-7f + 9g + 17$ (f) $9e + 6$
(g) $-11z - 14t - 5r$ (h) $-6y$ (i) $f + 5h$
(j) $-9 - v + 16w$
3 (a) $7x^2 - 12$ (b) $12y^2 + x$ (c) $-1 + 7c^2$
(d) $18x^2 + 7y$ (e) $5w^2 + 8w$ (f) $5b^2 - 2b + 7$
(g) $9k - 2k^2$ (h) $5ab - 3xy$ (i) $-xy + 4y$
(j) $11st$ (k) $10x^2y$ (l) $15ab^2 + 5a^2b$
(m) $8yz + 6y^2z + 4yz^2$ (n) $7m^2n - 8mn^2 - 6m$
(o) $-4gh + 4gh^2 - g^2h$

Exercise 2.3

1 (a) $10y - 35$ (b) $12 + 18x$ (c) $20z + 8w$
(d) $14a - 35b$ (e) $-12b - 9$ (f) $-5q + 15$
(g) $-42 + 14t$ (h) $12x - 10$ (i) $50 - 20a + 40b$
(j) $-12c + 24d + 28$ (k) $-32e - 16f + 48$ (l) $3x - 6y + 15z$
2 (a) $5x + 16$ (b) $20y - 27$ (c) $17c + 20d - 5e$
(d) $18x + 16 - 6y$ (e) $-9y - 21$ (f) $-12w + 13v$
(g) $4a - 16b - 8c$ (h) $4d + 12e - 3f$ (i) $6 + 15g - 5h$
(j) $7 - 7j$ (k) $5k + 9$ (l) $4m - 5n$
3 (a) $11a + 10b$ (b) $2e - 1$ (c) $3f^2 - 13f + 30$
(d) $4g + 13h$ (e) $5x + 8y + 7z$ (f) $2a + 18b - 6c$
(g) $-9 - 24y$ (h) $-7 + 9m$ (i) $-31d + 1$
(j) $-62x + 22y$ (k) $27a - 4b$ (l) $16y - 6x - 17$
(m) $18x + y - 8$ (n) $-18a - 24b + 6 - 2ab + 2b^2$

Exercise 2.4

1 (a) $2(x + 3)$ (b) $3(y + 8)$ (c) $4(y + 9)$
(d) $5(3m - 7)$ (e) $18(t + 2)$ (f) $5(4t - 7)$
(g) $10(3f + 5)$ (h) $4(8s + 4t - 5)$ (i) $7(5a - 11b + 7)$
2 (a) $2(3r + s - 4)$ (b) $4(4x + 1)$ (c) $5(4x + 3y - 5)$
(d) $9(2t + 5)$ (e) $4(5t + 9u - 7)$ (f) $3(11 - 7g)$
(g) $10(2f - g)$ (h) $8r + 49s - 14$ (i) $8(2f - g)$
(j) $5(6r + 5s - 3)$ (k) $6(3m + 6n - 4)$ (l) $5(f - 4g)$
3 (a) $5(8m - 5n - 11)$ (b) $2(5d + 14e - 6)$ (c) $11(r - 3s + 9)$
(d) $40(x - 2y)$ (e) $100(5f + 7g - 6)$ (f) $13(4x - 2y + 3)$
(g) $7(6m - 9n + 11p)$ (h) $7(x + 3y)$ (i) $2(2g + 3h - 7)$
(j) $2(8f - 7g)$ (k) $20(x + 4y)$ (l) $5(6s + 7t)$
(m) $15(2x + 3y - 5)$ (n) $21r + 40s$ (o) $11(2x - 5y + 8z)$
4 (a) $x(c + d)$ (b) $x(f + g)$ (c) $y(a + b)$
(d) $x(a - b)$ (e) $y(x - z)$ (f) $a(b + c)$
(g) $h(m - f)$ (h) $x(a + 1)$ (i) $y(b - 1)$
(j) $x(x - a)$ (k) $y(b - y)$ (l) $x(2 + a)$

Exercise 2.5

1 (a) $p = 4$ (b) $x = 5$ (c) $y = 6$
(d) $p = -2$ (e) $g = -3$ (f) $b = 2$
(g) $c = 2$ (h) $y = \frac{1}{2}$ (i) $x = -\frac{1}{3}$
2 (a) $x = 1$ (b) $y = 4$ (c) $f = 6$
(d) $y = \frac{2}{5}$ (e) $z = -4$ (f) $b = -3$
(g) $m = -2\frac{1}{2}$ (h) $x = \frac{2}{3}$ (i) $y = -\frac{3}{4}$
3 (a) $y = 2$ (b) $b = 1$ (c) $z = 10$
(d) $y = -3$ (e) $y = -2$ (f) $b = -5$
(g) $g = \frac{1}{2}$ (h) $y = \frac{2}{5}$ (i) $z = -\frac{3}{4}$
4 (a) $p = 1$ (b) $y = 4$ (c) $x = -2$
(d) $z = -5$ (e) $t = 2$ (f) $b = -1$
(g) $x = -\frac{2}{3}$ (h) $y = -\frac{1}{2}$ (i) $z = 1\frac{1}{2}$

Exercise 2.6

1 (a) $x = 2$ (b) $z = 8$ (c) $b = -3$
(d) $y = 1$ (e) $x = -\frac{1}{2}$ (f) $w = -4\frac{1}{2}$
(g) $t = -2\frac{1}{2}$ (h) $b = \frac{1}{4}$ (i) $x = -\frac{6}{7}$
(j) $x = 2\frac{1}{2}$ (k) $b = -\frac{3}{5}$ (l) $z = -3\frac{1}{2}$
2 (a) $y = 2$ (b) $b = 11$ (c) $x = +4$
(d) $t = \frac{1}{2}$ (e) $w = -4$ (f) $z = 1\frac{1}{2}$
(g) $x = \frac{1}{3}$ (h) $z = -1\frac{1}{3}$ (i) $g = 1$
(j) $x = -1\frac{2}{3}$
3 (a) $y = -5$ (b) $x = -2$ (c) $z = 8$
(d) $y = 31$ (e) $x = 8\frac{2}{5}$ (f) $x = 1$
(g) $z = 2\frac{4}{7}$ (h) $b = 1\frac{11}{13}$ (i) $w = \frac{2}{3}$

Exercise 2.7

1 (a) $y = 12$ (b) $b = -6$ (c) $x = -10$
(d) $z = -30$ (e) $x = 4$ (f) $x = 4$
(g) $y = 1\frac{1}{3}$ (h) $x = -10$ (i) $x = -18$
2 (a) $y = 6$ (b) $z = -9$ (c) $y = -14$
(d) $w = -7$ (e) $y = 33$ (f) $a = -7$
3 (a) $x = 2$ (b) $z = -5$ (c) $m = 6$
(d) $x = -1$ (e) $y = -1\frac{3}{4}$ (f) $b = \frac{2}{5}$

Exercise 2.8

1 $x = 11$
2 $x = -1$
3 $x = 4\frac{1}{2}$
4 (a) $x = 8$ (b) $x = 12$ (c) $x = 4$
5 10 sweets in each packet
6 6 cans in each crate
7 50 nails in each bag

Exercise 2.9

1 (a) $y < -7$ (b) $x > 6$ (c) $z \leq -10$
(d) $b \leq -4$ (e) $w > -6$ (f) $x \leq 3$
(g) $p > -2$ (h) $y \geq \frac{1}{2}$ (i) $w < -\frac{1}{5}$
(j) $z \geq 3\frac{3}{4}$ (k) $p > -\frac{1}{2}$ (l) $y \leq -2\frac{1}{2}$
2 (a) $\{6\}$ (b) $\{-6, -5, -4, -3, -2, -1, 0, 1\}$
(c) $\{2, 3, 4, 5, 6\}$ (d) $\{-6, -5, -4\}$
(e) $\{-1, 0, 1, 2, 3, 4, 5, 6\}$ (f) $\{-6\}$
(g) $\{-6, -5, -4, -3, -2, -1, 0\}$
(h) $\{-6, -5, -4, -3, -2, -1, 0, 1, 2\}$
(i) $\{-6, -5, -4, -3, -2, -1\}$
3 (a) $y < 8$ (b) $x \geq 3$ (c) $w < 6$
(d) $z \geq 2$ (e) $m < -8$ (f) $p \leq 3$
(g) $y < -2$ (h) $x \leq \frac{7}{9}$ (i) $x \leq 6\frac{3}{4}$
(j) $p \geq 4\frac{1}{2}$ (k) $w > 2\frac{4}{5}$ (l) $y < -2\frac{1}{3}$
4 (a) $y > 1$ (b) $z \geq 2$ (c) $w < 1$
(d) $x \geq -\frac{1}{2}$ (e) $y < 1\frac{1}{2}$ (f) $x \geq -5$
(g) $z \leq 2\frac{1}{4}$ (h) $x > 1$ (i) $z > 4$
(j) $y < \frac{4}{5}$ (k) $w \leq 10$ (l) $y \leq \frac{1}{2}$

Exercise 2.10

1 (a) $x < 5$ (b) $x > 1$ (c) $x \leq 5$
2 muffin 40p, cookie 20p
3 max. 60 boxes

Review exercise 2

1 (a) 22 (b) 123 (c) -12
(d) 12 (e) 10 (f) 9
2 (a) $-5x + 2y$ (b) $-10r - 10v$ (c) $9st - 8xy$
(d) $4c^2 + 3ab$ (e) $6gh^2 - 4gh$ (f) $x^3 + x^2 - 5x - 3$
3 (a) $18d - 12$ (b) $20x - 20y$ (c) $11x^2 - 27$
(d) $18 - 12f$ (e) $36z - 3$ (f) $24b + 32$

4 (a) $5(3x - 7y)$ (b) $7(4p + 3)$ (c) $6(a - 2b + 7)$
5 (a) $y = 10$ (b) $x = \frac{2}{3}$ (c) $z = -7$
  (d) $b = -\frac{3}{4}$ (e) $w = 3$ (f) $y = \frac{4}{9}$
6 (a) $x = -12$ (b) $y = \frac{1}{5}$ (c) $z = 3$
  (d) $w = -1$ (e) $b = \frac{1}{2}$ (f) $x = -4$
7 (a) $y = -6$ (b) $x = 10$ (c) $x = -4$
  (d) $w = -3$ (e) $x = -5\frac{1}{2}$ (f) $z = 5$
8 (a) $y \geqslant -3$ (b) $z \leqslant 2\frac{1}{2}$ (c) $x \leqslant -5$
  (d) $w < -8$ (e) $y > -\frac{3}{7}$ (f) $x \geqslant -3\frac{1}{3}$
9 (a) $x = 2$ (b) $x = 11$ (c) $x = 4$
10 $y = 2$ 11 $x = -2$
12 (a) $x < 2$ (b) $x \geqslant 2\frac{2}{3}$
13 crisps £0·15 juice £0·30

Chapter 3

Exercise 3.1

1 (a) £33   (b) £13·20
2 £2160   3 550 km   4 585 loaves   5 £14·40
6 19·2 kg   7 £477   8 £1476   9 41·3 m
10 (a) £98·88   (b) £183·63
11 £100
12 (a) £26·08   (b) £40·16
13 (a) 0·17 km   (b) 0·082 km
14 (a) 40 cm   (b) 123 cm
15 (a) 1·23 km   (b) 29·3 cm
16 42·75 m
17 Flour 750 g, Butter 225 g, Sugar 187·5 g
17 20 hrs
19 (a) 82 800 m/h   (b) 82·8 km/h

Exercise 3.2

1 (a) 513·6 cm   (b) 816·8 cm
2 27·13 m   3 49·4 kg   4 £800   5 460 pupils
6 9900 chairs   7 11·4 kg   8 £2600   9 £600 000

10
Distance on map (cm)	5·30	8·95	14·65	70·79
Distance on ground (km)	2·61	4·40	7·20	34·8

Exercise 3.3

1 6 days   2 2320 jotters   3 35 mins   4 30 slabs
5 15   6 16 books   7 8 days   8 275
9 5   10 3333   11 6 days   12 14
13 4

Exercise 3.4

1 (a) 64·40€   (b) 358·40€   (c) 499·10€   (d) 670·32€
2 (a) £25·71   (b) £63·57   (c) £247·14   (d) £561·07
3 1·36
4 (a) (i) 264€   (ii) $302·72   (iii) 2464 krone
  (b) (i) £303·33   (ii) 223·83   (iii) £44·57
5 $214·20
6 Bank of Caledonia   1·44   Euro Express has the best exchange rate
  Euro Express   1·50
  Burnfoot travel   1·325
7 £11·93
8 May £106·54

Review exercise 3

1 (a) £26·50   (b) 7 plants
2 120 l   3 £58·85   4 925
5 306 000 000 m/s   6 63·2 m   7 680
8 14·49 kg   9 10 days
10 (a) $125·56   (b) $233·92
11 (a) £134·33   (b) £6·22
12 Mike

Chapter 4

Exercise 4.1

1 (a) 0·45 m²   (b) 12·25 mm²   (c) 816 cm²
  (d) 3·5 cm²   (e) 0·44 m²   (f) 3·91 m²
2 (a) 1100 m²   (b) 202·5 cm²   (c) 35·8 cm²
  (d) 6·44 m²   (e) 1326 mm²   (f) 63·8 cm²
3 £3711·68
4 (a) 14 cm   (b) 30 cm

Exercise 4.2

1 (a) 384 mm²   (b) 4·73 cm²   (c) 67·45 cm²
  (d) 25·6 m²   (e) 24·34 mm²   (f) 385 cm²
2 (a) 10 cm   (b) 60 mm   (c) 1·21 m
3 (a) 60 cm²   (b) 480 cm²   (c) 720 cm²

Exercise 4.3

1 (a) 330 cm²   (b) 59·5 m²   (c) 4550 mm²
  (d) 630 mm²   (e) 36·55 cm²   (f) 3·63 m²
2 (a) 450 mm²   (b) 3600 mm²
3 (a) 12 m   (b) 10 cm   (c) 9·3 mm

Exercise 4.4

1 (a) 69·1 cm, 380 cm²   (b) 39·0 mm, 121 mm²
  (c) 48·7 m, 189 m²
2 £6·53   3 101
4 (a) 27·7 m²   (b) 1018·6 mm²   (c) 145 cm²
5 0·87 m²
6 (a) 4π cm²   (b) 25π mm²   (c) 100π cm²
7 (a) 3 cm   (b) 6·2 m   (c) 1·6 mm
8 15·6 cm

Exercise 4.5

1 (a) 23·6 cm   (b) 108 cm   (c) 43·5 mm
  (d) 25·7 m   (e) 65·0 cm   (f) 148 mm
2 (a) 60·4 cm   (b) 111 m
3 122 cm   4 52·4 m, 78·5 m, 105 m
5 121 cm   6 $\frac{5\pi}{3}$ cm
7 (a) $\frac{4\pi}{3}$ m   (b) 2π cm   (c) $\frac{10\pi}{3}$ mm

Exercise 4.6

1 (a) 113 cm²   (b) 3230 cm²   (c) 5·54 m²
  (d) 349 mm²   (e) 77·2 m²   (f) 13·7 m²
2 2904·2 cm²   3 13124·9 mm²
4 2 m   5 $\frac{49\pi}{3}$ m²
6 (a) 4π m²   (b) $\frac{50\pi}{3}$ m²   (c) 5π m²
7 (a) 50π cm²   (b) $263·25\pi$ mm²   (c) $6·48\pi$ m²

Exercise 4.7

1 $r = 5$ cm   2 12·6 m   3 60°
4 12 m   5 10 m
6 (a) 45°   (b) 4·71 cm   7 (a) 145°   (b) 7·29 m
8 (a) 22·5 cm   (b) 180°   9 (a) 48 cm²   (b) 37·5°

Review exercise 4

1 (a) 90 cm²   (b) 5625 mm²   (c) 5·2 m²
2 30·6 l
3 (a) 7·85 cm, 4·91 cm²   (b) 40·8 cm, 133 cm²   (c) 251 mm, 5030 mm²
4 9·2 m

5 **(a)** 38·4 cm, 154 cm² **(b)** 9·53 m, 20·0 m² **(c)** 10·4 mm, 88·3 mm²
6 **(a)** 7π m **(b)** 49π
7 30°
8 **(a)** 8·5 cm **(b)** 170°

3 **(a)** 1·5 **(b)** 2·5 **(c)** $\frac{4}{3}$
4 **(a)** $\frac{1}{2}$ **(b)** $\frac{1}{3}$ **(c)** $\frac{1}{4}$
5 **(a)** 4 **(b)** 4 **(c)** 3

Chapter 5

Exercise 5.1

1
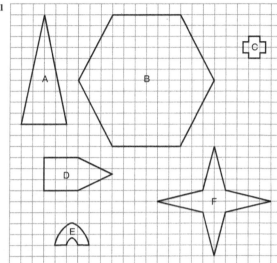

2
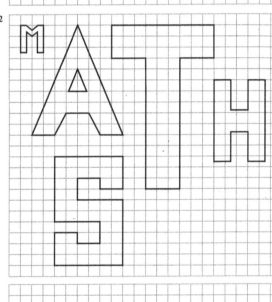

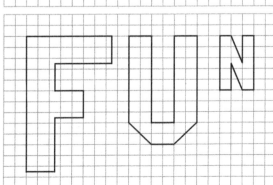

Exercise 5.2

1 **(a)** Similar. Equiangular; sides in equal ratio.
(b) Similar. Equiangular; sides in equal ratio.
(c) Not similar.
(d) Similar. Equiangular; sides in equal ratio.
(e) Not similar. Sides in equal ratio; not equiangular.
(f) Similar. Equiangular; sides in equal ratio.
2 B F H G
3 **(a) (d) (e)** are similar
4 No. They are equiangular but sides are not necessarily in equal ratio.
5 Yes. Equiangular and sides in equal ratio.
6 Yes. Only one dimension to compare.

Exercise 5.3

1 **(a)** Scale factor 3, $x = 4.5$ **(b)** Scale factor $\frac{1}{2}$, $x = 3.5$
(c) Scale factor 3·5, $x = 1.75$ **(d)** Scale factor 0·75, $x = 6$
(e) Scale factor 1·5, $x = 2.25$ **(f)** Scale factor 0·75, $x = 15$
2 **(a)** Scale factor 1·25, $x = 7.5$ **(b)** Scale factor 0·625, $x = 3.75$
(c) Scale factor 4, $x = 3.75$
3 2·2 m
4 **(a)** 148·5 mm by 105 mm **(b)** Scale factor $\frac{1}{2}$
(c) 74·25 mm by 52·5 mm **(d)** Yes. Scale factor is $\frac{1}{2}$
(e) Equal **(f)** 37·125 mm by 26·25 mm
(g) 1188 mm by 840 mm
5 **(c)** Yes. Sides are in equal ratio.
(d) Equiangular and sides are in equal ratio.
6 **(b)** Yes. Sides in equal ratio; equiangular.

Exercise 5.4

1 **(a)** Similar **(b)** Similar **(c)** Not similar
2 **(a)** $x = 11.55$ cm, $y = 5.85$ cm
(b) $x = 110°$, $y = 25°$
3 18·75 m
4 $x = 2$, $y = 2.125$, $z = 2.52$

Exercise 5.5

1 **(a)** $x = 7.5$ **(b)** $x = 24$ **(c)** $x = 15$
2 **(a)** AC = 15 cm, ED = 3·5 cm
(b) AE = 10 cm, AB = 5 cm
(c) BE = 28 cm
3 **(a)** $x = 4.5$ **(b)** $x = 16\frac{2}{3}$ **(c)** $x = 20$
(d) $x = 1.2$ **(e)** $x = 150$ **(f)** $x = 12.5$
4 **(a)** 5·25 m **(b)** Yes
5 18 m
6 61 m
7 **(a)** $x = 3.125$ **(b)** $x = 1.5$
8 $x = 6$, $y = 8$

Exercise 5.6

1 **(d)**

Scale factor	Area (cm²)
1	1
2	4
3	9
4	16

(e) (i) 25 cm² **(ii)** n^2 cm²

2 (d)

Scale factor	Area (cm²)
1	2
2	8
3	18
4	32

(e) (i) 50 cm²   (ii) $2n^2$ cm²

3 (d)

Scale factor	Area (cm²)
1	3
2	12
3	27
4	48

(e) (i) 75 cm²   (ii) $3n^2$ cm²

Exercise 5.7

1 (a) 20 cm²   (b) 50 cm²   (c) 40 cm²
2 Model B 1296 cm², Model C 1764 cm²
3 £1378·12
4 (a) size 4 8·125 m², size 3 5·2 m²   (b) 2·925 m²
5 0·1875 km²   6 78750 km²
7 (a) 4   (b) 2   (c) 10 cm
8 (a) 1·44   (b) 1·2   (c) 15·24 cm

Exercise 5.8

1 (a) 1 cm³   (b) 8 cm³

(d)

Scale factor	Volume (cm³)
1	1
2	8
3	27
4	64

(e) (i) 125 cm³   (ii) n^3 cm³
2 (a) 6 cm³   (b) 48 cm³

(d)

Scale factor	l	b	h	Volume (cm³)
1	2	1	3	6
2	4	2	6	48
3	6	3	9	162
4	8	4	12	384

(e) (i) 750 cm³   (ii) $6n^3$ cm³
3 (a) 6·28 cm³   (b) 50·24 cm³

(d)

Scale factor	v	h	Volume (cm³)
1	1	2	6·28
2	2	4	25·12
3	3	6	56·52
4	4	8	100·48

(e) (i) 785 cm³   (ii) $6·28n^3$ cm³

Exercise 5.9

1 (a) 675 ml   (b) 874·8 ml   (c) 87·5 ml
2 345·6 cm³   3 168·75 cm³   4 148·15 ml
5 Yes. Volume is 8 times greater but cost is 4 times greater.
6 0·98 l
7 (a) 72·8%   (b) 7·7%
8 101 mm, 243 mm   9 13·5 cm
10 (a) 12 cm   (b) 64 cm³

Review exercise 5

1 First, second and fourth sizes. Sides are in equal ratio.
2 (a) Scale factor 2, $x = 16·6$ (b) Scale factor 0·25, $x = 1·325$
   (c) Scale factor 0·5, $x = 3·2$
3 56 cm
4 (a) $x = 18$, $y = 8·775$ (b) $x = 69°$, $y = 77°$
5 46 m
6 (a) $x = 6·4$ (b) $x = 9·84$ (c) $x = 2·25$, $y = 0·625$
7 67·5 cm
8 Yes. The transmitter is only 3·85 m from the shed.
9 125 m
10 3·825 m
11 6·22 m²
12 Yes. Area is 1500 m²
13 (a) 2·25   (b) 1·5   (c) $x = 22·8$
14 683·59 ml
15 Smaller can at 5 ml per pence. Larger is 4·8 ml per pence.
16 No. Volume is 25·3125 ml
17 15 cm
18 The bigger biscuit is slightly more than 70% larger.

Chapter 6

Exercise 6.1

1

Triangle	A	B	C	D	E	F
Area of smallest square	9	25	36	81	49	100
Area of middle square	16	144	64	144	576	576
Area of largest square	25	169	100	225	625	676

2 (a) 74 cm²   (b) 63 cm²   (c) 33 cm²
   (d) 29 cm²   (e) 75 cm²   (f) 28 cm²

Exercise 6.2

1 (a) z   (b) r   (c) n   (d) LN   (e) XY
2 (a) $x = 5$ cm   (b) $x = 13$ cm   (c) $x = 17$ cm
3 (a) $x = 7$ cm   (b) $x = 9$ cm   (c) $x = 16$ cm
4 (a) $c = 6·7$ cm   (b) $b = 3·9$ cm   (c) PQ = 4·5 m
   (d) SU = 18·4 cm   (e) $m = 5·2$ cm   (f) $b = 12·0$ cm

Exercise 6.3

1 (a) $c = 4·6$ m   (b) $d = 3·1$ m
   (c) $a = 4$ m   (d) $b = 1·2$ m
   (e) $e = 8·9$ m, $f = 18·3$ m   (f) $g = 5$ m, $h = 2·0$ m
   (g) $i = 1·7$ m   (h) $j = 1·3$ m
   (i) $k = 3·7$ m, $l = 9·5$ m   (j) $m = 5·2$ m, $n = 1·5$ m
2 1·78 km
3 12·21 km
4 12·8 km
5 (a) (i) 1·2 m   (ii) 0·6 m²
   (b) (i) 1·6 m   (ii) 1·92 m²
6 (a) $x = 4$, $y = 7·2$ (b) $x = 10$, $y = 4·36$ (c) $x = 14·3$, $y = 16$

Exercise 6.4

1 (a) $x = 35·36$ mm   (b) $x = 1·77$ m   (c) $x = 30·86$ cm
2 91·92 m
3 (a) Square   (b) ∠GCB, BG = 7·07 cm
   (c) BH = 8·66 cm
4 (a) ∠RQP, PR = 10 cm   (b) PV = 10·77 cm
5 (a) 12 cm   (b) 8·06 cm
6 (a) TM = 12 cm   (b) TO = 10·91 cm
7 No. Space diagonal is less than 10 m.
8 $x = 2$ m

Exercise 6.5

1 (a) $AB = 5$ units   (b) $AB = 10$ units
2 (a) $PQ = 10$ (b) $ST = 9.43$ (c) $VW = 7.81$
   (d) $CD = 12.04$ (e) $EF = 9.22$ (f) $KL = 11.31$
3 (a) $SQ = 4.24$ (b) $PR = 7.07$
4 (a) $AB = 6.08, BC = 6.08, AC = 7.07$ (b) Isosceles

Exercise 6.6

1 (a) 5   (b) 10   (c) 13
   (d) 13   (e) 15   (f) 4.24
2 $AB = \sqrt{37}, BC = \sqrt{50}, AC = \sqrt{37}.$ $AB = AC.$
3 $AB = \sqrt{17}, BC = \sqrt{13}, CD = \sqrt{17}, AD = \sqrt{13}, AC = \sqrt{52}, BD = \sqrt{8}$

Exercise 6.7

1 (b), (c), (e)
2 No   3 No   4 No   5 Yes
6 (a) Yes   (b) No   (c) No   (d) Yes

Exercise 6.8

1 (a), (b), (c), (e), (g), (h), (i), (j), (k), (l)

4
x, y	a	b	c
2, 1	4	3	5
3, 1	6	8	10
3, 2	12	5	13
4, 1	8	15	17
4, 2	16	12	20
4, 3	24	7	25

5 (a) $x = 5$ (b) $x = 25$ (c) $x = 10$
   (d) $x = 12$ (e) $x = 40$ (f) $x = 10$

Review exercise 6

1 (a) $c = 10.8$ cm   (b) $d = 15.9$ cm   (e) $EG = 7.4$ cm
2 (a) $c = 20$ m, $d = 30.7$ m   (b) $e = 3$ m, $f = 2.7$ m
   (c) $s = 4.1$ m
3 14.42 km
4 9.9 cm
5 (a) $EG = 11.4$ cm   (b) $EC = 12.4$ cm
6 (a) $PQ = 8.94, QR = 8.94, PR = 12.65$ (b) No
7 No
8 Since $\triangle ABC$ is right angled, $AC = 5.$
   Hence $AC^2 + CD^2$
         $= 25 + 144$
         $= 169 = AD^2$

Review 1

1 (a) £3.45   (b) 45 kg   (c) £36   (d) 61 ml
2 (a) £61.25   (b) £411.25
3 (a) £75.60   (b) 14.35 kg   (c) 113 ml   (d) £41.42
4 £55.35   5 £36 864.87   6 $33\frac{1}{3}\%$
7 £10 798.25   8 £119.23
9 (a) 7   (b) -4 (c) $\frac{7}{36}$
10 (a) $-kl$ (b) $4x^3 - x^2 + 4x$
11 (a) $45z - 39w$ (b) 24
12 (a) $x = 7$ (b) $p = 2$ (c) $n = 0.2$
   (d) $d = -1$ (e) $x = -1$
13 (a) $a = -1$ (b) $v = -20$
14 (a) $x < -\frac{13}{2}$ (b) $y \geq 23$ (c) $x \leq -3$ (d) $z < 1$
15 -7 16 $x < 6.8$ 17 3.4 kg
18 30 hours   19 £547.59

20 (a) 65 cm^2 (b) 4550 mm^2 (c) 4.94 m^2
21 (a) $C = 10.05$ m   (b) $C = 34.5$ cm   (c) $C = 188.4$ mm
     $A = 8.04$ m^2 $A = 94.985$ cm^2 $A = 2826$ mm^2
22 9.312 m
23 (a) $L = 37.68$ cm   (b) $L = 10.26$ m   (c) $L = 11.86$ mm
     $A = 150.72$ cm^2 $A = 21.54$ m^2 $A = 100.83$ mm^2
24 (b) 18.84 m
25 $30°$
26 (a) Scale factor 3, $x = 14.7$ cm   (b) Scale factor 4, $x = 0.8$ cm
27 18 m
28 (a) $x = 16.5, y = 18$ (b) $x = 3, y = 5$
29 24 m
30 4125 cm^2
31 1500.625 ml
32 (a) $a = 9.5$ cm   (b) $b = 4.3$ cm   (c) $c = 57.7$ mm
33 51.5 m
34 (a) $TV = 15$ cm   (b) $TR = 17$ cm
35 $KM = KL = 8.544$
36 No
37 No

Chapter 7

Exercise 7.1

1 (a) $4y$ (b) $7w$ (c) ab (d) vw
   (e) $3pr$ (f) $20st$ (g) $28kn$ (h) $72ck$
   (i) $7gh$ (j) $30bds$ (k) $60pqr$ (l) $18atw$
   (m) $30p^2$ (n) $56y^2$ (o) $4p^2$ (p) $16k^2$
   (q) $25p^2q^2$ (r) $9r^2t^2$
2 (a) $-4f$ (b) $-10t$ (c) ab (d) wy
   (e) $-mp$ (f) $-et$ (g) $-15aw$ (h) $-42ty$
   (i) $30hj$ (j) $-15bds$ (k) $60pty$ (l) $18atw$
   (m) $-50p^2$ (n) $63s^2$ (o) $4k^2$ (p) $9g^2$
   (q) $16x^2y^2$ (r) $25m^2n^2$
3 (a) $8y^3$ (b) $27w^3$ (c) $-27k^3$ (d) $-64m^3$
   (e) $8z^3y^3$ (f) $27g^3h^3$ (g) $-27k^3m^3$ (h) $4p^4$
   (i) $25h^4$ (j) $6c^3d^2$ (k) $20w^3y^3$ (l) $-14g^3h^3$
   (m) $-72s^3t^3$ (n) $8a^3b^2$ (o) $-6w^3z^3$

Exercise 7.2

1 (a) $yz + y$ (b) $fy - 4y$ (c) $pq - 5p$
   (d) $rx + 8x$ (e) $3t - st$ (f) $xy + 4x$
   (g) $-2 - 7$ (h) $-d - 6$ (i) $-7r + r^2$
   (j) $x^2 - 3x$ (k) $w^2 - 4w$ (l) $at - t^2$
   (m) $-ab + b^2$ (n) $t2 - 7z^2$ (o) $-g - 2$
   (p) $-x^2 - 9x$ (q) $-w^2 + wz$ (r) $-g + h$
   (s) $st + t^2$ (t) $-x + y$
2 (a) $2x^2 + 4x$ (b) $3xy - 12y$ (c) $4qr - 28r$
   (d) $2dx + 10x$ (e) $18st - 12t$ (f) $8xy + 16x$
   (g) $-3wz - 6w$ (h) $-3de + 18e$ (i) $-63r + 18r^2$
   (j) $7x^2 + 63x$ (k) $6w^2 - 8w$ (l) $8t - 40t^2$
   (m) $35ab - 21b^2$ (n) $40yz + 20z^2$ (o) $-14g^2 - 14gh$
   (p) $-16x^2 - 72xy$ (g) $-15w^2 + 30vw$ (r) $-10gh + 14h^2$
   (s) $18st + 45t^2$ (t) $-49xy + 42y^2$ (u) $-3x + 5y$
   (v) $-5sy - 3y^2$ (w) $-6t^2 + 8ht$ (x) $-3p^2 + 9pq$
3 (a) $3b^2 + 15b$ (b) $8x + 12x^2$ (c) $2y - 4y^2$
   (d) $10w^2 - 15w$ (e) $-12z + 6z^2$ (f) $-10t^2 - 30rt$
   (g) $9x^2 - 3x^3$ (h) $-8xy - 6y^3$ (i) $24z^3 + 18z^4$
4 (a) $3y^2 - 3y$ (b) $7x^2 - 6x$ (c) $-9z^2 + 23z - 9$
   (d) $7r^2 + 2rs$ (e) $6y^2 + 10xy$ (f) $-18y^3 + 57y^2$
   (g) $-3b^2 - 19b$ (h) $12x^3 - 23x^2 + 3x$ (i) $-15z^3 + 11z^2 - 8z$
   (j) $11t^2 - 4at$ (k) $11tz - 16z^2$ (l) $-21r^2 - 15rt$
   (m) $-20p^2 - 12pq$ (n) $-7y^2 - 39wy$ (o) $44g^2 + 3gh$
   (p) $-21c^2 - 7cd$ (q) $-10a^2 - 3ab$ (r) $z^2 - 8yz - 3y^2$
5 (a) $x^2 + 2x$ (b) $y^2 + 7y$ (c) $z^2 + 3z$
   (d) $2p^2 + 2p$ (e) $x^2 + 4x$ (f) $20x^2 + 30x$

6 (a) $x^3 - 2x^2 - 14x + 3$
(b) $y^3 + 7y^2 + 7y - 15$
(c) $2z^3 + 9z^2 - 43z - 56$
(d) $3w^3 - 7w^2 + 7w - 3$
(e) $9x^2 - 13x + 5$
(f) $3b^3 - 7b^2 + 3b + 16$
(g) $23y^3 - 12y^2 + 30y$
(h) $7x^3 + 14x^2 - 14x$

Exercise 7.3

1 (a) $x^2 + 3x + 2$
(b) $z^2 + 4z + 3$
(c) $y^2 + 7y + 12$
(d) $w^2 + 5w + 6$
(e) $b^2 - 6b + 8$
(f) $x^2 - 7x + 10$
(g) $y^2 - 6y + 5$
(h) $x^2 - 9x + 18$
(i) $h^2 - 6h + 8$

2 (a) $a^2 + 2a - 8$
(b) $z^2 - z + 6$
(c) $y^2 + y - 20$
(d) $w^2 + 5w - 24$
(e) $y^2 - 8y + 15$
(f) $b^2 + 11b + 30$
(g) $x^2 + 2x - 35$
(h) $z^2 + 5z - 66$
(i) $96 + 4c - c^2$

3 (a) $x^2 - 4$
(b) $x^2 - 49$
(c) $y^2 - 9$
(d) $p^2 - 16$
(e) $q^2 - 36$
(f) $t^2 - 100$

Exercise 7.4

1 (a) $y^2 + 11y + 30$
(b) $a^2 + 10a + 24$
(c) $d^2 + 12d + 27$
(d) $z^2 + 14z + 49$
(e) $m^2 + 14m + 45$
(f) $k^2 + 15k + 56$
(g) $y^2 + 11y + 18$
(h) $x^2 + 8x + 15$
(i) $z^2 + 12z + 32$
(j) $z^2 + 13z + 42$
(k) $m^2 + 18m + 81$
(l) $k^2 + 16k + 64$

2 (a) $x^2 - 5x + 6$
(b) $y^2 - 10y + 9$
(c) $z^2 - 7z + 12$
(d) $b^2 - 14b + 48$
(e) $w^2 - 11w + 28$
(f) $x^2 - 13x + 40$
(g) $x^2 - 4x + 4$
(h) $y^2 - 10y + 25$
(i) $b^2 - 18b + 81$
(j) $z^2 - 10z + 21$
(k) $m^2 - 14m + 45$
(l) $k^2 - 15k + 56$

3 (a) $x^2 + 10x + 21$
(b) $y^2 + 7y - 18$
(c) $z^2 - 2z - 15$
(d) $b^2 - 9b + 18$
(e) $k^2 - 2k - 63$
(f) $x^2 - 17x + 72$
(g) $x^2 - 9x - 22$
(h) $g^2 - 17g + 30$
(i) $b^2 - b - 90$
(j) $z^2 - 9z - 52$
(k) $b^2 - 20b + 100$
(l) $y^2 - 144$

4 (a) $x^2 + 3x + 2$
(b) $x^2 + 3x - 10$
(c) $x^2 - 3x + 2$

5 (a) $x^2 + 2x$
(b) $x^2 + 6x + 8$
(c) $4x + 8$

6 (a) $8x + 32$
(b) $8x + 40$
(c) $10x + 72$
(d) $6x + 16$

Exercise 7.5

1 (a) $2x^2 + 7x + 3$
(b) $4y^2 + 14y + 6$
(c) $4z^2 + 10z + 6$
(d) $6b^2 + 13b - 5$
(e) $15z^2 - 31z - 24$
(f) $12a^2 + 4a - 21$
(g) $12y^2 - 35y + 18$
(h) $15w^2 - 63w + 54$
(i) $15 - 26y + 8y^2$
(j) $18m^2 + 15m - 63$
(k) $24x^2 - 63x + 30$
(l) $25y^2 - 1$
(m) $9k^2 - 25$
(n) $36z^2 - 16$
(o) $15b^2 - 71b + 84$

2 (a) $2z^2 + 16z + 30$
(b) $4x^2 + 28x + 24$
(c) $5w^2 - 10w - 40$
(d) $12k^2 + 4k - 8$
(e) $10y^2 - 25y + 15$
(f) $12z^2 - 84z + 144$
(g) $-12b^2 - 2b + 24$
(h) $-20 - 2m + 48m^2$
(i) $-70k^2 + 168k + 126$
(j) $-90x^2 - 180x + 70$
(k) $-96y^2 + 156y - 60$
(l) $x^3 + 4x^2 + 3x$
(m) $18k^3 - 50k$
(n) $-72z^3 + 32z$
(o) $-15y^3 + 55y^2 - 30y$

3 (a) $3x^2 + 12x + 9$
(b) $2x^2 + 16x + 30$
(c) $2x^2 + 10x - 12$
(d) $x^3 - 4x^2 + 4x$
(e) $2x^3 + 2x^2 - 16x$
(f) $5x^3 - 35x^2 + 60x$

Exercise 7.6

1 (a) $x^2 + 2x + 1$
(b) $w^2 + 4w + 4$
(c) $k^2 + 10k + 25$
(d) $z^2 = 8z + 16$
(e) $x^2 + 6x + 9$
(f) $m^2 + 14m + 49$
(g) $y^2 + 12y + 36$
(h) $k^2 + 18k + 81$

2 (a) $y^2 - 2y + 1$
(b) $x^2 - 6x + 9$
(c) $k^2 - 10k + 25$
(d) $b^2 - 8b + 16$
(e) $k^2 - 4k + 4$
(f) $m^2 - 18m + 81$
(g) $y^2 - 14y + 49$
(h) $y^2 - 24y + 144$

3 (a) $z^2 + 16z + 64$
(b) $w^2 - 10w + 25$
(c) $c^2 + 20c + 100$
(d) $d^2 - 12d + 36$
(e) $x^2 + 24x + 144$
(f) $m^2 - 22m + 121$
(g) $y^2 - 40y + 400$
(h) $x^2 - 60x + 900$

4 (a) $9x^2 + 12x + 4$
(b) $4y^2 + 4y + 1$
(c) $25w^2 + 30we + 9$
(d) $9x^2 - 12x + 4$
(e) $4y^2 - 20y + 25$
(f) $9m^2 + 36m + 36$
(g) $64z^2 - 16z + 1$
(h) $16y^2 + 48y + 36$
(i) $81x^2 - 144x + 64$
(j) $81 + 54z + 9z^2$
(k) $100 - 40y + 4y^2$
(l) $400 - 80y + 4y^2$

5 (a) $z^2 + 2z + 1$
(b) $16y^2 - 16y + 4$
(c) $49 - 42x + 9x^2$

Exercise 7.7

1 (a) $2w^2 + 12w + 18$
(b) $4y^2 + 8y + 4$
(c) $5x^2 + 40x + 80$
(d) $5k^2 - 20k + 20$
(e) $6z^2 - 48z + 96$
(f) $18m^2 + 12m + 2$
(g) $16y^2 + 48y + 36$
(h) $-3b^2 + 12b - 12$
(i) $-5y^2 - 30y - 45$
(j) $-8x^2 - 8x - 2$
(k) $-36y^2 + 48y - 16$
(l) $-48 + 48z - 12z^2$

2 (a) $3b^2 + 6b + 3$
(b) $k^2 - 18k + 50$
(c) $m^2 + 2m + 19$
(d) $-10y^2 + 39y - 36$
(e) $9x^2 + 32x - 3$
(f) $15z^2 - 44z + 21$
(g) $16b^2 + 83b + 95$
(h) $-2z^2 + 14z - 11$
(i) $-14x + 21$
(j) $2y - 19$
(k) $-8x + 17$
(l) $-w^2 - 10w - 19$
(m) $-8x^2 - 2x - 20$
(n) $-44y^2 + 40y - 21$

3 (a) $x^2 + 2 + \dfrac{1}{x^2}$
(b) $z^2 + 6 + \dfrac{9}{z^2}$
(c) $k^2 - 2 + \dfrac{1}{k^2}$
(d) $z^2 - 4 + \dfrac{4}{z^2}$
(e) $m^2 + 8 + \dfrac{16}{m^2}$
(f) $4x^2 + 4 + \dfrac{1}{x^2}$
(g) $9b^2 - 6 + \dfrac{1}{b^2}$
(h) $25y^2 + 40 + \dfrac{16}{y^2}$
(i) $\dfrac{25}{z^2} + 20 + 4z^2$
(j) $\dfrac{1}{x^2} - 8 + 16x^2$
(k) $\dfrac{9}{z^2} - 12 + 4z^2$
(l) $\dfrac{1}{x^2} + \dfrac{2}{xy} + \dfrac{1}{y^2}$
(m) $\dfrac{9}{x^2} + \dfrac{12}{xy} + \dfrac{4}{y^2}$
(n) $\dfrac{1}{a^2} - \dfrac{4}{ab} + \dfrac{4}{b^2}$
(o) $\dfrac{4}{z^2} - \dfrac{16}{z} + 16$

4 (a) $24x + 96$
(b) $24x - 24$
(c) $200 - 40x$

Exercise 7.8

1 (a) $xy + 2y + bx + 2b$
(b) $y^2 + by - 2y - 2b$
(c) $yz + xy + xz + x^2$
(d) $a^2 - b^2$
(e) $c^2 - 2cd + d^2$
(f) $q^2 - p^2$
(g) $5g - gh + 5h - h^2$
(h) $9y - 3xy - 27x + 9x^2$
(i) $15s^2 - 16st + 4t^2$

2 (a) $x^3 + 4x^2 + 8x + 5$
(b) $w^3 - 3w^2 - 7w + 6$
(c) $2k^3 + 13k^2 + 11k - 20$
(d) $3z^3 - z^2 - 7z - 6$
(e) $4x^3 - 17x^2 + 6x + 27$
(f) $3m^3 - 15m^2 - 38m - 28$
(g) $2y^3 + 7y^2 - 22y + 48$
(h) $7k^3 - 72k^2 + 86k - 45$
(i) $6x^3 + 56x^2 + 57x - 56$
(j) $7z^3 + 12z^2 - z + 6$
(k) $-4b^3 + 11b^2 + 26b - 24$
(l) $-2x^3 + 3x^2 + 13x - 12$
(m) $9y^3 + 3y^2 + 7y - 3$
(n) $15z^3 - 16z^2 - 30z - 9$
(o) $42a^3 - 39a^2 - 21a + 15$

3 (a) $x^3 + 5x^2 + 8x + 4$
(b) $y^3 + 5y^2 + 7y + 3$
(c) $z^3 + z^2 - 16z + 20$
(d) $2w^3 + 13w^2 + 24w + 9$
(e) $9x^3 - 3x^2 - 8x - 4$
(f) $9y^3 - 3y^2 - 5y - 1$
(g) $4x^3 - 16x^2 + 13x - 3$
(h) $18m^3 + 45m^2 - 36m - 108$
(i) $192z^3 - 368z^2 + 83z - 5$
(j) $-4y^3 + 8y^2 + 11y + 3$
(k) $-27b^3 + 90b^2 - 96b + 32$
(l) $-50x^3 + 55x^2 + 348x + 252$

4 (a) $b^3 + 6b^2 + 11b + 6$
(b) $y^3 + 8y^2 + 17y + 10$
(c) $x^3 + 3x^2 - 13x - 15$
(d) $k^3 - 3k^2 - 4k + 12$
(e) $z^3 - 3z^2 - 10z + 24$
(f) $3m^3 + m^2 - 3m - 1$
(g) $2y^3 - 3y^2 - 5y + 6$
(h) $8b^3 - 24b^2 - 2b + 6$
(i) $10y^3 + 51y + 2y - 15$
(j) $24 + 26y + 9y^2 + y^3$
(k) $-b^3 + 3b^2 + 1\S0b - 24$
(l) $2x^3 - 29x^2 + 123x - 126$

5 (a) $x^3 + 3x^2 + 3x + 1$ (b) $w^3 + 12w^2 + 48w + 64$
(c) $k^3 + 15k^2 + 75k + 125$ (d) $z^3 - 6z^2 + 12z - 8$
(e) $x^3 - 3x^2 + 3x - 1$ (f) $m^3 - 9m^2 + 27m - 27$
(g) $8y^3 + 12y^2 + 6y + 1$ (h) $8k^3 + 60k^2 + 150k + 125$
(i) $27x^3 - 27x^2 + 9x - 1$ (j) $27 - 27y + 9y^2 - y^3$
(k) $8 - 12b + 6b^2 - b^3$ (l) $64 - 96x + 48x^2 - 8x^3$
6 (a) $x^3 + 9x^2 + 20x + 12$ (b) $x^3 + 11x^2 + 39x + 45$
(c) $3x^3 - 14x^2 + 20x - 8$ (d) $2x^3 + 9x^2 + 12x + 5$
(e) $x^3 + 6x^2 + 12x + 8$ (f) $8x^3 - 60x^2 + 150x - 125$
7 (a) $2x^3 - 6x^2 + 6x - 2$ (b) $-3y^3 - 18y^2 - 36y - 24$
(c) $8k^3 - 65k^2 + 300k - 480$ (d) $21z^3 - 67z^2 + 67z - 30$
(e) $-3x^3 - 16x^2 - 36x - 40$ (f) $30y^3 - 56y^2 - 64y$
(g) $30x^4 - 15x^3 + 50x^2 - 25x$ (h) $12m^3 - 38m^2 + 26m - 4$
(i) $-18y^3 - 42y^2 + 42y + 18$ (j) $4k^3 - 17k^2 - 15k + 50$
(k) $-30x^2 - 14x - 5$ (l) $34y^3 - 177y^2 + 273y - 123$

Exercise 7.9

1 (a) $x = 4$ (b) $y = \frac{9}{4}$ (c) $z = -2$
(d) $b = -3$ (e) $k = -\frac{5}{2}$ (f) $x = -\frac{13}{3}$
(g) $y = -\frac{5}{3}$ (h) $a = -\frac{17}{8}$ (i) $x = -3$
(j) $y = -\frac{6}{7}$ (k) $z = \frac{3}{5}$ (l) $m = -1$
(m) $x = \frac{1}{3}$ (n) $z = 1$ (o) $y = 1$
(p) $x = \frac{1}{2}$ (q) $w = \frac{1}{2}$ (r) $y = -\frac{3}{4}$
(s) $z = -\frac{1}{6}$ (t) $b = \frac{3}{4}$
2 (a) $x = 5$ (b) $x = \frac{1}{2}$ (c) $z = 5$
3 (a) $x = \frac{1}{3}$ (b) $x = 8$ (c) $x = 2$
4 (a) 3 cm (b) OB $= r - 1$
(c) $r^2 = 3^2 + (r-1)^2$ (d) $r = 5$
5 (a) $r = 5$ (b) $r = 10$

Exercise 7.10

1 (a) $z = -10$ (b) $w = -10$ (c) $x = 6$
(d) $d = -45$ (e) $p = 33$ (f) $x = \frac{4}{3}$
(g) $y = -7$ (h) $b = -30$ (i) $z = 4$
(j) $a = \frac{12}{5}$ (k) $p = \frac{35}{3}$ (l) $z = -\frac{8}{7}$
(m) $w = -\frac{17}{8}$ (n) $x = 6$ (o) $y = \frac{1}{2}$
(p) $z = 15$

Review exercise 7

1 (a) $12z - 12$ (b) $28x + 28$
(c) $-12y - 30$ (d) $-15 + 10w$
(e) $3x^2 + 6x$ (f) $30z - 15z^2$
(g) $-2t + 4t^2$ (h) $-30b + 23b^2$
(i) $-4x^2 - 29x$
2 (a) $y^2 + 8y + 15$ (b) $x^2 - 7x + 6$
(c) $z^2 + 3z - 10$ (d) $2x^2 + 6x - 20$
(e) $3y^2 - 12$ (f) $8w^2 - 14w + 5$
(g) $15z^2 + 25z + 10$ (h) $3y^2 + 3y - 90$
(i) $-30x^2 - 25x + 30$
3 (a) $y^2 + 6y + 9$ (b) $z^2 - 10z + 25$
(c) $4x^2 + 32x + 64$ (d) $25k^2 - 60k + 36$
(e) $4y^2 + 16y + 16$ (f) $7w^2 - 42w + 63$
(g) $12y^2 + 4y + 2$ (h) $20x^2 - 60x + 36$
(i) $13z^2 - 2z + 2$
4 (a) $3x^3 - x^2 - 6x + 4$ (b) $5y^3 + 23y^2 + 30y + 18$
(c) $18b^3 + 33b^2 - 40b - 75$ (d) $y^3 + 10y^2 + 31y + 30$
(e) $10b^3 - 14b^2 - 56b + 24$ (f) $27k^3 - 135k^2 + 225k - 125$
(g) $8x^3 + 84x^2 + 294x + 343$ (h) $-30y^3 + 20y^2 + 60y + 10$
(i) $4x^3 - 13x^2 - 16x + 38$ (j) $3y^3 - 17y^2 + 2y + 60$
5 (a) $x = 2$ (b) $z = -\frac{1}{2}$ (c) $k = -3·5$
(d) $y = 5$ (e) $x = \frac{7}{3}$ (f) $y = -2$
6 (a) $x = 4$ (b) $x = 37$
7 $x = -3·5$
8 (a) $y = 4$ (b) $x = 6$ (c) $x = 7$ (d) $w = \frac{12}{11}$

Chapter 8

Exercise 8.1

1
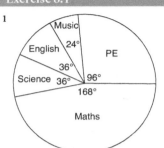

2
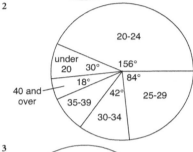

3
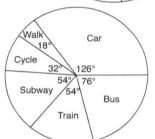

4

	Home News	Sport	Entertainment	Foreign	Politics
(a)	$\frac{7}{36}$	$\frac{1}{4}$	$\frac{1}{3}$	$\frac{1}{9}$	$\frac{1}{9}$
(b)	14	18	24	8	8

5

Europe	Aus. & NZ	Asia	North America	UK
360	160	200	480	240

Exercise 8.2

1 (a) (i) 3 (ii) 14 m (iii) Ben (iv) Ali
(b) Bob threw further than expected for his weight. (c) 20 m
2 (a) 2 (b) Mike (c) Mike
(d) 22 laps (e) Ron and Gus
3 (a)

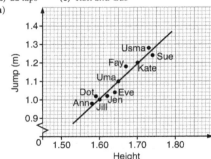

(b) Sue (c) Usma (d) Ann
(e) Ann (f) Yes. Positive correlation. (g) 1·12 m

4

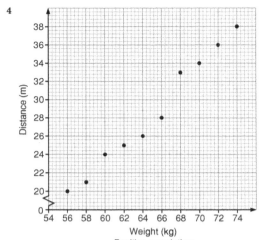

Weight (kg)
Positive correlation

5

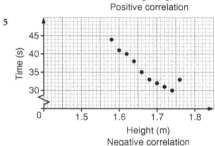

Height (m)
Negative correlation

6 No correlation

Exercise 8.3

1 (a) £0·95   (b) 4·9 hours   (c) 5·5°C
2 (a) 14 (b) 67 (c) 3·5 (d) 6·0
3 (a) 5 (b) 12·4 (c) 240
4 Group A 120, Group B 122. Group B appears taller.
5 (a) mean = 18·8, median = 19, mode = 22
  (b) mode
6 (a) (i) 21·5°C (ii) 20·5°C (iii) 25°C or 19°C
  (b) Either mean or median would give a typical temperature.
7 (a) 69   (b) 69·5
  (c) 70·1   (d) The winner's score of 63.
8 42 kg   9 8 cm   10 £71·25
11 (a) 12 (b) Most of the dresses sold are likely to be this size.

Exercise 8.4

1 (a) 13 seconds   (b) skewed to the left
2 (a) 49 tacks   (b) 50 tacks
  (c) roughly symmetrical
  (d) 18 of the 30 packets had fewer than 50 tacks.
3 (a)

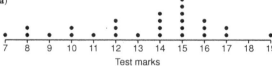

Test marks
  (b) (i) 15 (ii) 14
  (c) 4 pupils   (d) skewed to the right
4 (a)

Daily absences
  (b) 19   (c) roughly symmetrical

5 (a)

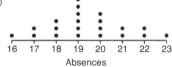

  (b) roughly symmetrical   (c) 5
  (d) 45·1   (e) No. They are almost the same.

Exercise 8.5

1 (a) 25, 30, 35, 40, 40, 45, 45, 50, 50, 55, 55, 60, 60, 65, 65, 70, 70, 90, 95
  (b) (i) 55 (ii) 40 (iii) 65
2 (a) 3·5 (b) 2 (c) 6
3 (a) 26 (b) 17 (c) 36·5
4 (a) 3·35 (b) 2·8 (c) 3·5
5 (a) 3·5 (b) 1·5 (c) 7
6 (a)

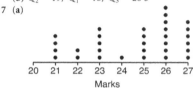

Absences
  (b) $Q_2 = 19$, $Q_1 = 18$, $Q_3 = 20·5$
7 (a)

Marks
  (b) $Q_2 = 25$, $Q_1 = 23$, $Q_3 = 26$
8 (a) 41   (b) 46 years

Exercise 8.6

1 (b) (i) 21 (ii) $Q_1 = 15$, $Q_3 = 21$, 6 (iii) 3
  (b) (i) 9 (ii) $Q_1 = 42·5$, $Q_3 = 46$, 3·5 (iii) 1·75
  (c) (i) 435 (ii) $Q_1 = 320$, $Q_3 = 404$, 84 (iii) 42
  (d) (i) 123 (ii) $Q_1 = 186$, $Q_3 = 244·5$, 58·5 (iii) 29·25
  (e) (i) 39·7 (ii) $Q_1 = 44·7$, $Q_3 = 61·0$, 16·3 (iii) 8·15
2 (a) 13·5   (b) 14
  (c) 15   (d) 9
3 (a) Chemistry 55, Maths 55
  (b)

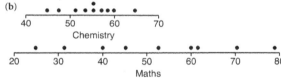

Chemistry

Maths
  (c) Chemistry 20, Maths 60
  (d) Chemistry 7, Maths 31
  (e) Chemistry better – second top mark.
4 (a) Physics 52·1, English 52·1
  (b)

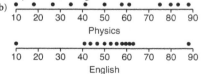

Physics

English
  (c) Physics 79, English 79
  (d) Physics 23·5, English 7·5
  (e) English was better since it was second top mark but in Physics it was fifth top.

Exercise 8.7

1 (b) (i) 57 mins (ii) 2 mins (b) 40
  (c) 36·5, 46·5, 25·5   (d) 21

2 (a)   **Seedling lengths (mm)**

```
2 | 9 9
3 | 5 6 7 9
4 | 1 2 3 4 5 6 6 7 8 8 9 9
5 | 0 1 2 2 3 3 4 6 8
6 | 0 1 2
```

$n = 30$ Key 2 | 9 represents 29 mm

(b) $Q_1 = 42$, $Q_2 = 48$, $Q_3 = 53$

3 (a) 29   **(b)** 2·7 kg   **(c)** 3·4   **(d)** 0·5 kg

4 (a) £106

(b)   **Rents (£)**

```
 9 | 4 5
10 | 0 6
11 | 0 5 5 7
12 | 5 5 7 8 8
13 | 0 2 5 5 5 6
14 | 0 4 5
15 | 4 5 7
16 | 3 5
17 |
18 | 5
19 | 0
20 | 0
```

$n = 30$ Key 19 | 0 represents £190

(c) Yes

Exercise 8.8

1 (a)

English		Mathematics
	2	9
	3	5 8
9 5 2	4	0 1 2 2 5 7 9
9 8 6 4 3 3 2 0	5	2 3 3 4 4 5 6 8 9
9 8 8 6 5 2 2 2 1	6	5 6 6 7 8 9
9 9 7 5 2	7	0 3 7
8 6 0	8	2
5 2	9	0 $n = 30$

Key 2 | 4 represents 42   Key 2 | 9 represents 29

(b) English

(c) Mathematics appears more difficult since marks are generally poorer.

2 (a)

Smokers		Non-smokers
8 3 2	3	5
9 6 5 1	4	2
8 6 6 5 2	5	5 8
9 8 7 6 6 4 3	6	8 9 9 9
6 5	7	0 1 2 4 5 5 6 8 9
2	8	0 2 5 9
	9	3

$n = 22$ $n = 22$
Key 2 | 3 represents 32   Key 3 | 5 represents 35

(b) 82   **(c)** 35   **(d)** Smokers generally die younger.

3 (a)

Boys		Girls
	1	6 7 8 8
9 8 8 8 7 7 6 5 5 5	2	0 1 1 1 2 2 3 3 5 5 5 5 6 7 7 7 8 9
9 9 8 8 7 6 5 5 2 2 0 0 0	3	0 0 0 2 3 4 5
5 5 4 0 0 0	4	5
0	5	

$n = 30$ $n = 30$
Key 5 | 2 represents 25   Key 1 | 6 represents 16

(b) 16   **(c)** 4

(d) Boys 11, Girls 9.   The Boys data is more spread out.

Exercise 8.9

1 (a) 18 kg   **(b)** 81 kg
(c) 76 kg, 85 kg   **(d)** 9 kg
2 (a) £550   **(b)** £450, £350, £575
(c) £112·50

3 (a)

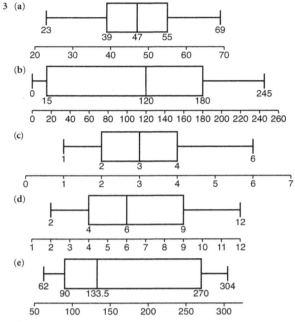

4 (a) 74·75 years   **(b)** 83 years   **(c)** 2·5 years   **(d)** 6·25 years
(e) In general, females can expect to live about 6 years more.
(f) No   **(g)** Slightly longer.

5 (a)

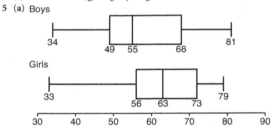

(b) Although ranges are similar, in general, girls' marks are better since Q_1, Q_2 and Q_3 are all higher.

6 (a)

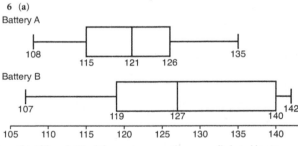

(b) Although B had the greater range, they generally lasted longer with Q_1, Q_2 and Q_3 all higher.

7 (a)

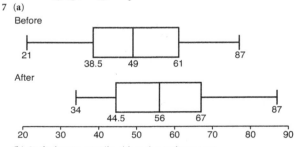

(b) In the lowest quartile, although not the poorest.
(c) He improved more than others.

(d)

	Range	SIQR
Before	66	11·25
After	53	11·25

Although the semi-interquartile range is the same for both, the range is greater in the 'before' marks.

(e) Yes. Although the top mark was the same, marks generally improved.

Review exercise 8

1

Walk	Bus	Car	Cycle	Taxi
130°	100°	70°	40°	20°

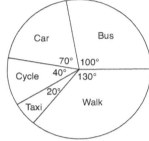

2

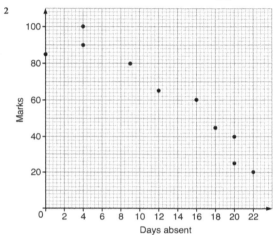

(b) Yes, there is a negative correlation since marks, in general, go down as days absent go up.

3 (a) (i) £19·96   **(ii)** £1   **(iii)** £1

(b) Below the mean.

4 3·48 absences per day

5 56 kg

6 (a)

(b) Skewed slightly to the right   **(c)** 3·35 kg

7 (a) 28   **(b)** 40   **(c)** 14·5

8 (a)

	July		August
		0	2 4 8 8
9 8 3 2		1	0 1 2 4 7 8 9 9
7 4 4 3 1 0		2	2 3 3 4 5 6 7 8 8 9 9
9 8 8 7 6 6 5 3 3 2 1 1 0 0		3	0 1 1 2 2
5 2		4	
		5	

$n = 28$ $n = 28$
Key 2 | 1 represents 12   Key 2 | 3 represents 23

(b)

	July	August
Range	38	30
IQR	13	15·5

9 (a) 4·25

(b) $Q_2 = 22\cdot75$, $Q_1 = 21\cdot75$, $Q_3 = 23\cdot5$

(c) 1·75

10 (a)

3C_A

```
22                                              91
        41      54    62
```

3C_B

```
22                                              89
             46     59    70
20   30   40   50   60   70   80   90
```

(b) Although the top mark is from $3C_A$, the marks between the quartiles are slightly better for $3C_B$.

Chapter 9

Exercise 9.1

1 (a) 42   **(b)** 17   **(c)** 13   **(d)** 27
(e) 22   **(f)** 3   **(g)** 17   **(h)** 21
2 (a) −22   **(b)** −27   **(c)** −8   **(d)** −7
(e) −5   **(f)** 0·8   **(g)** $\frac{1}{2}$ **(h)** −2
3 (a) 13·8   **(b)** 8·3   **(c)** 10·7   **(d)** 12·65
(e) 0·9   **(f)** 1·1   **(g)** 2·475   **(h)** 1·325
4 (a) (i) 900   **(ii)** −52
(b) (i) 56   **(ii)** 636
(c) (i) 25·56   **(ii)** 6
(d) (i) 72   **(ii)** 33·5
5 (a) 77°F   **(b)** 212°F   **(c)** 176°F   **(d)** 150·8°F
6 (a) 210 miles   **(b)** 56·25 miles   **(c)** 11·4 km

Exercise 9.2

1 (a) 16   **(b)** 32   **(c)** 64   **(d)** 64
(e) 7·2   **(f)** 12   **(g)** 36   **(h)** 3
(i) 33   **(j)** −18   **(k)** 40·5   **(l)** 6
2 (a) 12   **(b)** −18   **(c)** 36   **(d)** 36
(e) −5   **(f)** 16   **(g)** 64   **(h)** 12
(i) −7
3 (a) (i) 144   **(ii)** 5·76
(b) (i) 144   **(ii)** 64
(c) (i) −116   **(ii)** 40
(d) (i) 150   **(ii)** 9·6
(e) (i) 529   **(ii)** 81
(f) (i) 113·1   **(ii)** 523·6
(g) (i) 82·5   **(ii)** 84·375
4 (a) 100°C   **(b)** −10°C   **(c)** −25°C   **(d)** 0°C
5 (a) 5   **(b)** 27   **(c)** 54

Exercise 9.3

1 (a) 13   **(b)** 8   **(c)** 8   **(d)** 24
(e) 2   **(f)** 25   **(g)** 34   **(h)** 1·728
2 (a) 6   **(b)** 30   **(c)** 10   **(d)** 40
(e) 10   **(f)** 12·2   **(g)** 30   **(h)** 4
3 (a) 4   **(b)** −6   **(c)** 10   **(d)** 33
(e) 2   **(f)** −0·3   **(g)** −4·44   **(h)** 8·1
4 (a) (i) 7   **(ii)** 2003
(b) (i) 49   **(ii)** 1·445
(c) (i) 10   **(ii)** 0·5
(d) (i) 5   **(ii)** 2·65
(e) (i) 13   **(ii)** 9·7
(f) (i) 0·277   **(ii)** 6
(g) (i) 8·4   **(ii)** 12·48
5 (a) 14   **(b)** 16·9
6 (a) 427·3 cm²   **(b)** 2·62 m²
7 (a) 786·4 newtons   **(b)** $1\cdot964 \times 10^{20}$ newtons

Exercise 9.4

1 (a) 4·77 cm (b) 0·796 m (c) 0·283 m
2 (a) 11·3 cm (b) 0·69 m
3 (a) 15·9 cm (b) 6·3 cm (c)
4 (a) 12 (b) 20 (c) 400 (d) 6
  (e) 11 (f) −65 (g) 2·1 (h) 4·57
5 2·53 m

Exercise 9.5

1 (a) 11 (b) $16 - a$ (c) $b - a$ (d) 15
  (e) $3 + a$ (f) $b + 2$ (g) 2 (h) $\frac{a}{3}$
  (i) $\frac{p}{q}$ (j) $\frac{10}{b}$ (k) $\frac{5}{2}$ (l) $\frac{2}{5}$
  (m) $\frac{3}{7}$ (n) $\frac{7}{3}$ (o) $\frac{b}{a}$ (p) $\frac{a}{b}$
2 (a) 6 (b) $\frac{b-a}{2}$ (c) 6 (d) $\frac{a+b}{3}$
  (e) 10 (f) $y + z$ (g) $\frac{b-a}{2}$ (h) $\frac{a-6}{4}$
3 (a) $\frac{6}{p}$ (b) $\frac{3s}{2t}$ (c) $\frac{a}{2t}$ (d) $\frac{r}{5p}$
4 (a) −1 (b) $4 - b$ (c) $\frac{a}{2} - b$ (d) 10
  (e) $6 + a$ (f) $\frac{p}{3} + a$ (g) $\frac{18}{r} + 4$ (h) 1
  (i) $\frac{v}{10} - \frac{a}{2}$ (j) $\frac{c}{12} - \frac{b}{3}$ (k) $\frac{d}{p} + 2b$ (l) $\frac{10}{3a} + \frac{r}{3}$

Exercise 9.6

1 (a) 72 (b) $6a$ (c) bc (d) $\frac{5}{L}$
  (e) $\frac{s}{r}$ (f) $\frac{8}{a}$ (g) $\frac{a}{2}$ (h) $\frac{a}{b}$
  (i) 8 (j) $\frac{40}{P}$ (k) $\frac{r}{2p}$ (l) $\frac{4}{3s}$
2 (a) $\frac{12}{(3+a)}$ (b) $\frac{18}{(5-b)}$ (c) $\frac{b}{a-y}$
3 (a) −12 (b) $-\frac{b}{5} - 6$ (c) $-\frac{b}{d} + 5$
4 (a) $\frac{b-a}{2}$ (b) $\frac{p-q}{5}$ (c) $\frac{s-r}{d-q}$ (d) $\frac{c-a}{b+d}$
  (e) $\frac{5}{a+b}$ (f) $\frac{2}{c-b}$

Exercise 9.7

1 (a) $t - 3$ (b) $a - c$ (c) $g + h$ (d) $\frac{y+d}{a}$
2 (a) $\frac{y}{x}$ (b) $\frac{y}{x}$ (c) $\frac{V}{R}$ (d) $\frac{p}{s+t}$
3 (a) $2g$ (b) cr (c) $\frac{q}{a}$ (d) $\frac{T}{Q}$
4 (a) $\frac{y-c}{m}$ (b) $\frac{y+d}{m}$ (c) $\frac{y-d}{a}$ (d) $\frac{r+2}{t}$
5 (a) $2(B + a)$ (b) $b(R - f)$ (c) $c(T - r)$ (d) $T(V + g)$
6 (a) $\frac{R}{ac}$ (b) $\frac{6L}{b}$ (c) $\frac{ty}{R}$ (d) $\frac{VR}{TQ}$
7 (a) $\frac{Gy+x}{2}$ (b) $\frac{5y-d}{x}$ (c) $4(g - B)$ (d) $l(c - g)$
8 (a) $a - r$ (b) $\frac{3-r}{t}$ (c) $5y - aX$ (d) $b - aG$
9 (a) $\frac{R}{a+b}$ (b) $\frac{Q}{a-b}$ (c) $\frac{R}{t-s}$ (d) $\frac{X}{2(5t-a)}$
10 (a) $I = \frac{V}{R}$ (b) $d = \frac{c}{\pi}$ (c) $c = y - mx$ (d) $m = \frac{2k}{v^2}$
  (e) $x = Pz - y$ (f) $z = \frac{x+y}{P}$ (g) $b = \frac{c(L-3)}{2}$ (h) $q = \frac{f}{E}$
  (i) $T = \frac{pV}{nR}$ (j) $R = \frac{100I}{PT}$ (k) $h = \frac{A}{x+y}$ (l) $h = \frac{2A}{a+b}$

Exercise 9.8

1 (a) $a = \frac{R}{c} - b$ (b) $a = \frac{Q}{v} + b$
  (c) $t = \frac{R}{q} - s$ (d) $a = 5t - \frac{X}{P}$
2 (a) $b = \frac{r}{ax}$ (b) $x = \frac{P}{Q} - y$
  (c) $d = \frac{c}{V} + e$ (d) $t = \frac{g}{2r} - 2$
3 (a) $b = r^2$ (b) $A = l^2$
  (c) $b = \frac{R^2}{a}$ (d) $y = \frac{(Pt)^2}{x}$
  (e) $x = \frac{bL^2}{a}$ (f) $b = P^2 - a$
  (g) $A = (T - 7)^2$ (h) $b = \left(\frac{R}{a}\right)^2$
4 (a) $b = \sqrt{T}$ (b) $L = \sqrt{A}$
  (c) $b = \sqrt{D - a}$ (d) $b = \sqrt{R} - a$
  (e) $b = \sqrt{\frac{X}{a}}$ (f) $b = \frac{\sqrt{X}}{a}$
  (g) $b = \sqrt{\frac{a}{R}}$ (h) $b = \sqrt{\frac{xt}{a}}$
5 (a) $r = 2A - l$ (b) $b = aD + c$
  (c) $b = \frac{Ax}{a} + c$ (d) $a = \frac{2A}{h} - b$
6 (a) $m = \frac{R}{a+b}$ (b) $r = \frac{Q}{t+s}$
  (c) $l = \frac{A}{b+s}$
7 (a) $r = \frac{V^2}{a}$ (b) $r = \sqrt{\frac{A}{\pi}}$
  (c) $v = \sqrt{\frac{2k}{m}}$ (d) $d = \frac{\sqrt{A}}{2}$
  (e) $d = \frac{\sqrt{A}}{4}$ (f) $b = \sqrt{D + 4ac}$
  (g) $x = \sqrt{G} - 3$ (h) $x = \sqrt{z^2 - y^2}$
  (i) $a = \frac{5p^2}{b}$ (j) $m = \frac{3RT}{V^2}$
  (k) $v = \sqrt{\frac{Fr}{m}}$ (l) $l = g\left(\frac{T}{2\pi}\right)^2$
  (m) $T = \frac{mV^2}{3R}$ (n) $x = \frac{A}{h} - y$
  (o) $m = \frac{nIr}{nE - IR}$
8 (a) $l = \frac{A}{\pi r} - r$ (b) $r = \sqrt{\frac{Gm_1m_2}{F}}$
  (c) $r = l - \frac{a}{s}$ (d) $F = \frac{9c}{5} + 32$
  (e) $r = \frac{100A}{P} - 100$ (f) $h = \frac{1}{(T - \frac{1}{g})} = \frac{g}{gT - 1}$
  (g) $b = \frac{a(1-f)}{(1+f)}$ (h) $l = \frac{s}{2\pi r} - r$
9 $u = \frac{fv}{v - f}$ 10 $v_1 = \frac{Rr_2}{r_2 - R}$

Exercise 9.9

1 (a) 74 km (b) $D - 7p$
2 $C = 0·8t$
3 (a) 8 m (b) $\left(L - \frac{nr}{100}\right)$ metres
4 (b) 700 (b) $\frac{4000}{c} - kt$
5 (a) 19·1 litres (b) $R = \frac{2000}{c} - dt$
6 $T = 0·99x + 0·75y$

7 **(a)**

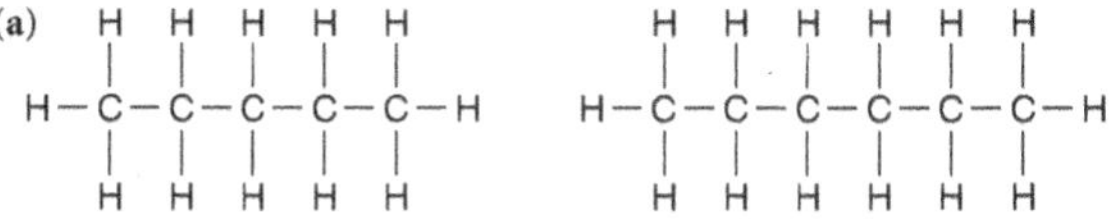
H H H H H
H–C–C–C–C–C–H
H H H H H
H H H H H H
H–C–C–C–C–C–C–H
H H H H H H

Pentane Hexane

(b) 18 **(c)** 19 **(d)** $h = 2C + 2$

8 **(a)** 16 **(b)**

Number of floors	1	2	3	4	5	6
Number of pillars	0	8	16	24	32	40

(c) $P = 8(x - 1)$ **(d)** 80

9 **(a)** **(i)** £76 **(ii)** $C = 5p + 8(d - 1)$
(b) **(i)** £102 **(ii)** $C = 4p + 7(d - 2)$
(c) **(i)** £143 **(ii)** $C = 3p + 7(d - 3)$

10 **(a)** **(i)** £2·60 **(ii)** $C = \frac{4m + 10(t - 4)}{100}$
(b) **(i)** £2·355 **(ii)** $\frac{3{\cdot}5m + 10(t - b)}{100}$

Review exercise 9

1 **(a)** −42 **(b)** −20 **(c)** 0 **(d)** 63
(e) 147 **(f)** 441 **(g)** 20 **(h)** 27
(i) 81 **(j)** 2·8 **(k)** 21 **(l)** −2

2 **(a)** 5·3 **(b)** 400 **(c)** −3 **(d)** 16·9
(e) 259 **(f)** 2·14 **(g)** 4·47 **(h)** 0·325

3 **(a)** 7·7 **(b)** 21

4 **(a)** 10 **(b)** $\frac{b - a}{2}$ **(c)** $\frac{3s}{2t}$
(d) $\frac{a}{2} - b$ **(e)** $\frac{8}{a}$ **(f)** $-\frac{b}{d} + 5$

5 **(a)** $m = \frac{y - c}{x}$ **(b)** $v = \sqrt{\frac{2k}{m}}$ **(c)** $y = Pz - x$
(d) $b = \frac{d(L - a)}{2}$ **(e)** $T = \frac{pV}{nR}$ **(f)** $a = \frac{2A}{h} - b$
(g) $p = \frac{\sqrt{A}}{3}$ **(h)** $b = \sqrt{P} - a$ **(i)** $b = \sqrt{D + 4ac}$
(j) $r = \sqrt[3]{\frac{3V}{4\pi}}$ **(k)** $y = \sqrt{z^2 - x^2}$ **(l)** $c = \frac{ab}{p^2}$
(m) $R = \frac{mV^2}{3T}$ **(n)** $v = \sqrt{\frac{Fr}{m}}$ **(o)** $l = \frac{T}{2\pi r} - r$

6 **(a)** 54·8 **(b)** $R = \frac{4000}{c} - dt$

Chapter 10

Exercise 10.1

1 **(a)** 10·125 l **(b)** 129·8 m³
2 **(a)** 286 l **(b)** 120 l **(c)** 393·75 l
3 0·4 m
4 **(a)** 12 cm **(b)** 0·6 m **(c)** 42 mm
5 1·3 m **6** 151·875 l

Exercise 10.2

1 **(a)** 9275 mm³ **(b)** 177·56 cm³ **(c)** 0·108 m³ **(d)** 1882·5 cm³
(e) 725 mm³ **(f)** 3·432 m³
2 **(a)** 3510 m³ **(b)** 896 cm³ **(c)** 34 000 mm³ **(d)** 6292·8 cm³
(e) 35·557 m³ **(f)** 79·344 m³
3 1·584 m³
4 **(a)** 2262 cm³ **(b)** 95 426 mm³ **(c)** 6·73 m³
5 **(a)** 1924 m³ **(b)** 61 359 cm³ **(c)** 2·95 m³ **(d)** 10·4 m³
6 Weight 4536 g Value £22 634·64
7 0·3 m **8** 0·45 m **9** 9·3 m³
10 **(a)** 219·4 m³ **(b)** 3 m

Exercise 10.3

1 **(a)** 37·5 cm³ **(b)** 346·56 m² **(c)** 4450 mm² **(d)** 11·37 m²
(e) 24·48 cm² **(f)** 4200 mm²
2 **(a)** 78 cm, 48 cm, 40 cm **(b)** 149 760 cm³ **(c)** 18 920 cm²
3 **(a)** 28 cm, 21 cm **(b)** 10 cm **(c)** 2548 cm²

Exercise 10.4

1 **(a)** 452·4 cm² **(b)** 731·4 cm² **(c)** 3456 cm²
2 **(a)** 24 504 mm² **(b)** 86 m² **(c)** 2983 cm²
3 **(a)** 339 cm² **(b)** 78·5 m² **(c)** 49 480 mm²
4 459 cm² **5** 5 m² **6** 204 cm²
7 **(a)** 20 m **(b)** 5·2 cm **(c)** 3·1 m
8 1370 m²
9 **(a)** 20π m² **(b)** 6π cm² **(c)** 60π m²

Exercise 10.4

1 **(a)** 452·4 cm² **(b)** 731·4 cm² **(c)** 3456 cm²
2 **(a)** 24 504 mm² **(b)** 86 m² **(c)** 2983 cm²
3 **(a)** 339 cm² **(b)** 78·5 m² **(c)** 49 480 mm²
4 459 cm² **5** 5 m² **6** 5 m²
7 **(a)** 20 m **(b)** 5·2 cm **(c)** 3·1 m
8 1370 m²
9 **(a)** 20π m² **(b)** 6π cm² **(c)** 60π m²

Exercise 10.5

1 **(a)** 524 cm³ **(b)** 1289 cm³ **(c)** 2145 m³ **(d)** 70 555 mm³
(e) 89 535 cm³ **(f)** 106 m³
2 56·5 cm³ **3** 112·785 l **4** 737 cm³
5 15 000 **6** 131·36 l

Review exercise 10

1 **(a)** 768 m³ **(b)** 129·6 cm³ **(c)** 1296 cm³
2 **(a)** 24·4 m³ **(b)** 87 965 mm³ **(c)** 1257 cm³
3 3·23 m
4 **(a)** 18 060 mm² **(b)** 27 529 cm³ **(c)** 130·6 m²
5 **(a)** 91 952 cm³ **(b)** 213 059 cm³ **(c)** 0·16 m³

Review 2

Exercise 2A

1 **(a)** $20x + 15$ **(b)** $6x - 15$ **(c)** $-18 + 6x$
(d) $2x^2 - 10x$ **(e)** $6x^2 - x$ **(f)** $30x - 21x^2$
2 **(a)** $x^2 + 7x + 10$ **(b)** $x^2 + x - 20$ **(c)** $x^2 - 11x + 24$
(d) $6x^2 + 5x - 6$ **(e)** $x^2 + 8x + 16$ **(f)** $25x^2 - 20x + 4$
3 **(a)** $2x^3 + 7x^2 + 7x + 2$ **(b)** $x^3 + 2x^2 - 5x - 6$
(c) $8x^2 + 12x + 12$
4 **(a)** $x = 7$ **(b)** $x = \frac{16}{5}$
5 $3\frac{1}{3}$ cm **6** $x = 5$ cm
7 **(a)** 75 **(b)**

Marks

2	3	3	7	8	8	
3	4	4	7	7	9	
4	4	5	5	7		
5	2	4	6	6	6	8
6	5	7				
7	6	6				
8	7	7	9			
9	5	5	8			

$n = 30$ Key 2 | 3 represents 23

(c) Yes **(d)** $Q_1 = 37$, $Q_2 = 53$, $Q_3 = 76$

(d)

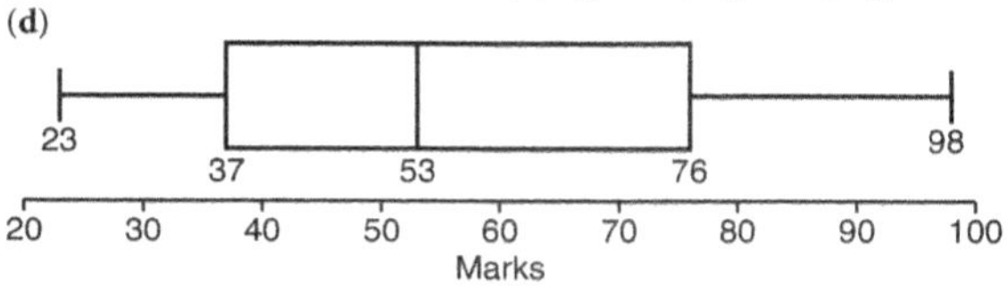
23
37
53
76
98
20
30
40
50
60
70
80
90
100
Marks

8 Less rubbish collected after. Median and quartiles lower. Ranges similar but interquartile range less afterwards.

9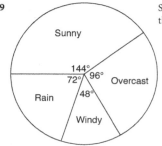

Shows how June was divided into the different types of weather.

10 28

11 12·75

12 (a) $v = \frac{KT}{P}$ (b) $t = 2S + T$ (c) $a = \sqrt{r^2 + b^2}$

13 (a) £28 (b) $C = 20 + 2(h - 5)$

14 9·1 m³

15 (a) 2·75 m³ (b) 688 kg

16 (a) 311 cm³ (b) 222·5 cm3 (c) 14 137 cm3

17 (a) 23·58 cm

(b)
Hexagonal Prism	Cylinder
756 cm²	794 cm²

(c) Hexagonal Prism

Exercise 2B

1 (a) $13x - 3y$ (b) $3xy$
2 (a) $11x - 4$ (b) $10 - 6y$ (c) $13x - 6$
3 (a) -9 (b) -7 (c) $\frac{4}{3}$ (d) $-\frac{25}{2}$
4 (a) $x < \frac{9}{2}$ (b) $y \leqslant 11$ (c) $x \leqslant \frac{22}{21}$ (d) $x > 1$
5 22 245 **6** 170 mg **7** 400 g
8 £9000 **9** £5 **10** 41 605 cm³
11 $x = y - 2Z$ **12** 1047 m² **13** $2 \cdot 64 \times 10^5$ km
14 (a) 3·46 cm (b) 6·93 cm² (c) 41·57 cm² (d) 332·6 cm³
15 Yes **16** 60 m **17** 288 cm²
18 (a) 644·5 ml
(b) Cost per ml   Small 0·136p,
Large 0·132p   i.e. Large is better value

Chapter 11

Exercise 11.1

1 (a) 1 metre (b) 6·5 cm
2 (a) 1 cm : 10 km $\frac{1}{1\,000\,000}$ (b) 1 cm : 5 km $\frac{1}{500\,000}$
(c) 1 cm : 50 km $\frac{1}{5\,000\,000}$ (d) 1 cm : 10 km $\frac{1}{1\,000\,000}$
3 (a) 7·5 km, 24·75 km, 1·35 km (b) 3 cm, 16 cm, 0·5 cm
(c) $\frac{1}{150\,000}$
4 (a) 1·8 km, 3·84 km, 1·8 km (b) 40 cm, 30·5 cm, 0·5 cm
5 31·2
6 (a) 1 : 15 (b) 1·8 m
7 (a) $\frac{1}{500\,000}$ (b) 28·2
8 1·3 km, 1·95 km, 0·9 km **9** No the space is 6 cm
10 1 : 90
11 (a) 1·8 m (b) 21·6 m
12 (a) 4 cm (b) 21·6 cm

Exercise 11.2

1 (a) 11·2 m (b) 1·8 m (c) 7·8 m (d) 4·4 m
2 10·3 m **3** 50 m **4** 240 m
5 4·6 m **6** 146 m **7** 9·6 m

Exercise 11.3

1 (a) 245° (b) 315° (c) 162°
2 67° **3** 23°
4 PS = 5·1 km SQ = 2·6 km **5** C₁P = 48 km C₂P = 78 km
6 210 km **7** A – 38 km B – 34 km
7 49 km

Exercise 11.4

1 (a) 8 cm, 6 cm (b) 3·7 kg, 3·3 kg
(c) 2·93 ml, 2·87 ml (d) 2·59 m, 2·57 m
(e) 7·651 cm³, 7·649 cm³ (f) 8·045 g, 8·035
(g) 6·92 l, 6·88 l (h) 4·88 g, 4·78 g
(i) 9·7 s, 8·7 s
2 (a) 0·5 m (b) 0·05 cm (c) 0·05 kg (d) 0·005 s
(e) 0·005 s (f) 0·0005 mm (g) 0·005 km (h) 0·5 g
(i) 0·00005 s (j) 0·5 m (k) 0·005 cm (l) 0·05 ml
3 (a) 0·5 s, 4·5 s, 3·5 s
(b) 0·5 cm, 21·5 cm, 20·5 cm
(c) 0·005 m, 6·755 m, 6·745 m
(d) 0·05 kg, 0·95 kg, 0·85 kg
(e) 0·005 m, 45·805 m, 45·795 m
(f) 0·005 mm, 1·005 mm, 0·995 mm
(g) 0·05 km, 120·55 km, 120·45 km
(h) 0·0005 g, 0·0015 g, 0·0005 g
(i) 0·0005 h, 32·0055 h, 32·0045 h
(j) 0·5 kg, 4500·5 kg, 4499·5 kg
(k) 0·0005 ml, 30·7755 ml, 30·7745
(l) 0·00005 mg, 0·55605 mg, 0·55595 m
4 (a) 6 ± 1 cm (b) 6·4 ± 0·1 km
(c) 8·2 ± 0·2 mm (d) 0·54 ± 0·03 ml
5 (a) 6·52 cm, 6·31 cm, 6·78 cm (b) 1·201 cm, 1·199 cm, 1·198 cm
6 1·234 mm, 1·261 mm
7
	(a)	(b)	(c)	(d)	(e)	(f)
max	38·25	27·6	59·9	39·8	3959	963
min	26·25	26·5	58·1	35·3	3837	955·1
8
	max	min
(a)	91·125	42·875
(b)	70·7	65·3
(c)	1580·7	1539·5
(d)	2499	1888

Review exercise 11

1 (a) 3·6 m (b) 1·2 m **2** 43·3 cm, 153·3 cm, 28·2 cm
3 $\frac{1}{250\,000}$ **4** (a) 315 m (b) 8·8 cm
5 92 m **6** (a) 236° (b) 100°
7 74 km
8 (a) 4·7, 4·3 (b) 16·551, 16·549 (c) 0·048, 0·042
9 (a) 0·5 km (b) 0·005 cm (c) 0·0005 kg
10 (a) 30·25, 20·25 (b) 51·6375, 50·0075

Chapter 12

Exercise 12.1

1 (a) CB (b) AB (c) AB (d) CB
2 (a) (b) (c) (d)
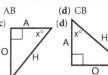

3 (a)
Triangle	O	A	$\frac{O}{A}$
P	4·7	6·8	0·7
Q	2·7	3·9	0·7
R	5·7	8·2	0·7
S	3·2	4·6	0·7

(b) Pupils' own answers (c) all round to 0·7 to 1 dp
2 (a) All similar (b) 0·4, 0·4, 0·4
(c) All the same answer.
Corresponding sides increase in the same ratio

Exercise 12.2

1 (a) 0·625   (b) 4·011   (c) 1·000   (d) 0·325   (e) 1·881
2 (a) 5·16 m   (b) 20·4 m   (c) 2·85 m
  (d) 42·9 m   (e) 5·67 m   (f) 4·05 m
3 1·19 m   4 10·3 m   5 17·7 km   6 8·08 m
7 (a) 60·6 cm   (b) 60·7 cm   (c) 86·2 cm
8 (a) 20 cm   (b) 20·7 cm   9 (a) 10·5 cm   (b) 28 cm
10 (a) 9·75 m   (b) 11·47 m   11 21·89 m
12 (a) 8·58 m   (b) 5·12 m   (c) 3·46 m
13 13·7 m

Exercise 12.3

1 (a) 27° (b) 19° (c) 45° (d) 60° (e) 85°
2 (a) 39° (b) 61° (c) 41° (d) 34°
3 (a) 20° (b) 36° (c) 36° (d) 46° (e) 51° (f) 23°
4 32°   5 (a) 58° (b) 36°
6 (a) 38° (b) 16°   7 29°
8 Yes, the angle is 16°

Exercise 12.4

1 (a)

Triangle	O_1	H	$\frac{O}{H}$
P	3·9	7·9	0·5
Q	2·2	4·5	0·5
R	2·7	5·6	0·5
S	4·7	9·4	0·5

(b) Pupils' own answers
(c) all 0·5 to 1 dp

Exercise 12.5

1 (a) 4·3 cm   (b) 41·3 cm   (c) 0·989 cm   (d) 9·90 cm
  (e) 3·61 cm   (f) 2·49 cm   (g) 10·9 cm   (h) 5·54 cm
2 (a) 18°   (b) 43°   (c) 65°   (d) 37°
  (e) 28°   (f) 50°   (g) 37°   (h) 67°
3 530 m   4 51°, 90°, 39°   5 yes
6 1·3 m   7 16·6° meets regulations.

Exercise 12.6

1 (a) 11·2 cm   (b) 17·4 cm   (c) 3·04 cm   (d) 4·10 cm
  (e) 1·35 cm   (f) 12·0 cm   (g) 9 cm   (h) 13·7 cm
2 (a) 42°   (b) 51°   (c) 52°   (d) 50°
  (e) 54°   (f) 54°   (g) 62°   (h) 67°
3 45°
4 (a) 0·57   (b) 3·14   (c) 3·71
5 (a) 15·7 m   (b) 44·6 m
6 (a) 4·3   (b) 15·9   (c) 10·1

Exercise 12.7

1 (a) 4·2 m   (b) 2·7 m   (c) 5·8 m   (d) 7·7 m
  (e) 5 m   (f) 7·1 m   (g) 1·6 m   (h) 1·5 m
2 (a) 22°   (b) 55°   (c) 73°   (d) 35°
  (e) 55°   (f) 9°   (g) 33°   (h) 45°
3 (a) 64°   (b) 14·9 m   (c) 13°   (d) 31·2 mm
4 (a) 17·5 m   (b) 26·0 m
5 31°   6 5·47 m
7 (a) 20·1 cm   (b) 11·4 cm   (c) 115 cm^2
8 (a) 12·6 cm (b) 19·6 cm   9 $a = 1·06$ m $b = 2$ m
10 (a) 022°   (b) 202°
11 (a) 72°   (b) 8·09 cm   (c) 11·76 m   (d) 238 cm^2

Exercise 12.8

1 (a) 23·2 cm   (b) 42·9 cm   (c) 25·7 cm   (d) 16·0 cm
  (e) 22·8 cm   (f) 7·53 cm   (g) 4·41 cm   (h) 13·9 cm
2 (a) 5·36 cm   (b) 18·8 cm   (c) 5·08 cm
3 4·45 m   4 3·20 m   5 3·58 m   6 46·5 m

Exercise 12.9

1 76·1 km   2 80·8 km   3 157 km
4 $a = 26·0$ cm $b = 20·3$ cm   5 $x = 0·909$ $y = 1·78$
6

	(a)	(b)	(c)
(i)	6·12 cm	10·1 cm	10·7 cm
(ii)	7·39 cm	10·9 cm	19·3 cm
(iii)	22·6 cm^2	55·0 cm^2	103 cm^2

7 29° Yes, it meets regulations.   8 17·8 m
9 46 metres   10 1·83 m
11 (a) 24·9 cm
  (b) proof of equal corresponding angles   (c) 8·3 cm
12 ∠CBA = 70°   ∠CDA = 30°
  ∠BCD = ∠BAD = 130°
  CB = AB = 20·8 cm   CD = AD = 45·6 cm

Review exercise 12

1 (a) 21·0 cm   (b) 16°   (c) 31·4 cm   (d) 50°
  (e) 50·5 cm   (f) 81°   (g) 6·60 cm   (h) 17·6 cm
2 11·1 metres   3 2·07 m   4 34·0 km
5 6·03 m   6 2·60 m

Chapter 13

Exercise 13.1

1 (a) $\frac{1}{8}$ (b) $\frac{3}{20}$ (c) $\frac{9}{20}$ (d) $\frac{3}{10}$
2 (a) 28   (b) (i) $\frac{2}{7}$ (ii) $\frac{9}{28}$ (iii) $\frac{5}{28}$
3 (a) $\frac{3}{11}$ (b) $\frac{7}{11}$ (c) $\frac{4}{11}$ (d) $\frac{15}{22}$
4 30   5 (a) $\frac{5}{14}$ (b) $\frac{5}{28}$
6 (a) (i) $\frac{1}{11}$ (ii) $\frac{4}{11}$ (b) (i) $\frac{1}{8}$ (ii) $\frac{1}{2}$
7 (a) 164   (b) (i) $\frac{35}{82}$ (ii) $\frac{6}{41}$ (iii) $\frac{8}{41}$
8 (a) 22   (b) 180   (c) (i) $\frac{1}{52}$ (ii) $\frac{9}{52}$ (iii) $\frac{19}{208}$
9 (a) 55 dresses, 29 skirts, 38 trousers
  (b) $\frac{17}{55}$, $\frac{9}{29}$ (c) $\frac{27}{38}$

Exercise 13.2

1 (a) 0   (b) $\frac{1}{2}$ (c) 1   (d) 0   (e) $\frac{1}{2}$
2 $\frac{1}{2}$, $\frac{1}{2}$, $\frac{1}{6}$, 0, $\frac{2}{3}$
3 (a) $\frac{1}{6}$ (b) $\frac{1}{2}$ (c) $\frac{1}{3}$ (d) $\frac{2}{3}$
4 $\frac{1}{25}$ 5 (a) $\frac{1}{3}$ (b) $\frac{5}{12}$
6 $\frac{20}{29}$
7 (a) (i) $\frac{1}{10}$ (ii) $\frac{1}{30}$ (iii) $\frac{1}{6}$ (b) (i) $\frac{1}{13}$ (ii) 0 (iii) $\frac{2}{13}$
8 $\frac{1}{60} > 0·015$ No
9 (a) $\frac{74}{109}$ (b) $\frac{35}{109}$ (c) No, only 68%
10 (a) (i) $\frac{1}{20}$ (ii) $\frac{41}{200}$ (b) $\frac{193}{400}$ (c) $\frac{62}{105}$

Exercise 13.3

1 (a) $\frac{1}{12}$ (b) $\frac{1}{6}$ (c) $\frac{1}{3}$
2 (a) $\frac{1}{4}$ (b) $\frac{1}{6}$ (c) $\frac{1}{6}$ (d) $\frac{5}{18}$ (e) $\frac{5}{9}$ (f) $\frac{1}{4}$
3 (a) $\frac{1}{4}$ (b) $\frac{5}{16}$ (c) $\frac{3}{16}$ (d) $\frac{1}{8}$
4 (a) $\frac{1}{18}$ (b) $\frac{1}{9}$ (c) $\frac{2}{3}$ (d) $\frac{4}{9}$
5 (a) $\frac{1}{8}$ (b) $\frac{1}{8}$ (c) $\frac{3}{8}$
6 (a) $\frac{1}{18}$ (b) $\frac{1}{6}$ (c) $\frac{2}{9}$
7 (a) $\frac{1}{6}$ (b) $\frac{1}{6}$ (c) $\frac{1}{12}$

Exercise 13.4

1 (a) 30   (b) 62   (c) 1500
2 (a) 2   (b) 10   (c) 70
3 (a) $\frac{3}{5}$ (b) 60   4 1275
5 (a) 3   (b) 9   6 (a) $\frac{1}{4}$, $\frac{2}{5}$, $\frac{7}{20}$ (b) 45, 72, 63
7 171, 66   8 36, 15, 6, 3

Review exercise 13

1 (a) $\frac{2}{15}$ (b) $\frac{1}{6}$ (c) $\frac{11}{30}$ (d) $\frac{7}{15}$
2 (a) $\frac{5}{13}$ (b) $\frac{3}{13}$ (c) $\frac{2}{13}$
3 (a) 130 (b) $\frac{33}{130}$ (c) $\frac{37}{130}$
4 $\frac{1}{3}, \frac{1}{2}, 0, 1$ 5 $\frac{1}{15}$
6 (a) (i) $\frac{2}{5}$ (ii) $\frac{3}{5}$ (iii) $\frac{11}{15}$ (b) (i) $\frac{6}{13}$ (ii) $\frac{7}{13}$ (iii) $\frac{11}{13}$
7 (a) $\frac{42}{95}$ (b) $\frac{71}{95}$ (c) Yes, only 25%
8 (a) $\frac{1}{6}$ (b) $\frac{1}{2}$ (c) $\frac{1}{6}$ (d) $\frac{1}{12}$
9 (a) $\frac{1}{6}$ (b) $\frac{1}{3}$
10 (a) 20 (b) 60 (c) 80
11 78, 36, 6

Review 3

Exercise 3A

1 $\frac{1}{350\,000}$ 2 1·26 km 3 11·5 km
4 (a) 6·5, 7·5 (b) 18·2, 18·4 (c) 0·017, 0·023
5 (a) 6·93 cm (b) 6·43 (c) 23·39 (d) 5·75 (e) 4·72
6 (a) 22° (b) 38° (c) 50°
7 165·50 m 8 67·41 km 9 51·32 cm
10 (a) $\frac{1}{8}$ (b) $\frac{1}{2}$ (c) $\frac{1}{4}$
11 (a) $\frac{5}{12}$ (b) $\frac{4}{11}$
12 (a) $\frac{1}{5}$ (b) $\frac{2}{5}$ (c) $\frac{8}{15}$
13 (a) $\frac{1}{30}$ (b) $\frac{1}{10}$ (c) $\frac{1}{5}$
14 21

Exercise 3B

1 (a) -34 (b) -3 (c) -28 (d) -27
2 (a) $3x + 5y$ (b) $7x^2 - 3x + 7$ (c) $6pq - 3p$ (d) $2x^3 + 2$
3 (a) $y - 10x$ (b) $2 + 4y$
4 (a) 8 (b) -1 (c) -6 (d) $-\frac{1}{3}$
5 (a) 5 (b) 3 (c) 0 (d) 7
6 (a) 24 (b) 19 7 3
8 (a) $m < 4$ (b) $p > \frac{2}{5}$ 9 $x > 10$
10 (a) 96p (b) 24·1 kg (c) £18·20
11 4·09% 12 (a) £25 (b) £78
13 £1 = €1.40 14 (a) 9 days (b) 27 kg
15 (a) $\frac{4}{3}$, 2 cm (b) $\frac{4}{5}$, 5·2 cm 16 (b) $x = 6·3$ cm, $y = 2·8$ cm
17 (a) $6\frac{2}{3}$ cm (b) 3·9 cm 18 (a) 48 cm² (b) 12·5 cm²
19 1·44 l
20 (a) 8·06 cm (b) 9·22 cm (c) 11·31 cm
21 Proof 22 12·73 cm
23 (a) 5·78, 6, 6 (b) 14, 14, 14 24 (a) dot plot (b) 8
25 (a)
```
        9 | 2
9 9 8 7 6 5 1 1 0 | 3
  9 9 4 4 2 2 2 0 | 4
          6 0 0 | 5
```
(b) 40; 58
(c) $35\frac{1}{2}, 46\frac{1}{2}$; 42, 64
26 (a) $6b - 4b^2$ (b) $15x^2 + 19x - 10$ (c) $12m^2 - 60m + 75$
(d) $7x^2 + 20x - 3$ (e) $16y^3 + 20y + 12$
27 (a) 3 (b) -2
28 (a) $6\frac{2}{3}$ (b) -31 (c) 17·5
29 (a) $\frac{V}{I}$ (b) $\frac{v - u}{t}$ (c) $\frac{2(s - ut)}{t^2}$ (d) $\frac{t^2}{r - s}$
30 (a) $pq - r^2$ (b) 84 cm 31 100 km
32 (a) 3·25 (b) 1·72 33 156 tails
34 (a) (i) $\frac{1}{3}$ (ii) $\frac{5}{6}$ (b) (i) $\frac{3}{11}$ (ii) $\frac{6}{11}$

Chapter 14

Exercise 14.1

1 (d) (i) PN (ii) 90°
2 (d) (i) S (ii) RT (iii) right angle
3 (e) (i) OB (ii) MB (iii) isosceles (iv) ∠BOM (v) 90°
4 equilateral

Exercise 14.2

1 (a) KH (b) 5 cm (c) 21° (d) kite
2 (a) 90° (b) 106°
3  4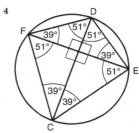

5 (a) WY (b) ∠XYW
6 Centre of circle

Exercise 14.3

1 (a) 5 (b) 8 cm
2 (a) 12 cm (b) 32 cm
3 24 cm
4 (a) 7 mm (b) 32 mm (c) 768 mm²
5 49 cm
6 (a) 1·2 m (b) 3·2 m (c) 3·6 m
7 15·2 cm
8 (a) 19·1 cm (b) 17·3 cm
9 3·32 m 10 8·2 m 11 32 cm 12 72 cm

Exercise 14.4

1 (e) all 90° (f) The angle in a semicircle is 90°.

Exercise 14.5

1 $a = 28$ $b = 41$ $c = 52$
2 (a) 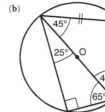 (b)

(c) 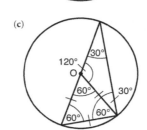 (d)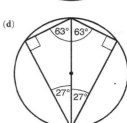

(e) (f)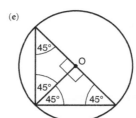

3 Rectangle – all angles are 90°
4 (a) 33 (b) 64 (c) 55
(d) 38 (e) 70 (f) $r = 27·5, v = 62·5$

Exercise 14.6

1 (a) 35° (b) 58° (c) 113°
2 (a) kite (b) (i) 27° (ii) 27° (iii) 63°
3 $a = 50$ $b = 90$ $c = 40$
4 $a = 18$ $b = 144$ $c = 36$ $d = 54$ $e = 72$ $f = 48$ $g = 45$
 $h = 132$ $i = 57$ $j = 66$ $k = 66$ $l = 24$
5 PQ is parallel to SR, PS is parallel to QR and PQ = QS = RS = PS

Exercise 14.7

1 9.9 cm   2 (a) kite (b) 16.6 cm
3 11.1 cm   4 (a) rectangle (b) 24.6 cm
5 (a) 3.5 cm (b) 2.5 cm   6 10.6 cm
7 6.4 m   8 36 cm

Exercise 14.8

1 (a) 12 cm (b) 9.5 cm (c) 3.1 cm
2 (a) 2.9 cm (b) 6.2 cm (c) 8.8 cm
3 (a) 4.4 cm (b) 21.5 cm (c) 22.8 cm
4 (a) 36.9° (b) 22.6° (c) 65.9°
5 (a) 12 cm (b) 20.8 cm
6 (a) 13.8 cm (b) 5.8 cm

Coursework task

1 220 mm × 132 mm
2 (a) 60° (b) 38.1 mm (c) side 253 mm
3 (a) 60° (b) 12.7 mm (c) side 183 mm
4 (a) 30° (b) 85 mm (c) diameter 214 mm
5 5 balls

Review exercise 14

1 (a) (i) 9 cm (ii) 15 cm (b) (i) 53° (ii) 37°
2 (a) 90° (b) 122°
3 (a) $n = 55$ $m = 49$ (b) $p = 49$ $q = 41$ (c) $r = 45$ $s = 47$
4 $a = 38$ $b = 90$ $c = 52$ 5 2.8 cm
6 19.8 cm   7 (a) 8.4 m (b) 90°, 42°, 48°
8 19.2 cm   9 5.2 cm
10 26.7 cm   11 36.9°

Chapter 15

Exercise 15.1

1 (a) Pupil answers
 (b) No, there is an infinite number of solutions.
 (d) CD £6 DVD £4
 (e) (i) £6 (ii) £4
2 (c) (i) £4 (ii) £2
3 adult – £3 child – £2
4 (a) adult – £3 child – £1 (b) adult – £4 child – £1
 (c) adult – £3 child – £2 (d) adult – £3 child – £1

Exercise 15.2

1 $a = 3$ $c = 1$ 2 $a = 4$ $c = 1$ 3 $a = 3$ $c = 1$
4 $a = 6$ $c = 2$ 5 $x = 4$ $y = 1$ 6 $x = 5$ $y = 3$
7 $x = 2$ $y = 2$ 8 $x = 4$ $y = 3$

Exercise 15.3

1 $a = 3$ $b = 1$ 2 $a = 3$ $c = 3$ 3 $e = 6$ $f = -1$
4 $p = 5$ $q = 2$ 5 $x = 2$ $y = 0$ 6 $x = -3$ $y = 2\frac{1}{2}$
7 $x = -1$ $y = -2$ 8 $x = -1$ $y = 1$ 9 $a = 5$ $b = 2$
10 $x = 1$ $y = -3$ 11 $x = -3$ $y = -3$ 12 $x = -1$ $y = 1$

Exercise 15.4

1 $a = 1$ $b = 1$ 2 $a = 3$ $c = 2$ 3 $x = 1$ $y = 3$
4 $p = -1$ $q = -1$ 5 $x = 3$ $y = -3$ 6 $x = 7$ $y = 1$
7 $x = 1$ $y = -1$ 8 $x = 1$ $y = -1$ 9 $a = 5$ $b = 2$
10 $x = 5$ $y = 1$ 11 $x = 9$ $y = 8$ 12 $p = 4$ $q = \frac{1}{2}$

Exercise 15.5

1 $a = 2$ $c = 2$ 2 $a = 5$ $c = 1$ 3 $e = 3$ $f = -2$
4 $x = -3$ $y = 4$ 5 $x = 2$ $y = -3$ 6 $x = 2$ $y = 1$
7 $x = -2$ $y = 5$ 8 $x = 1$ $y = 4$ 9 $x = 4$ $y = 2$
10 $x = 1$ $y = 4$ 11 $a = -2$ $b = -3$ 12 $a = 1.5$ $c = 1$

Exercise 15.6

1 $a = 7$ $b = -2$ 2 $a = 2$ $c = 3$ 3 $e = -1$ $f = 2$
4 $p = 1$ $q = 1\frac{1}{2}$ 5 $x = -8$ $y = -9$ 6 $x = -3$ $y = 4$
7 $x = 1\frac{1}{2}$ $y = \frac{1}{2}$ 8 $x = -22$ $y = 31$ 9 $a = 5$ $b = -2$
10 $x = 1$ $y = 8$ 11 $x = 2$ $y = 3$ 12 $x = \frac{1}{2}$ $y = -\frac{1}{2}$

Exercise 15.7

1 $x = 4$ $y = 1$ 2 $x = 5$ $y = 0$ 3 $x = 3$ $y = 8$
4 $x = 6$ $y = -10$ 5 $x = 10\frac{1}{2}$ $y = -3$ 6 $x = -1$ $y = 8$
7 $x = 7$ $y = 5$ 8 $x = 2\frac{2}{3}$ $y = 4\frac{2}{3}$

Exercise 15.8

1 (a) £14 (b) £4 (c) £44
2 (a) £8 (b) £5 (c) £39
3 38 years old   4 £25
5 $x = 124$ $y = 56$ 6 6 cars 4 motorcycles
7 £12.30   8 50 metres
9 15 correct 5 incorrect   10 144
11 (a) $u = 5$ $a = 10$ (b) 155

Exercise 15.9

1 $a = 5$ $b = 5$ 2 $a = 2$ $c = 4$ 3 $e = -6$ $f = -3$
4 $p = 12$ $q = 4$ 5 $x = 2$ $g = -1$ 6 $x = 3$ $y = 2$
7 $x = 3$ $y = 4$ 8 $x = -2$ $y = -1$
9 (a) $x = -\frac{1}{3}$ $y = -3$ (b) $p = 2$ $q = 3$
 (c) $x = -2$ $y = 5$ (d) $a = 1\frac{1}{3}$ $c = -3$

Coursework task

1 A $w = 10\,\text{ft}^2$ $g = 6\,\text{ft}^2$ 2 $6g + 10w = 56.20$
 B $w = 9\,\text{ft}^2$ $g = 9\,\text{ft}^2$ $9g + 9w = 72.90$
 C $w = 8\,\text{ft}^2$ $g = 12\,\text{ft}^2$ $12g + 8w = 82.40$
 D $w = 27\,\text{ft}^2$ $g = 20\,\text{ft}^2$ $20g + 27w = 171.50$
 E $w = 15\,\text{ft}^2$ $g = 11\,\text{ft}^2$ $11g + 15w = 94.70$
 F $w = 13\frac{1}{2}\,\text{ft}^2$ $g = 18\,\text{ft}^2$ $18g + 13\frac{1}{2}w = 127.35$
2 (a) box B (b) £69.30

Review exercise 15

1 (a) $a = 1$ $b = 2$ (b) $x = 3$ $y = 1$ (c) $a = 8$ $b = -10$
 (d) $p = 5$ $q = 3$ (e) $x = 5$ $y = 3$ (f) $x = -1$ $y = 5$
 (g) $x = 4$ $y = 4.5$ (h) $x = 1, y = -\frac{1}{2}$
2 (a) $x = 2$ $y = 1$ (b) $c = 7$ $d = 3$ (c) $x = -2$ $y = -2$
 (d) $p = 4$ $q = 3$
3 (a) $x = 2$ $y = 1$ (b) $x = 2$ $y = -1$ (c) $x = 1$ $y = 2$
 (d) $p = 4$ $q = -1$ (e) $x = 3$ $y = 2$ (f) $a = -4$ $b = 5$
 (g) $x = 2$ $y = 1$ (h) $p = 12$ $q = 2$
4 90 kg
5 (a) £14 (b) £8 (c) £60
6 (a) large $0.7\,l$ small $0.33\,l$ (b) 4.16 litres
7 40 small 20 large

Chapter 16

Exercise 16.1

1 (a) 5 (b) 6 (c) $\frac{1}{2}$ (d) $\frac{1}{5}$ (e) $\frac{1}{15}$
2 (a) 1 (b) $\frac{3}{2}$ (c) $\frac{1}{10}$ (d) $\frac{2}{3}$ (e) $\frac{4}{3}$
3 (a) gradient $= \frac{1}{2}$; regulations met
   (b) gradient $= 1\cdot25$; regulations met
   (c) gradient $= 2$; regulations not met
   (d) gradient $= 0\cdot5$; regulations met
   (e) gradient $= 2$; regulations not met
4 (a) 5 m (b) $4\cdot125$ m (c) $3\cdot12$ m (d) $1\cdot275$ m
5 (a) side $= 1\cdot5$ m; gradient $= \frac{3}{4}$ (b) side $= 2\cdot5$; gradient $= \frac{12}{5}$
   (c) side $= 1\cdot25$; gradient $= \frac{5}{12}$
6 $0\cdot251$

Exercise 16.2

1 (a) -6 (b) -8 (c) $-\frac{1}{3}$ (d) $-\frac{1}{20}$ (e) $-\frac{1}{5}$
2 (a) 2 (b) 1 (c) $\frac{1}{2}$ (d) -3
   (e) $-\frac{2}{3}$ (f) 3 (g) 3 (h) $\frac{5}{3}$
   (i) 1 (j) -3 (k) -3 (l) $-\frac{2}{5}$
   (m) $\frac{2}{5}$ (n) 0 (o) undefined
3 (a) -80 (b) $89\cdot3°$ (c) $19\cdot5$ (d) $0\cdot097$

Exercise 16.3

1 (a) 2 (b) $\frac{1}{2}$ (c) -1 (d) $\frac{3}{2}$
2 (a) 2 (b) $\frac{1}{2}$ (c) 1 (d) -3
   (e) 0 (f) undefined (g) 2 (h) 3
3 (b) $m_{AB} = 2$ $m_{CD} = 2$ $m_{EF} = 2$
   (c) lines are parallel
4 (b) $m_{AB} = -4$ $m_{CD} = -4$ $m_{EF} = -4$
   (c) lines are parallel
5 (a) (ii) $m_{AB} = 2$ $m_{BC} = 2$ $m_{AC} = 2$
       (iii) $y = 2x$
       (iv) gradient = coefficient of x
   (b) (ii) $m_{AB} = 1$ $m_{BC} = 1$ $m_{AC} = 1$
       (iii) $y = x$
       (iv) gradient = coefficient of x
   (c) (ii) $m_{AB} = \frac{1}{2}$ $m_{BC} = \frac{1}{2}$ $m_{AC} = \frac{1}{2}$
       (iii) $y = \frac{1}{2}x$
       (iv) gradient = coefficient of x
   (d) (ii) $m_{AB} = -2$ $m_{BC} = -2$ $m_{AC} = -2$
       (iii) $y = -2x$
       (iv) gradient = coefficient of x

Exercise 16.4

1 (a) 4 (b) -2 (c) $\frac{3}{4}$ (d) 3 (d) $\frac{5}{3}$
2 (a) $y = 3x$ (b) $y = 2x$ (c) $y = -x$ (d) $y = -2x$
3 (a) $y = 3x$ (b) $y = 3x$ (c) $y = \frac{1}{2}x$ (d) $y = -\frac{1}{3}x$
4 B
5 (a) $a = 6$ $b = 4$ $c = -3$ $d = -2$
6 (a) $a = 3$ $b = 16$ $c = -4$ $d = 6$

Exercise 16.5

1–3 (i) same gradient (ii) different y-intercept
4 (a) $m = 5$ y-intercept $= (0, 4)$
   (b) $m = -3$ y-intercept $= (0, -1)$
   (c) $m = \frac{1}{2}$ y-intercept $= (0, 10)$

Exercise 16.6

1 (a) $m = 3$ y-intercept $= (0, 2)$
   (b) $m = -2$ y-intercept $= (0, 6)$
   (c) $m = -1$ y-intercept $= (0, 6)$
   (d) $m = \frac{1}{2}$ y-intercept $= (0, -4)$
   (e) $m = -\frac{1}{3}$ y-intercept $= (0, 6)$

2 (a)   (b)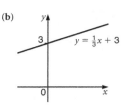

   (c) 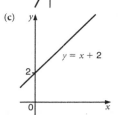 (d)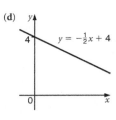

   (e)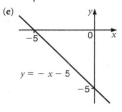

Exercise 16.7

1 (a) $y = 2x + 2$ (b) $y = x + 4$ (c) $y = \frac{1}{2}x + 1$
   (d) $y = 2x - 3$ (e) $y = \frac{3}{2}x + 3$ (f) $y = -2x + 6$
   (g) $y = -\frac{1}{4}x + 2$ (h) $y = -\frac{1}{2}x - 2$
2 (a) $y = 2x + 3$ (b) $y = 4x - 2$ (c) $y = -3x + 5$
   (d) $y = \frac{1}{2}x + 4$ (e) $y = \frac{3}{4}x - 5$ (f) $y = -\frac{2}{3}x + \frac{1}{2}$
3 (a) $y = x + 5$ (b) $y = -x - 3$ (c) $y = \frac{5}{2}x - 2$
   (d) $y = \frac{1}{3}x + 5$ (e) $y = -\frac{8}{3}x + 4$ (f) $y = -\frac{5}{4}x - 5$
4 (b) $AB = \sqrt{13}$ $AC = \sqrt{26}$ $BC = \sqrt{13}$
   (d) $AB: y = \frac{3}{2}x + 5$ $CB: y = -\frac{2}{3}x + 5$
   (e) $m_{AB} \times m_{AC} = -1$
5 (b) $AB = 5$ $AC = \sqrt{125}$ $BC = 10$
   (d) $AB: y = \frac{4}{3}x + 3$ $CB: y = -\frac{3}{4}x + 3$ (e) $m_{AB} \times m_{AC} = -1$
6 all horizontal lines (a) $y = 4$ (b) $y = 6$ (c) $y = 3$ (d) $y = -2$
7 all vertical lines (a) $x = 2$ (b) $x = 1$ (c) $x = -1$ (d) $x = -4$

Exercise 16.8

1 (a) $d = 15t + 10$ (b) $d = 7t + 15$ (c) $V = -\frac{1}{2}b + 6$
   (d) $V = -\frac{3}{4}b + 3$ (e) $d = 0\cdot2t + 0\cdot2$ (f) $d = 1\cdot5t + 0\cdot75$
   (g) $p = -2q + 14$ (h) $r = -\frac{1}{3}s + 0\cdot5$
2 (c) $E = 10w + 25$
3 $F = \frac{9}{5}c + 32$
   (b) (i) $77°F$ (ii) $149°F$ (iii) $168\cdot8°F$ (iv) $-4°F$
4 (a) 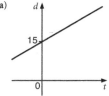 (b) $d = 2t + 15$
                             (c) 39 cm

5 (b) $c = \frac{1}{5}w + 20$ (c) 60p (d) 400 g
6 (a) 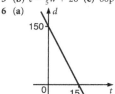 (b) $d = -10t + 150$
                             (c) 75 cm

7 (a)

Time (t)	0	10	20	30	40
Distance (d)	80	70	60	50	40

(c) $d = -t + 80$ **(d)** 35 km   **(e)** 80 min

Exercise 16.9

1 (a) 2; $(0, 1)$ **(b)** -2; $(0, 3)$ **(c)** $\frac{1}{2}$; $(0, 1\frac{1}{2})$
   (d) $-\frac{3}{2}$; $(0, -2)$ **(e)** -2; $(0, -3)$ **(f)** -3; $(0, 4)$
2 A **(iii)**   B **(iv)**   C **(i)**   D **(ii)**
3 (a) $y = -x + 2$ **(b)** $y = -2x + 5$ **(c)** $y = 3x + 1$
   (d) $y = -2x + 4$ **(e)** $y = -\frac{1}{2}x + 2$ **(f)** $y = -4x + 5$
   (g) $y = -\frac{1}{3}x + \frac{7}{3}$ **(h)** $y = -\frac{1}{2}x + \frac{5}{2}$ **(i)** $y = -\frac{2}{3}x + 2$
   (j) $y = -\frac{3}{2}x + \frac{3}{2}$ **(k)** $y = 2x - 1$ **(l)** $y = 3x - 5$

Exercise 16.10

1 A **(iii)**   B **(iv)**   C **(i)**   D **(ii)**
2 (a) $(3, 0)$ $(0, -3)$ **(b)** $(-3, 0)$ $(0, 2)$
   (c) $(-4, 0)$ $(0, 6)$ **(d)** $(1, 0)$ $(0, 2)$
   (e) $(2, 0)$ $(0, 1\frac{1}{2})$ **(f)** $(-2, 0)$ $(0, \frac{8}{3})$
   (g) $(2, 0)$ $(0, 12)$ **(h)** $(\frac{3}{2}, 0)$ $(0, -6)$
   (i) $(6, 0)$ $(0, 4)$

Exercise 16.11

1 (a) $(3, 5)$ **(b)** $(4, 5)$
   (c) $(2, 5)$ **(d)** $(6, 3)$
2 (a) $(1, 3)$ **(b)** $(3, 3)$
   (c) $(-1, 6)$ **(d)** $(2\frac{1}{2}, -3)$
3 (a) $(2, 1)$ **(b)** $(1, -1)$
   (c) $(1, -1)$ **(d)** $(2, -3)$
4 (a) $(3, -3)$ **(b)** $(1, 1)$
   (c) $(2, 3)$ **(d)** $(-1, -1)$

Exercise 16.12

1 (a) $(5, 5)$ **(b)** $(2, 4)$ **(c)** $(-4, -12)$
2 (a) $(2, 0)$ **(b)** $(-1, -2)$
   (c) $(-1, 1)$ **(d)** $(-1, 1)$
   (e) $(-1, 2)$ **(f)** $(2, 3)$
   (g) $(3, 4)$ **(h)** $(-2, -1)$

Exercise 16.13

1 (a) $c = 5h + 30$ $c = 8h + 15$
   (c) Mental Rentals are best value until $h = 5$,
     Higher Cars are best value after $h = 5$.
2 (a) $c = 8h$ $c = 4h + 12$ **(c)** 3 hours   **(d)** £24
3 City Cabs until 2 miles, Town Taxis after 2 miles.
4 Aligator better until 10 CDs, Crocodile after 10 CDs.
5 Sinking Feeling until 2h, Shower of Cowboys after 2h.
6 $(3, 2)$
7 Bank of Scotia until £200, Alba Bank after £200.

Exercise 16.14

1 (a) $y = \frac{3}{2}x + 3$ **(b)** $y = -2x + 6$
   (c) $y = -\frac{1}{2}x + 4$ **(d)** $y = -\frac{1}{2}x - 2$
2 (a) $y = 1.25x + 225$ **(b)** $y = 2.5x - 125$
   (c) $y = 0.5x + 420$ **(d)** $y = 4x + 2.5$
   (e) $y = -2x + 11$ **(f)** $y = -3.9x + 6.525$
   (g) $x = -34$ **(h)** $y = 0.6$
3 (a) $3m + 2r = 46$, $2m + 3r = 44$
   (b) Mountain £10   Road £8

Review exercise 16

1 (a) 4   **(b)** $\frac{1}{2}$ **(c)** -3 **(d)** $\frac{3}{5}$
2 (a) 2   **(b)** $-\frac{5}{8}$
3 (a) $y = 2x$ **(b)** $y = \frac{7}{5}x$ **(c)** $y = -\frac{2}{3}x$ **(d)** $y = \frac{1}{4}x$
4 (a) $m = 4$ y-intercept $= (0, 1)$
   (b) $m = -3$ y-intercept $= (0, 4)$
   (c) $m = \frac{1}{2}$ y-intercept $= (0, -4)$
   (d) $m = -\frac{1}{2}$ y-intercept $= (0, \frac{5}{2})$
   (e) $m = -\frac{3}{2}$ y-intercept $= (0, -2)$
5 (a) $y = 2x + 3$ **(b)** $y = 4x - 2$
   (c) $y = -\frac{1}{2}x + 3$ **(d)** $y = -\frac{2}{5}x - 2$
6 Both P and Q
7 (a) $d = \frac{35}{2}t + 15$ **(b)** $s = \frac{3}{2}r + 1.5$
   (c) $C = -\frac{5}{6}h + 100$ **(d)** $p = -\frac{1}{2}q + 0.2$
8 (a) 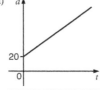   **(b)** $d = 5t + 20$
   (c) 70 cm

9 (a)

t	0	1	2	3
d	5	25	45	65

(b)

   (c) $d = 20t + 5$
   (d) 115 km
   (e) 4 hr 45 min
10 (a) $y = 2x + 2$ **(b)** $y = -3x + 6$ **(c)** $y = -\frac{1}{2}x + 3$
11 (a)   **(b)**
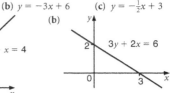
   (c)
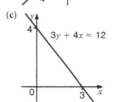
12 (a) $(2, 5)$ **(b)** $(1, 7)$
13 Sparky until 5h, Wired after 5h
14 (a) $(5, 3)$ **(b)** $(3, 1\frac{1}{2})$
15 (a) $3a + 2c = 44$, $2a + 3c = 41$ **(c)** adult £10   child £7
16 (a) $y = -x + 61$ **(b)** $y = -\frac{11}{8}x + 13\frac{1}{8}$
17 (a) $y = 2x - 3$ **(b)** $y = 0.2x + 3.8$
   (c) $y = -3x + 18$ **(d)** $y = \frac{8}{3}x + 18$

Review 4

Exercise 4A

1 2 m   **2** 5.9 cm   **3** 30.1 cm
4 10.3 m   **5 (a)** $2a + c = 16$, $3a + 4c = 34$ **(b)** $a = 6$, $c = 4$
6 (a) $x = 4$ $y = -2$ **(b)** $x = 2$ $y = 6$ **(c)** $x = 3$ $y = -1$
7 200   **8** 140
9 (a) $y = x + 3$ **(b)** $y = \frac{1}{2}x - 2$ **(c)** $y = -3x - 2$
10 (a) 2, $(0, 4)$ **(b)** 1, $(0, -3)$
   (c) -3, $(0, -1)$ **(d)** -2, $(0, 5)$
11 $d = 3t + 12$

Exercise 4B

1 (a) $x^2 + 4x - 21$ (b) $x^2 - 16$
   (c) $6x^2 - 13x + 5$ (d) $8x^2 - 12xy + 26x - 9y + 15$

2 7·5 cm   3 25·7%

4 $a = 18{·}2$ cm $b = 19{·}6$ cm   5 110·25

6 (a) $x = 2$ $y = -7$ (b) $x = 2$ $y = 5$

7 (a) $\dfrac{P + 2a + b}{2}$ (b) $\dfrac{As + dt}{d}$ (c) $\dfrac{mv^2}{3t}$

8 (a) 180 m   (b) 1500 m²

9 £18·75   10 £4240·55

11 (a)

1	2 4 7 8	LQ = 18
2	0 0 0 3 4 7	Med = 23
3	0 1 2 4 6	UQ = 31

           $1 \mid 2 = 12$, $n = 15$

   (b) 6·5   (c)

12 (a) (i) $y = 2x + 8$ (ii) $y = -3x - 2$ (b) $x = -2$, $y = 4$

13 (a) $w = -10$ (b) $w < \frac{7}{3}$ (c) $x = -\frac{4}{5}$ (d) $a = \frac{7}{4}$

14 (a) 3·7 m   (b) 3·9 m²

15 No, proof by converse of Pythagoras.   16 £290·70

17 (a) (i) $\frac{1}{2}$ (ii) $\frac{1}{9}$ (b) 10

18 (a) 378 000 cm³   (b) 47 250 cm³

19 (a) 1·4 km   (b) 6 cm

20 27·7   21 $x = 2$

Chapter 17

Exercise 17.1

1 (a) 3   (b) 8   (c) 6   (d) 10
2 (a) $2x$ (b) $5x$ (c) x (d) $3a$
3 (a) 6   (b) 4   (c) 2   (d) 3
   (e) $5x$ (f) $6y$ (g) $3x$ (h) $7p$
4 (a) x^2 (b) $2x$ (c) $5p$ (d) a
   (e) b^2 (f) ab (g) $3x$ (h) $3p$

Exercise 17.2

1 (a) $3(x + 6)$ (b) $2(x + 5)$
   (c) $2(x - 3 + 4y)$ (d) $3(x - 7 - 9z)$
   (e) $2(2y + 3)$ (f) $7(-5 + 7t + 4x)$
   (g) $3(-5x + 16)$ (h) $16(4 - z)$
   (i) $15(3y - 5 + 10t)$
2 (a) $8x + 9$ (b) $6x - 2$
   (c) $3x - 2$ (d) $8 - 5x$
3 (a) $a(2b + \pi)$ (b) $x(2x + 3 + 5a)$
   (c) $t(7 - a)$ (d) $p^2(2t + 11q)$
   (e) $x(5 + x - 2p)$ (f) $x^2(x^3 - 1)$
   (g) $v^2(10 - \pi v^3)$ (h) $x(1 + x^3 - x^4)$
   (i) $a(bc + 3t)$
4 (a) $2\pi(2x - b)$ (b) $5x(2x - 1)$
   (c) $3v(4av - 1)$ (d) $2z(3x + z)$
   (e) $5x(1 + 2t)$ (f) $2a(b - 2c - 6a)$
   (g) $4ab(1 + 2b)$ (h) $3x(y + 1)$
   (i) $y^2(1 + y)$ (j) $\pi v^2(v^3 - 1)$
   (k) $x^3(5 + x)$ (l) $\pi x^2(x + 2)$
   (m) $5pq^2r^2(1 - 5r)$ (n) $4atr(1 + a)$
   (o) $x(6ax - 3a + 5)$
5 (a) $2(3a + 5b + 6c)$ (b) $\pi a(x + b + y)$
   (c) $x(12ax + 5 - 10b)$ (d) $x^3(1 + x + x^2)$
   (e) $xy(x + y + y^2)$ (f) $2(px^2 + 6px + 9)$
   (g) $2(3x^2 + 5x - 2)$ (h) $3(3y^2 - 4x - 1)$
   (i) $5(\pi x + 3\pi x^2 + 4)$ (j) $2(p^2 - 10p + 3)$
   (k) $3(q^2 - q + 5)$ (l) $10(r^2 - 2r + 10)$

6 (a) $xy^1(2z + t)$ (b) $ab(70c + 3)$
   (c) $xy(xz + a)$ (d) $xyz(x + y)$
   (e) $2ast(a + 2)$ (f) $pq(5qr + 6a)$
7 (a) 420   (b) 1440
   (c) 180

Exercise 17.3

1 (a) $b^2 - a^2$ (b) $t^2 - 7^2$
   (c) $4^2 - r^2$ (d) $2^2 - x^2$
2 (a) $(x + 4)(x - 4)$ (b) $(y + 5)(y - 5)$
   (c) $(t + 2)(t - 2)$ (d) $(f + 8)(f - 8)$
   (e) $(g + 20)(g - 20)$ (f) $(b + 30)(b - 30)$
   (g) $(t + 13)(t - 13)$ (h) $(x + 15)(x - 15)$
   (i) $(x + b)(x - b)$ (j) $(x + t)(x - t)$
   (k) $(x + a)(x - a)$ (l) $(z + \pi)(z - \pi)$
3 (a) $(2x + b)(2x - b)$ (b) $(z + 9y)(z - 9y)$
   (c) $(x + 7a)(x - 7a)$ (d) $(8t + x)(8t - x)$
   (e) $(10x + 11b)(10x - 11b)$ (f) $(10z + 7p)(10z - 7p)$
   (g) $(6x + 13a)(6x - 13a)$ (h) $(5x + 9t)(5x - 9t)$
4 (a) $5(y + a)(y - a)$ (b) $11(z + t)(z - t)$
   (c) $\pi(r + x)(r - x)$ (d) $5(3x + 2t)(3x - 2t)$
   (e) $3(10x + 9b)(10x - 9b)$ (f) $3(4z + 3p)(4z - 3p)$
   (g) $3(5x + 2a)(5x - 2a)$ (h) $8(2y + x)(2y - x)$
   (i) $t(x + y)(x - y)$ (j) $2s(r + q)(r - q)$
   (k) $2c(2t + r)(2t - r)$ (l) $ab(y + r)(y - r)$
5 (a) $(ab + st)(ab - st)$ (b) $(ty + ds)(ty - ds)$
   (c) $(fg + 2pq)(fg - 2pq)$ (d) $(3ab + 2xy)(3ab - 2xy)$
   (e) $(7ab + 9xy)(7ab - 9xy)$ (f) $(6ab + 10xy)(6ab - 10xy)$
   (g) $(x^2 + 3y)(x^2 - 3y)$ (h) $(4x^2 + 5r)(4x^2 - 5r)$
6 (a) $(x + b)(x - b)$ (b) $9(2z + 3p)(2z - 3p)$
   (c) $(a + \pi)(a - \pi)$ (d) $(3a + 5x)(3a - 5x)$
   (e) $(a^2 + 4y)(a^2 - 4y)$ (f) $(t + 20)(t - 20)$
   (g) $(7x + 10a)(7x - 10a)$ (h) $\pi(y + 2)(y - 2)$
   (i) $7(3x + 2t)(3x - 2t)$ (j) $(9x^2 + 5y)(9x^2 - 5y)$
   (k) $5(3x + 2t)(3x - 2t)$ (l) $3(4z + 3t)(4z - 3t)$
7 (a) $x(x - 6)$ (b) $(x - 1)(x - 9)$
   (c) $(x + 1)(x - 9)$
8 (a) $4(t - 2)$ (b) $7(2r - 3)$
   (c) $3(2x - 1)$

Exercise 17.4

1 (a) $x^2 + 9x + 14$ (b) $p^2 + 5p + 4$
   (c) $t^2 + 5t + 6$ (d) $x^2 + 14x + 40$
   (e) $y^2 + 18y + 45$ (f) $x^2 + 6x + 9$
2 (a) 2, 12   (b) 3, 8
   (c) 4, 6   (d) 1, 24
3 (a) 2, 10   (b) 5, 7
   (c) 3, 9   (d) 4, 8
4 (a) $(x + 2)(x + 6)$ (b) $(x + 10)(x + 5)$
   (c) $(x + 3)(x + 7)$ (d) $(x + 2)(x + 5)$
   (e) $(x + 1)(x + 2)$ (f) $(x + 8)(x + 7)$
5 (a) $x + 1$ (b) $x + 3$
   (c) $x + 4$
6 (a) $2(x + 2)(x + 1)$ (b) $3(x + 3)(x + 7)$
   (c) $4(x + 3)(x + 2)$ (d) $4(x + 4)^2$
   (e) $3(x + 4)(x + 2)$ (f) $2(x + 5)(x + 1)$
   (g) $5(x + 4)(x + 7)$ (h) $7(x + 3)^2$
   (i) $3(x + 2)(x + 7)$ (j) $3(x + 8)(x + 1)$
   (k) $5(x + 3)(x + 5)$ (l) $2(x + 6)(x + 4)$

Exercise 17.5

1 (a) $x^2 - 7x + 12$ (b) $x^2 - 9x + 14$
   (c) $x^2 - 7x + 6$ (d) $x^2 - 4x + 4$
   (e) $x^2 - 14x + 45$ (f) $x^2 - 16x + 48$

2 (a) $(x-2)(x-3)$ (b) $(x-4)(x-6)$
  (c) $(x-1)^2$ (d) $(x-2)(x-8)$
  (e) $(x-7)^2$ (f) $(x-11)(x-4)$

3 (a) $(x-5)(x-6)$ (b) $(x-4)(x-2)$
  (c) $(x-10)(x-1)$ (d) $(x-3)(x-5)$
  (e) $(x-10)(x-2)$ (f) $(x-5)^2$
  (g) $(x-8)(x-3)$ (h) $(x-1)(x-9)$
  (i) $(x-4)(x-11)$ (j) $(x-5)(x-10)$
  (k) $(x-3)(x-4)$ (l) $(x-7)^2$

4 (a) $2(x-8)(x-2)$ (b) $3(x-3)(x-1)$
  (c) $2(x-3)^2$ (d) $10(x-9)(x-1)$
  (e) $6(x-4)(x-5)$ (f) $4(x-6)^2$
  (g) $x(x-6)(x-2)$ (h) $x(x-4)(x-2)$

Exercise 17.6

1 (a) x^2-x-6 (b) x^2+x-6
  (c) $x^2-3x-28$ (d) $x^2+3x-28$
  (e) $x^2+2x-35$ (f) $x^2-6x-27$
  (g) $x^2-8x-48$ (h) x^2+5x-6
  (i) x^2-x-42

2 (a) $(x+3)(x-8)$ (b) $(x-1)(x+12)$
  (c) $(x+2)(x-7)$

3 (a) $(x+3)(x-2)$ (b) $(x+10)(x-6)$
  (c) $(x+5)(x-4)$ (d) $(x+9)(x-7)$
  (e) $(x+5)(x-8)$ (f) $(x+1)(x-12)$
  (g) $(x+4)(x-6)$ (h) $(x+9)(x-3)$
  (i) $(x+1)(x-3)$ (j) $(x+8)(x-5)$
  (k) $(x+10)(x-2)$ (l) $(x+4)(x-9)$

4 (a) $2(x+3)(x-2)$ (b) $3(x+3)(x-7)$
  (c) $5(x+4)(x-1)$ (d) $4(x+6)(x-1)$
  (e) $2(x+2)(x-5)$ (f) $x(x+2)(x-4)$
  (g) $7x(x+2)(x-6)$ (h) $6(x+2)(x-7)$

Exercise 17.7

1 (a) $2x^2+7x-15$ (b) $3x^2-10x+7$
  (c) $5x^2-6x-8$ (d) $2x^2+13x+21$
  (e) $6x^2-19x-36$ (f) $8x^2+2x-21$
  (g) $12x^2-23x+5$ (h) $20x^2-4x-3$
  (i) $56x^2+11x-12$

2 (a) $(2x+1)(x+5)$ (b) $(x+1)(5x+3)$
  (c) $(3x+2)(x+1)$ (d) $(2x+3)(x+1)$
  (e) $(5x+2)(x+1)$ (f) $(3x+1)(x+3)$

3 (a) $(2x+5)(x+1)$ (b) $(3x+1)(x+7)$
  (c) $(7x+1)(x+1)$ (d) $(11x+1)(x+3)$
  (e) $(2x+1)(x+3)$ (f) $(5x+1)(x+2)$
  (g) $(2x+3)(x+7)$ (h) $(2x+1)(x+5)$

4 (a) $(2x-1)(x+2)$ (b) $(3x-1)(x+3)$
  (c) $(2x+1)(x-5)$ (d) $(3x-5)(x+1)$
  (e) $(2x+1)(x-2)$ (f) $(5x+1)(x-5)$
  (g) $(2x+1)(x-1)$ (h) $(3x-1)(x+2)$
  (i) $(5x+7)(x-1)$ (j) $(7x-1)(x+2)$
  (k) $(3x+2)(x-3)$ (l) $(3x-1)(x-5)$
  (m) $(3x+1)(x-2)$ (n) $(5x+1)(x-1)$
  (o) $(2x+3)(x-5)$ (p) $(3x-1)(x+2)$
  (q) $(7x-1)(x+5)$ (r) $(3x-5)(x+3)$

Exercise 17.8

1 (a) $(2x-1)(2x-3)$ (b) $(4x+1)(x+1)$
  (c) $(2x+7)(4x+1)$ (d) $(2x+3)(6x+1)$
  (e) $(4x+1)(x-1)$ (f) $(2x+1)(x-8)$

2 (a) $(2x+5)(x+3)$ (b) $(3x-2)(2x+1)$
  (c) $(2x-2)(x-3)$ (d) $(2x+5)(2x-1)$
  (e) $(3x+1)(4x-3)$ (f) $(3x-2)(x-5)$
  (g) $(8x+1)(2x+7)$ (h) $(5x-4)(x+3)$
  (i) $(6x+1)(2x-1)$ (j) $(3x-4)(x+4)$
  (k) $(10x+1)(2x+1)$ (l) $(2x-3)(x-4)$
  (m) $(6x-1)(x+3)$ (n) $(2x-1)(x-9)$
  (o) $(3x+5)(x+3)$

3 (a) $2(2x+1)(x+6)$ (b) $3(5x+3)(x-2)$
  (c) $7(3x+1)(x-2)$ (d) $2(7x-1)(2x-3)$
  (e) $4(x+1)(3x-2)$ (f) $2(2x+1)(4x-3)$

4 (a) $(5x+2)(2x+3)$ (b) $(3x-2)(2x-3)$
  (c) $(3x-4)^2$ (d) $(4x-3)(2x+3)$
  (e) $2(3x-2)(2x+1)$ (f) $(5x-2)^2$

5 (a) $(5x-4)(2x+3)$ (b) $(2x-3)(2x-5)$
  (c) $(3x+4)^2$ (d) $(4x+3)(2x-5)$
  (e) $(2x+3)^2$ (f) $(3x-2)(2x+5)$

6 (a) $3x-7$ (b) $3x-5$
  (c) $2x-3$ (d) $4x-1$

Exercise 17.9

1 (a) $(3x+1)(x+2)$ (b) $(3+2x)(3-2x)$
  (c) $(4a-1)(2a+3)$ (d) $(2y+5)(y-1)$
  (e) $3(x-1)(x+2)$ (f) $(3x+2)(2x+3)$
  (g) $(x-5)(x+7)$ (h) $(x-7)(x-3)$
  (i) $(2x+9)(x-3)$ (j) $(x+3)(6x-1)$
  (k) $(2y-9)(2y+3)$ (l) $(5b+6)(b+3)$

2 (a) $(3x+2)(5x-4)$ (b) $(2x-1)(x-12)$
  (c) $(3x+10)(3x-10)$ (d) $3(x+2)(x-2)$
  (e) $3(x-3)^2$ (f) $12(1+3x)(1-3x)$
  (g) $2(2x+1)(x-3)$ (h) $(6x-5)(2x+5)$
  (i) $(5x+1)(x+2)$ (j) $(5x-4)(3x+2)$
  (k) $(7x-5)(x+4)$ (l) $(3x-8)(x+2)$

3 (a) $(3-x)(4+x)$ (b) $(3+x)(5-x)$
  (c) $(3+x)(2-x)$ (d) $(3-x)(4-x)$
  (e) $(2-x)(1+x)$ (f) $(2-3x)(1+x)$
  (g) $(5-2x)(1+x)$ (h) $(2-3x)(1-2x)$
  (i) $2(3-2x)(2+x)$ (j) $(3-x)(1+3x)$
  (k) $(1+6x)(1-3x)$ (l) $(1+3x)(1-4x)$

4 (a) $(x^2+5)(x^2+6)$ (b) $(y^2+5)(y^2-3)$
  (c) $(s^2+1)(s-1)(s+1)$ (d) $a(a+1)(a-1)$
  (e) $(1+x-y)(1-x+y)$ (f) $b^4(1+b)(1-b)$

5 (a) $(3x-7)(2x-3)$ (b) $(2x+3)(2x+5)$
  (c) $(x+4)(x-2)$ (d) $(x+1)^2$
  (e) $(3x-5)(x+1)$ (f) $2(4x+11)$
  (g) $2(x+1)(x-1)$ (h) $(2x+5)(x-1)$

6 (a) $(c+b)^2$ (b) $(a+b)(a+2b)$
  (c) $(t+s)(t-2s)$ (d) $(p-2t)(p+3t)$
  (e) $(5t+p)(t-2p)$ (f) $(3t+2q)(t+q)$
  (g) $(2q+3s)(q+s)$ (h) $(2x+y)(x+5y)$
  (i) $(2p-q)(p+3q)$ (j) $(3x-2y)(3x+4y)$
  (k) $(6a+b)(a+2b)$ (l) $(2r+t)(3r-4t)$

Exercise 17.10

2 $(2x+1)^2-(x-1)^2$
  $=(4x^2+4x+1)-(x^2-2x+1)$
  $=3x^2+6x=3x(x+2)$

3 $\pi(4x)+\pi(2x-6)$
  $=4\pi x+2\pi x-6\pi$
  $=6\pi x-6\pi$
  $=6\pi(x-1)$

4 $2x(x+5)+(x+5)(x-2)$
  $=(3x-2)(x+5)$

5 $(n+1)^2-1$
  $=n^2+2n$
  $=n(n+2)$

Review exercise 17

1 (a) $(x+3)^2$ (b) $(x+2)^2$
  (c) $(x+4)(x-6)$ (d) $(x+6)(x-6)$
  (e) $(x-3)(x+6)$ (f) $(x+3)(x-2)$
  (g) $(x-3)(x+4)$ (h) $(x-4)(x+18)$
  (i) $(x+1)(x-3)$ (j) $(x+10)(x-10)$
  (k) $(x-8)(x+3)$ (l) $(x+3)(x+15)$

2 (a) $(3x + 5)(x + 3)$ **(b)** $(x - 1)(x - 2)$
  (c) $(2a + 1)(a - 3)$ **(d)** $(2y + 5)(y - 1)$
  (e) $(2x - 1)(x - 3)$ **(f)** $(2x + 1)(x + 3)$
  (g) $(3 + 2x)(3 - 2x)$ **(h)** $(5b + 6)(b + 3)$
  (i) $(3x - 2)(x - 3)$ **(j)** $(6x - 1)(x + 3)$
  (k) $(2y + 3)(2y - 9)$ **(l)** $(3x + 7)(3x - 7)$

3 (a) $2(x - 3)^2$ **(b)** $3(x - 3)(x + 5)$
  (c) $2(x + 2)(x - 2)$ **(d)** $2(x + 6)(x - 12)$
  (e) $4(x + 7)(x - 1)$ **(f)** $3(x + 3)(x + 6)$
  (g) $5(x - 3)(x - 6)$ **(h)** $2(3x + 4)(3x - 4)$

4 (a) $(x + 6)^2$ **(b)** $(x - 2y)^2$
  (c) $x(2x + 3)(2x - 3)$ **(d)** $(3 - x)(1 + 3x)$
  (e) $(4x + 3y)(x - 2y)$ **(f)** $(1 + 6x)(1 - 3x)$
  (g) $(3 - 2x)(5 + x)$ **(h)** $2x(x + 7)(x + 8)$
  (i) $(x^2 + 6)(x^2 - 6)$ **(j)** $(x - y)(2x - 3y)$
  (k) $(x^2 - 7)(x^2 + 9)$ **(l)** $(x + 2)(x - 6)$

5 (a) $(3x - 1)(2x - 3)$ **(b)** $x(x - 2)$
  (c) $(x - 3)(x + 10)$

Chapter 18

Exercise 18.2

1 (a)

Age	Tally	Frequency	Cumulative frequency
50	I	1	1
51		0	1
52	IIII	4	5
53	I	1	6
54	IIII	5	11
55	IIII	4	15
56	III	3	18
57	I	1	19
58	IIII	5	24
59	II	2	26
60	III	3	29
61	I	1	30

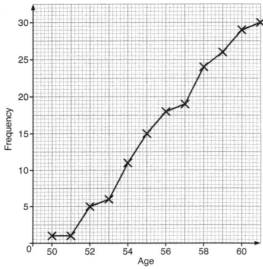

(b) 11   **(c)** 14

2 (a)

Age	Tally	Frequency	Cumulative frequency
17	II	2	2
18	I	1	3
19	II	2	5
20	II	2	7
21	I	1	8
22	II	2	10
23	II	2	12
24	I	1	13
25	I	1	14
26	II	2	16
27	IIII	4	20
28	III	3	23
29	IIII	4	27
30	II	2	29
31	I	1	30
32	III	3	33
33	II	2	35
34	II	2	37
35		0	37
36		0	37
37		0	37
38	II	2	39
39		0	39
40		0	39
41	I	1	40

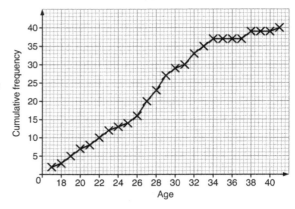

(b) 23
(c) 57.5%

3

Women

Age	Tally	Frequency	Cumulative frequency
19	|	1	1
20		0	1
21	||	2	3
22	||	2	5
23	||	2	7
24	|	1	8
25		0	8
26	|	1	9
27	|	1	10
28	|||	3	13
29	|||	3	16
30		0	16
31		0	16
32		0	16
33		0	16
34		0	16
35		0	16
36		0	16
37		0	16
38	|	1	17
39		0	17
40		0	17
41		0	17
42		0	17
43		0	17
44		0	17
45	|	1	18
46		0	18
47		0	18
48		0	18

Men

Age	Tally	Frequency	Cumuative frequency
19		0	0
20		0	0
21		0	0
22	||	2	2
23		0	2
24		0	2
25	|	1	3
26		0	3
27	||	2	5
28	|	1	6
29	||	2	8
30	|||	3	11
31	|	1	12
32	|	1	13
33		0	13
34	|	1	14
35	|	1	15
36	|	1	16
37		0	16
38	|	1	17
39		0	17
40		0	17
41		0	17
42		0	17
43		0	17
44		0	17
45		0	17
46	|	1	18
47		0	18
48		0	18

(a)

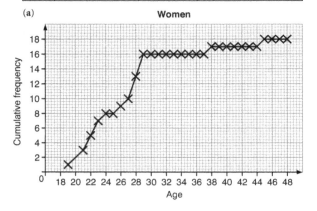

Women

(a)

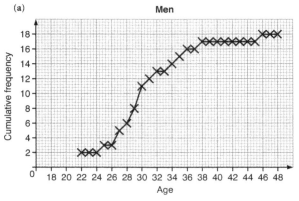

Men

(b) 36

(c) (i) 3 **(ii)** 8

(d) 18

(e) Yes, on average men marry later.

4 (a)

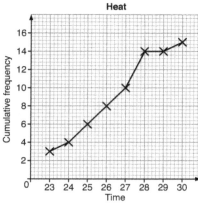

Heat

No heat

(b) 3   **(c)** On average times are shorter with heat.

3 (a)

Total spend	Cumulative frequency	
40	4	range = £25
0	4	mean = £18·17
70	9	median = £18
32	11	mode = £20
108	17	
180	26	
50	28	
30	29	
35	30	
Total 545		

(b) No, 13 people get more

4

Total eggs	Cumulative frequency	
0	8	range = 5
9	17	mean = 2·3
32	33	median = 2
51	50	mode = 3
12	53	
35	60	

(b) No, on average it is 2·3. The mode could be used to justify.

5

Total cost	Cumulative frequency	
800	20	range = £80
750	35	mean = £85·23
1080	53	median = £90
1540	75	mode = £100
3200	115	
4050	160	
5000	210	
2860	236	
2880	260	
Total 221 60		

(b) No, you couldn't justify it at all

6 (a) range = 7   mean = 4·9   median = 4   mode = 4

(b) Probably as median and mode are both 4

Exercise 18.3

1

Number of children	Frequency	Total number of children	Cumulative frequency
0	11	0 × 11 = 0	11
1	14	1 × 14 = 14	25
2	22	2 × 22 = 44	47
3	11	3 × 11 = 33	58
4	4	4 × 4 = 16	62
5	6	5 × 6 = 30	68
6	2	6 × 2 = 12	70
Total	70	149	

range = 6   mean = 2·1   median = 2   mode = 2

2

Power output	Frequency	Total power output	Cumulative frequency
1	4	1 × 4 = 4	4
1·25	6	1·25 × 6 = 7·5	10
1·5	16	1·5 × 16 = 24	26
1·75	2	1·75 × 2 = 3·5	28
2	6	2 × 6 = 12	34
2·25	1	2·25 × 1 = 2·25	35
Total	35	53·25	

range = 1·25   mean = 1·5   median = 1·5   mode = 1·5

Exercise 18.4

1 (a)

Cumulative frequency	
22	LQ = 15
39	median = 24
44	UQ = 30
56	SIQR = 7·5
77	
86	
98	

(b)

Cumulative frequency	
4	LQ = 45
15	median = 52
23	UQ = 52
44	SIQR = 3·5
51	
57	

2 (a) 1·5   **(b)** 2

(c) 2   **(d)** 10

Exercise 18.5

1 (a) 211·5 g
(b)

x	$x - \bar{x}$	$(x - \bar{x})^2$
150	−61·5	3782·25
220	8·5	72·25
225	13·5	182·25
240	28·5	812·25
195	−16·5	272·25
245	33·5	1122·25
230	18·5	342·25
190	−21·5	462·25
255	43·5	1892·25
165	−46·5	2162·25
		11 102·5

mean square deviation = 1110·25
standard deviation = 33·3

2 (a) 6·05, 2·46   **(b)** 25·27, 5·03   **(c)** 0·235, 0·48   **(d)** 29, 5·39

Exercise 18.6

1 (a) 5·1, 1·29   **(b)** 15·29, 1·15   **(c)** 4·18, 1·40
  (d) 7·83, 1·72   **(e)** 30·7, 1·77   **(f)** 26·92, 8·68
2 21·77, 1·35
3 (a) 72·6, 2·12   **(b)** No: mean is less than 75 ml
4 (a) $5C_1 - 23, 3·07$ $5B_1 - 22·75, 3·85$ $5B_2 - 17·5, 2·78$ **(b)** $5B_2$
5 (a) 5·23, 1·07   **(b) (i)** mean = 4·94: yes   **(ii)** less variation
6 (a) Start − 82·5, 10·54   End − 76·2, 9·25
  (b) No, on average it was less than 1 kg

Exercise 18.7

1 (a) 1998 − 3·11, 1·45   2006 − 6·67, 1·73
  (b) median = 3   SIQR = 0·75   median = 7   SIQR = 1
  (c)

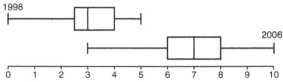

  (d) Yes, on average temperature is higher.
2 (a)

before		after
8	1	1 8
	2	1 1
	3	8 9
3	4	7
6	5	
9 7	6	9
2 2 1 0	7	5

1|8 = 18   1|1 = 11
$n = 9$ $n = 9$

  (b) Before − 59·78, 18·40
    Now − 37·67, 22·69
  (c) yes

3 (a) 1956 − 26·42, 2·61   2006 − 29·42, 2·78
  (b) On average weight is increased.
4 (a) A − 14·92, 1·75   B − 15·14, 0·62   C − 15·94, 2·56
  (b) A   LQ − 13·8   med − 14·75   UQ − 16
    B   LQ − 14·8   med − 15·1   UQ − 15·7
    C   LQ − 15·4   med − 16·15   UQ − 17·5

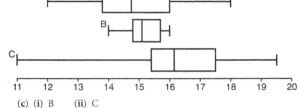

  (c) (i) B   **(ii)** C

Review exercise 18

1 Make of car – categorical, test scores – numerical, discrete
  Flight destination – categorical, arm spans – numerical, continuous
2 (a)

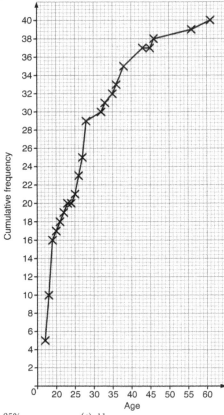

  (b) 95%   **(c)** 11
3 (a)

Time	Freq.	Cumulative frequency
49	1	1
59	6	7
60	1	8
61	2	10
63	1	11
64	4	15
65	4	19
66	4	23
67	7	30
68	2	32
69	3	35
70	5	40
71	2	42
72	5	47
73	2	49
79	1	50

  (b) range = 30
    mean = 66·34
    median = 67
    mode = 67
  (c) UQ = 70
    LQ = 64
    IQR = 6

4 (a) A − 13·25, 1·83   B − 14, 2·39
  (b) Branch B has larger average size but more variability.

Chapter 19

Exercise 19.1

1 (a) £12 317   **(b)** £3095   **(c)** £3699   **(d)** £2922
2 (a) £14 092·10   **(b)** £37 833·60   **(c)** £11 927·80   **(d)** £58 175·60

3 (a) False   **(b)** True
4 (a) £10 372·75   **(b)** £10 616·11   **(c)** £92 451·20   **(d)** £13 585·10
5 (a) £389·17   **(b)** £444·75   **(c)** £510·85

Exercise 19.2

1 (a) 1253   **(b)** £104·12   **(c)** 114·49   **(d)** 5·72
(e) £120·21
2 (a) 298   **(b)** £169·07   **(c)** £178·26
3 (a) 79 577   **(b)** £110·02   **(c)** 88 997   **(d)** £854·87
(e) £974·02   **(f)** £969   **(g)** £48·45   **(h)** £1017·45
4 (a) 94 859   **(b)** £82·93   **(c)** 681   **(d)** £61·80
(e) £6·99   **(f)** £153·86   **(g)** £150·53   **(h)** £7·53
(i) £158·06
5 (a) £36·31   **(b)** £1·88   **(c)** £99·19   **(d)** £6·13
(e) £143·51   **(f)** £7·18   **(g)** £150·69
6 (a) £264·12   **(b)** £10·60   **(c)** £265·16   **(d)** £13·26
(e) £278·42   **(f)** £8·30

Exercise 19.3

1 (a) (i) £624   **(ii)** £816   **(iii)** £690
(b) £360   **(c)** £702
2 (a) £3133·40   **(b)** 379%
3 (a) £17·28   **(b)** 24·7%   **(c)** £491·40
4 £530   **5** £52·60   **6** pay bill
7 (a) £89·14   **(b)** £147·33   **(c)** £64·61
8 (a) (i) £40·48   **(ii)** £41·45   **(iii)** £123·33
(b) high medical bills
9 £112·50
10 (a) (i) £4000   **(ii)** £4000   **(iii)** 0   **(b)** 250%

Exercise 19.4

1 (a) £282   **(b)** −£8·88   **(c)** −£1282·05   **(d)** £322
2 (a) (i) £302·55   **(ii)** £55·45   **(b) (i)** £33·53   **(ii)** £11·47
(c) (i) £311·14   **(ii)** £798·86   **(d) (i)** £2125·66   **(ii)** £979·34
3 (a) 6 months   **(b)** £3·

Exercise 19.6

1 (a) £107·20   **(b)** £169·50   **(c)** £139·77   **(d)** £959·20
2 (a) £198 000   **(b)** £26 000   **(c)** £237 000
3 (a) £67·01   **(b)** £1611·37

Exercise 19.7

1 (a) All could   **(b)** yes

Review exercise 19

1 (a) £1503·40   **(b)** £4804·72
2 £377·20   **3** £44·46
4 (a) yes   **(b)** cover and extras   **5 (a)** 7 months   **(b)** £3·29
6 (a) £119·79   **(b)** £222·44
7 Premium bonds – capital is guaranteed·

Review 5

Exercise 5A

1 (a) $2(3y + 4)$ **(b)** $7a(2 - 5a)$
(c) $(b + 6)(b - 6)$ **(d)** $(x + 5)(x + 1)$
(e) $(3z + 1)(3z - 1)$ **(f)** $9xy(4y - 2x + 3xy)$
(g) $6(w + 2v)(w - 2v)$ **(h)** $(b - 9)(b + 1)$
(i) $2(3s + 5)(s - 1)$ **(j)** $3y(y + 3)(y - 3)$
(k) $4(2y - 1)(y - 2)$ **(l)** $4g^3(3g^2h^3 - 2 + 5h)$
(m) $(7 + 2x)(3 + x)$ **(n)** $4x^2y(2xy + 1)(2xy - 1)$
(o) $(3a + 2b)(a - 3b)$
2 $(3x + 1)(x - 1)$ **3** $\pi(R + r)(R - r)$, $5000\pi = 15\,708\,mm^2$
4 (b) LQ = 44   med = 58   UQ = 73·5

5 (a) 47·225, 9·7   **(b)** Average and variability both increased.
6 £427
7 (a) £34·83   **(b)** £7·95   **(c)** £42·78
(d) £2·14   **(e)** £44·92
8 (a) £56·42   **(b)** £169·86

Exercise 5B

1 (a) −10   **(b)** 42   **(c)** −9   **(d)** −1   **(e)** −20   **(f)** −10
2 (a) $b = 4\frac{1}{2}$ **(b)** $z = \frac{1}{2}$ **(c)** $w = -3$ **(d)** $m = -5\frac{1}{2}$
3 (a) $10y + 14$ **(b)** $40y - 8$ **(c)** $152\,cm^2$
4 (a) 16 m   **(b)** £48   **(c)** 41 g   **(d)** £12·82
5 £145   **6** $4·86 \times 10^6$ **7** 7·51   **8** 45°
9 (a) $8\frac{1}{3}$ mm   **(b)** 4·8 cm   **(c)** 6 m
10 160 ml   **11 (a)** 16·2 cm   **(b)** 18 cm
12 No, proof by converse of Pythagoras.
13 (a)

9 9 7	1
8 8 7 6 5 4 2 1	2
8 6 6 5 5 5 5 3 2	3
8 7 7 6 5 4 4 3 3 2	4
6 6 4 4 3 3 2	5
6 2	6

(b) (i) 35   **(ii)** 37   **(iii)** LQ = 28   UQ = 47·5
14 (a) 130 mm, 184 mm
(b) LQ = 144   UQ = 163   **(c)** 19
(d)

(e) This year's plants were less varied in height.
15 (a) $32t + 32$ **(b)** $-30x + 23x^2$
(c) $-20z^2 + 61z$ **(d)** $a^2 + 3a - 10$
(e) $3h^2 + 21h - 54$ **(f)** $-18x^2 + 3x + 36$
(g) $3p^2 - 22p + 40$ **(h)** $3y^2 + 24y + 48$
(i) $38f^2 - 24f + 6$ **(j)** $3x^3 - 4x^2 - 11x - 12$
(k) $32d^3 + 32d^2 - 70d - 75$ **(l)** $-12y^3 + 14y^2 + 14y + 2$
16 (a) $y = -\frac{1}{2}$ **(b)** $x = 0$ **(c)** $x = \frac{1}{3}$
(d) $z = -2$ **(e)** $p = -\frac{7}{2}$ **(f)** $x = \frac{1}{6}$
17 190   **18** 2700
19 (a) $2(y - 5)$ **(b)** $\frac{2yp}{a}$ **(c)** $\frac{2T + mn^2}{mn}$
(d) $x = \sqrt{\frac{5 - 6p}{3}}$ **(e)** $\frac{9K^2L^2}{4}$ **(f)** $x = \sqrt[3]{\frac{z}{9wy}}$
20 (a) $5700\,m^3$ **(b)** $3·40\,m^3$ **(c)** $675\,000\,cm^3$
21 11·4 cm   **22** 122
23 (a) 5·5 m, 5·3 m   **(b)** 20·352, 20·348   **(c)** 32·5 s, 31·5 s
24 (a) 18·4 m   **(b)** 22°   **(c)** 8·3 km
25 1038 m
26 (a) (i) $\frac{1}{4}$ **(ii)** $\frac{1}{4}$ **(iii)** $\frac{7}{9}$ **(b)** $\frac{3}{17}$
27 Chicken 75   mushroom 24   salmon 22
28 (a) $x = 65°$ $y = 52°$ **(b)** $x = 30$
29 8·8 cm
30 (a) $y = 1, x = 2$ **(b)** $p = -2, q = 7$ **(c)** $n = -10, m = 6$
31 £45   **32 (a)** 2   **(b)** $-\frac{5}{8}$
33 (a) $-2\,(0, 9)$ **(b)** $-\frac{3}{2}\,(0, -8)$ **(c)** $\frac{7}{8}\,(0, -5)$
34 (a) $y = \frac{1}{2}x + 11$ **(b)** $y = -\frac{4}{7}x + 9$ **(c)** $y = \frac{1}{2}x + 4$
35 (a) $(z + 6)(z - 1)$ **(b)** $uv(vw + uz)$
(c) $x^2(x - 1)$ **(d)** $(3g + 5h)(3g - 5h)$
(e) $3(1 + 3c)(1 - 3c)$ **(f)** $(p + 5)(p - 1)$
(g) $(2y + 3)(2y + 5)$ **(h)** $f(f - 3)(f + 8)$
(i) $4b(b + 4)(b - 4)$ **(j)** $(2p + 1)(p + 5)$
(k) $(1 + v^2)(1 - v)(1 + v)$ **(l)** $(x + 6y)(x - 4y)$
36 (a) (i) 140   **(ii)** 55   **(iii)** 20   **(b) (i)** $\frac{1}{4}$ **(ii)** $\frac{39}{80}$ **(iii)** $\frac{11}{80}$
(c) 15
37 (a) mean = 50   SD = 4·4
(b) On average the number of sweets has decreased slightly but the number in the bag is more consistent.

Index